earth

A VISUAL GUIDE

Michael Allaby

earth

A VISUAL GUIDE

BONNIER
BOOKS

Bonnier Books
Appledram Barns
Birdham Road
Chichester
West Sussex
PO20 7EQ

Bonnier Books Edition
First Published 2008

Bonnier Books Website
www.bonnierbooks.co.uk

Conceived and produced by Weldon Owen Pty Ltd
61 Victoria Street, McMahons Point
Sydney, NSW 2060, Australia
Copyright © 2008 Weldon Owen Inc

Group Chief Executive Officer John Owen
President and Chief Executive Officer Terry Newell
Publisher Sheena Coupe
Creative Director Sue Burk
Vice President, International Sales Stuart Laurence
Vice President, Sales and New Business Development Amy Kaneko
Vice President Sales, Asia and Latin America Dawn Low
Administrator, International Sales Kristine Ravn

Project Editors Stephanie Goodwin and Jennifer Losco
Editor Robert Coupe
Proofreader Barbara Sheppard
Editorial Coordinator Mike Crowton
Designer Hilda Mendham
Picture Researcher Joanna Collard
Art Buyer Trucie Henderson
Illustrators Mick Posen, The Art Agency; Peter Bull Art Studio
Information Graphics Andrew Davies/Creative Communication

ISBN 978-1-905825-70-7

Color reproduction by Chroma Graphics (Overseas) Pte Ltd
Printed by SNP Leefung Printers Ltd
Printed in China

A WELDON OWEN PRODUCTION

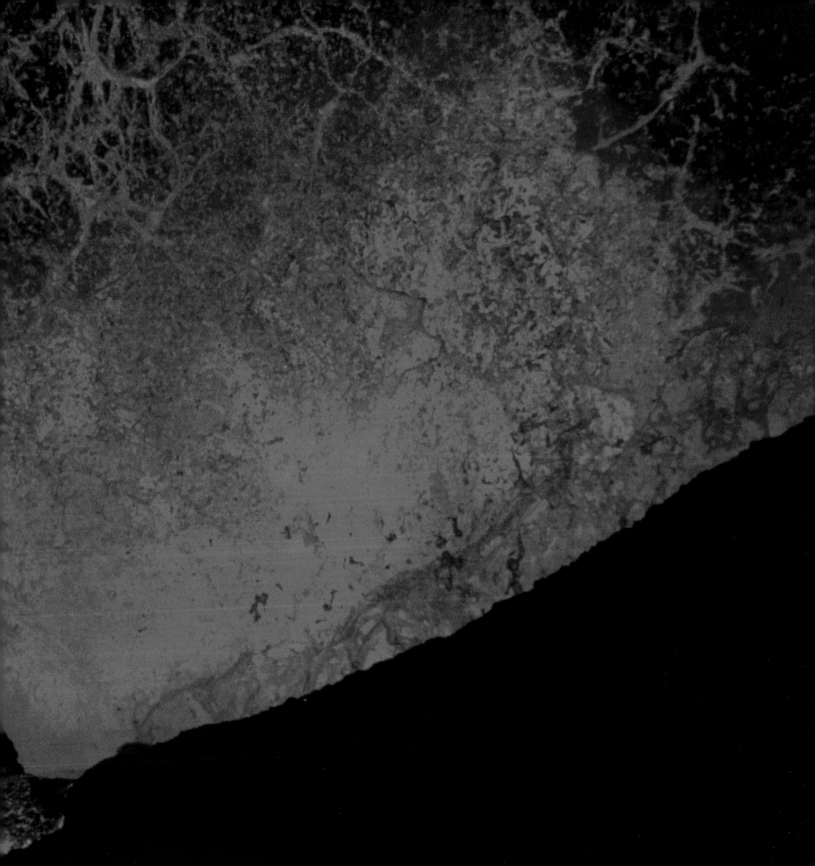

Contents

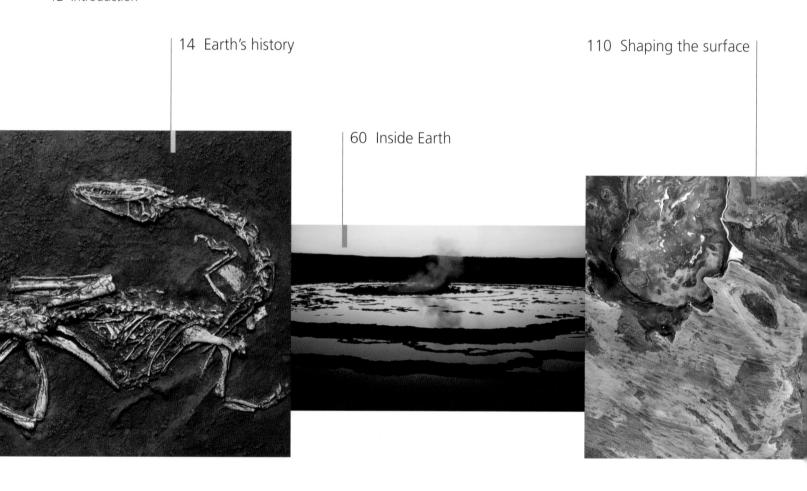

Introduction

Earth is our home. In the black vastness of the Universe, this planet is the only place humans can live. Whenever our astronauts travel away from Earth, they carry a little of the terrestrial environment with them, as a life-support system without which they would perish.

The more we learn, the more fascinating Earth becomes. Start with the planet in its context as a member of the Solar System, within the Milky Way galaxy, and discover how cosmologists believe the Universe began. The steps that transformed a cloud of dust and gas into a star—the Sun—orbited by planets, moons, asteroids and comets are described in detail.

The history of Earth is divided into eons of barely imaginable time, during which life on Earth emerged and evolved. Ours is a rocky planet, and a study of the various categories of rock and how they are made leads to the exploration of Earth's moving continents, constantly changing surface, volcanic eruptions and violent earthquakes.

Water covers more than two-thirds of Earth's surface, which is why it is often called the Blue Planet. Living organisms have colonized almost every corner of the planet, but their characteristics are not everywhere the same. Explore Earth's different habitats, their plants and animals, and the role humans have played in their protection or demise.

Finally, look to the heavens and discover the atmosphere, the gaseous envelope, thin as the blush of moisture on the skin of an orange. It produces our climates and provides us with air to breathe.

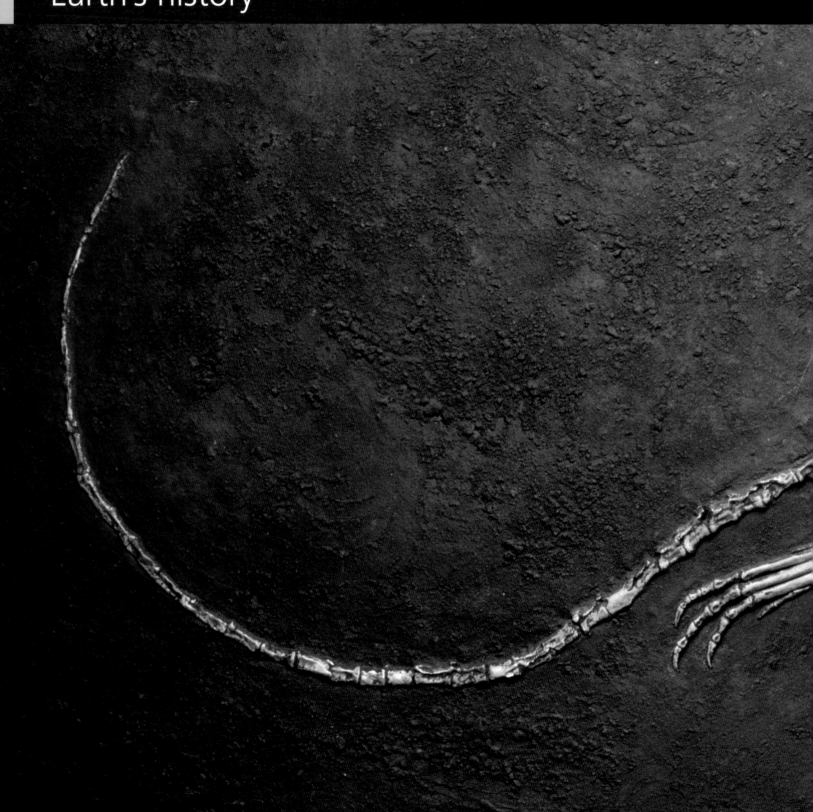

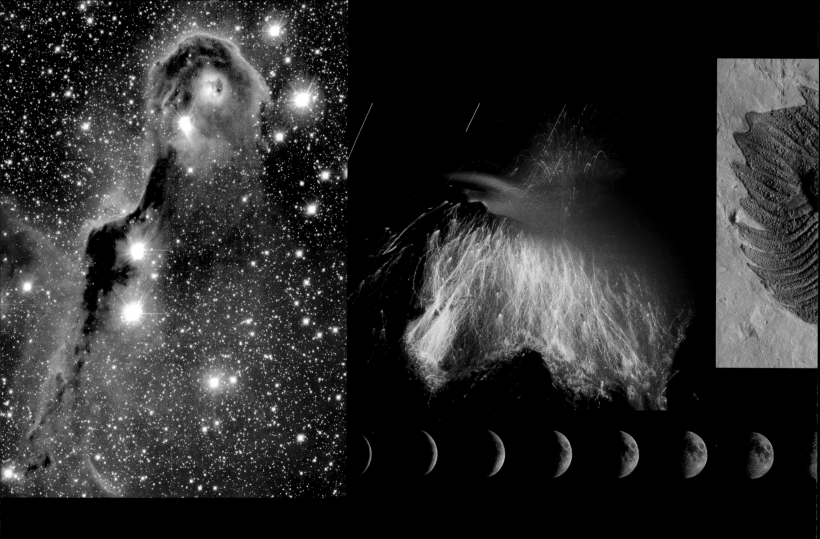

Previous page This fossil of the dinosaur *Coelophysis* was unearthed at Ghost Ranch, New Mexico, USA, in 1947.

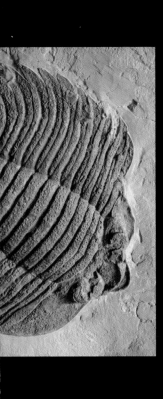

Earth's history

The Universe had its beginnings between 12 and 14 billion years ago, and the history of Earth spans more than 4.6 billion years from its origins as a rocky mass in the Solar System. During Earth's long history, life has diversified into ever more complex forms and the environment itself has changed dramatically.

Earth in space

Viewed from space, Earth is predominantly blue—the color of its air—with patterns of white clouds showing shapes of the weather systems that move water from oceans to land. Surrounded by air, and with 70 percent of its surface covered by water, Earth is unlike any other planet in the Solar System.

Earth and its companions formed at the same time, about 4.6 billion years ago. A cloud of gas and dust, perturbed by an injection of matter from a distant stellar explosion, began to condense. Particles, attracted by their mutual gravitational pull, formed denser masses, into which more particles fell. The densest part of the cloud lay at the center. Eventually this cloud comprised a central mass surrounded by much more tenuous matter, and the entire mass began to rotate. When the gravitational pressure in the central mass reached a critical value, atomic nuclei were forced to merge, which resulted in the release of electromagnetic radiation—light of all wavelengths. At this point, the central mass had become a star—the Sun—and it had begun to shine. As material in the cloud orbiting the Sun was also collecting, the cloud became lumpy. It formed rings, and eventually the planets. The densest, rocky planets formed closest to the Sun, and immense gas giants developed farther away.

→ **Artists and scientists** compiled this true-color image of Earth from a variety of satellite images and surface observations. It is centered on North America and the Great Lakes are visible between the clouds.

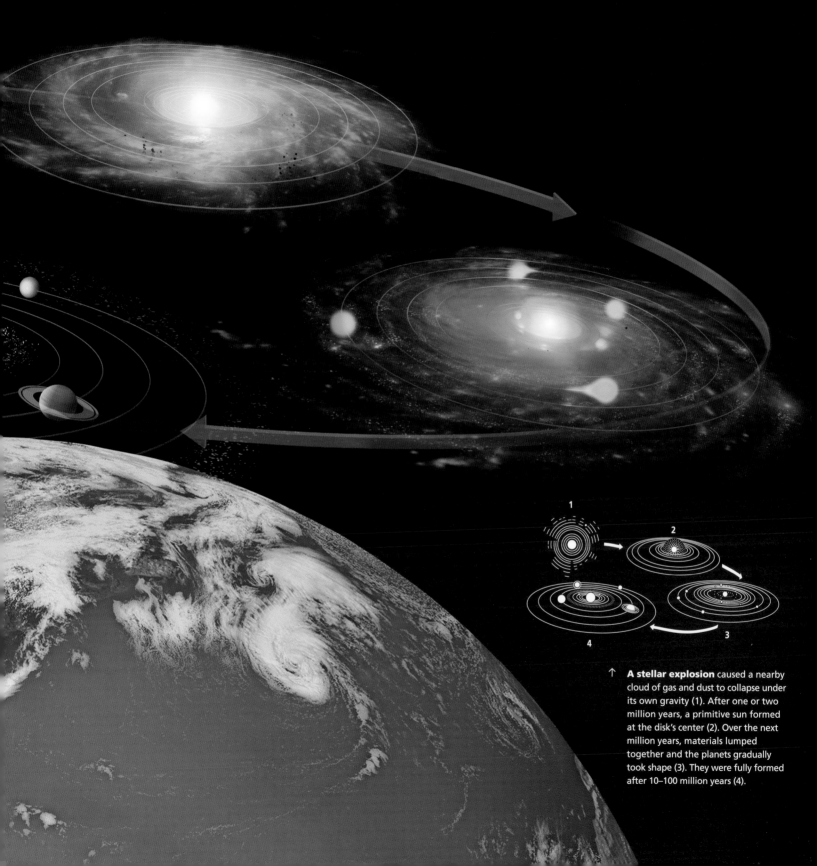

↑ **A stellar explosion** caused a nearby cloud of gas and dust to collapse under its own gravity (1). After one or two million years, a primitive sun formed at the disk's center (2). Over the next million years, materials lumped together and the planets gradually took shape (3). They were fully formed after 10–100 million years (4).

The Universe

The Sun is one of about 100 billion stars that make up the Milky Way Galaxy, so called because the view toward its center contains so many stars that it resembles a milky white path across the night sky. A concentration of stars is called a galaxy, and the visible Universe comprises countless billions of galaxies.

The Universe began in an immensely hot explosion—the "Big Bang"—between 12 and 14 billion years ago. In its first few seconds this explosion expanded rapidly. As it cooled, subatomic particles, then the first atoms, mainly of hydrogen and helium, formed. Matter was distributed unevenly and denser regions drew in material to form clouds of gas that contracted gravitationally, eventually forming stars and galaxies. After about 400 million years, the first stars began to shine.

↓ **Slight differences in the background temperature of the sky** resulted from the uneven distribution of energy following the Big Bang. They appear as color variations in this map, with reds and yellows indicating warmer regions and greens and blues cooler regions.

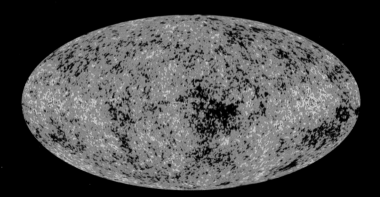

BIRTH OF THE STARS
The colors at left show uneven distribution of matter after the Big Bang. In the next frame matter is condensing by gravity, forming the first stars, seen in the following frame. Next, more stars ignite as internal pressures trigger nuclear fusion. The right-hand frame shows the present Universe, with its countless stars.

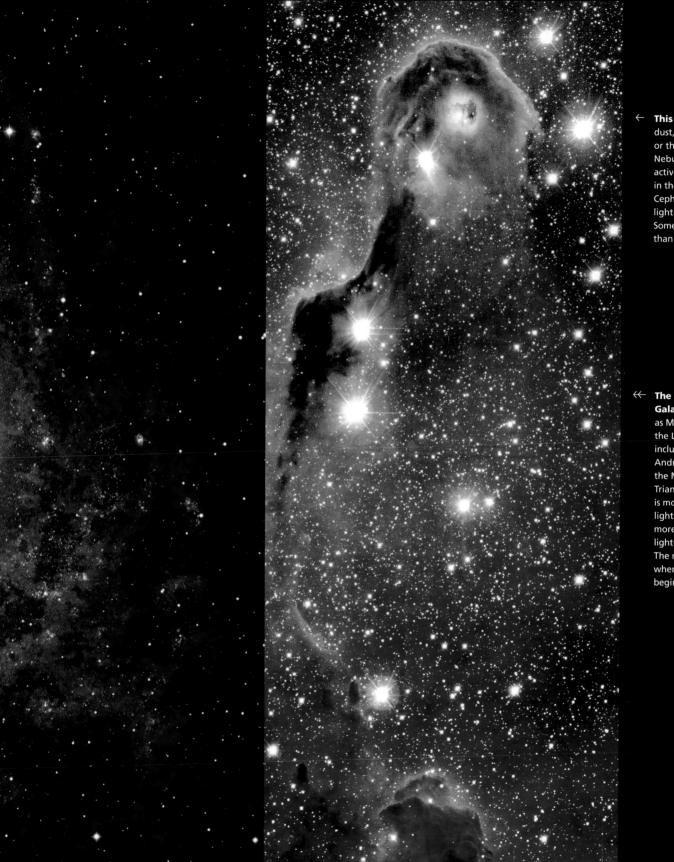

← **This cloud of gas** and dust, known as IC 1396 or the Elephant's Trunk Nebula, is a site of active star formation in the constellation Cepheus, about 2400 light-years from Earth. Some of its stars are less than 100,000 years old.

←← **The Triangulum Galaxy,** also known as M33, belongs to the Local Group that includes the galaxies Andromeda and the Milky Way. The Triangulum Galaxy is more than 30,000 light-years across and more than 2 million light-years from Earth. The reddish areas are where new stars are beginning to form.

The Solar System

As the cloud of gas and dust condensed into what was to become the Sun, temperatures were highest near the center. That is where chemical reactions produced oxides and, with further cooling, silicates of elements such as calcium, magnesium, aluminum and iron. These solid particles adhered to one another to form rocks and the rocks formed the inner planets: Mercury, Venus, Earth and Mars.

Farther out, carbon compounds and water condensed, producing the gas giants: Jupiter and Saturn. Beyond them, water, methane and ammonia froze to produce the ice giants: Uranus and Neptune. Pluto, the faint dot far to the right of Neptune in the illustration below, is no longer classed as a planet. In 2005 Eris, a body slightly larger than Pluto, was discovered. Rather than making Eris the tenth planet, all such bodies, including Pluto, are now called dwarf planets.

Between Mars and Jupiter, tidal forces produced by the gravitational attraction of Jupiter prevented a planet from forming. The millions of rocks that failed to form a planet comprise the Asteroid Belt.

→ **Planets travel around the Sun** in an elliptical orbit. Several have their own satellites, or moons, orbiting them. Earth has one satellite: the Moon; Mars has two: Deimos and Phobos; Jupiter has more than 60; Saturn has 56; Uranus has more than 20; and Neptune has 13.

↓ **The planets vary greatly in size.** The gas giant Jupiter, with a diameter of 89,357 miles (143,800 km), is the largest. The inner planets are much smaller. Mercury, with a diameter of 3032 miles (4880 km), is the densest planet—its gravity is 3.7 times that of Earth's. Venus and Earth are almost the same size: 7521 miles (12,104 km) and 7918 miles (12,742 km) across respectively. Mars has a diameter of 4213 miles (6780 km).

← **Billions of comets,** made from dust and ice, orbit the Sun as the Oort Cloud beyond the planets. Perturbations to their orbits send some of them along elliptical paths. Particles streaming from the Sun erode these comets, producing two tails: one of dust; the other of ionized gases.

Earth | Venus | Mars | Mercury | The Moon

Earth | Jupiter | Saturn | Uranus | Neptune

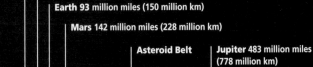

Sun

Mercury 36 million miles (58 million km)

Venus 67 million miles (108 million km)

Earth 93 million miles (150 million km)

Mars 142 million miles (228 million km)

Asteroid Belt

Jupiter 483 million miles (778 million km)

Saturn 890 million miles (1432 million km)

Uranus 1784 million miles (2871 million km)

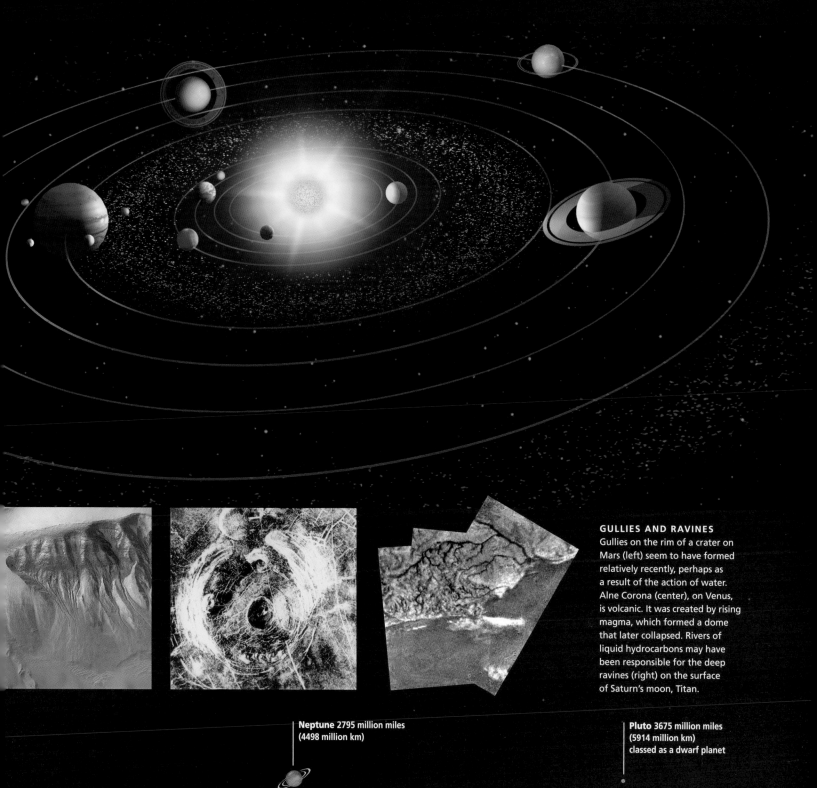

GULLIES AND RAVINES
Gullies on the rim of a crater on
Mars (left) seem to have formed
relatively recently, perhaps as
a result of the action of water.
Alne Corona (center), on Venus,
is volcanic. It was created by rising
magma, which formed a dome
that later collapsed. Rivers of
liquid hydrocarbons may have
been responsible for the deep
ravines (right) on the surface
of Saturn's moon, Titan.

Neptune 2795 million miles
(4498 million km)

Pluto 3675 million miles
(5914 million km)
classed as a dwarf planet

Earth's Sun

The Sun came into existence about 4.6 billion years ago and will remain much as it is now for about another five billion years. This means that it is middle-aged—and an ordinary star. It has a radius of about 430,000 miles (696,000 km); Earth's radius is 3959 miles (6371 km). Because the Sun is made up of 73 percent hydrogen, 25 percent helium and 2 percent heavier elements, its average density is only 88 pounds per cubic foot (1410 kg/m³). Earth consists predominantly of rock and has a density of 344 pounds per cubic foot (5517 kg/m³). Despite this, the Sun is 330,000 times as massive as Earth. Our star shines so brightly because it is very close. Its average distance from Earth is 93 million miles (149.6 million km).

Gravitational pressure forces hydrogen nuclei to fuse in the Sun's core. This reaction releases radiation that pushes outward, but the weight of the overlying material prevents the Sun from expanding. The Sun's stability is maintained by the balance of gravitational and radiation pressures, but eventually, when its hydrogen fuel is depleted, the reaction will change and the Sun will expand into a red giant.

THE SUN IN SPACE
The Milky Way Galaxy has a spiral structure and the Sun is located on one of the arms of the spiral. The galaxy is turning and the Sun turns with it. So far, the Sun has made approximately 21 complete galactic orbits. Astronomers measure large distances in parsecs and the Sun is 25.3 kiloparsecs (82,500 light-years) from the black hole at the center of the Milky Way Galaxy.

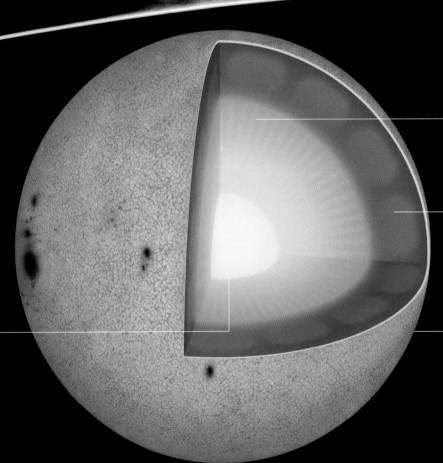

THE SUN'S STRUCTURE

→ **Radiant heat from the Sun** drives the thermonuclear reactions driving the Sun take place in its core, which is about 249,000 miles (400,000 km) across and surrounded by a radiative zone. About 320,000 miles (515,000 km) from the center there is a convective zone. The outermost layer is called the photosphere.

The core The core, where hydrogen nuclei fuse together to form helium, is the Sun's powerhouse. The temperature here is about 28,000,000°F (15,500,000°C).

Radiative zone The radiative zone is the region where energy is transported outward by the pressure of radiation generated in the core.

Convective zone In this zone, energy is carried to the solar surface by convection, the same process that causes cool air to sink beneath warmer air, pushing it upward.

Photosphere This is the visible surface of the Sun, where sunspots and solar granulation are observed. The temperature here is about 9900°F (5500°C).

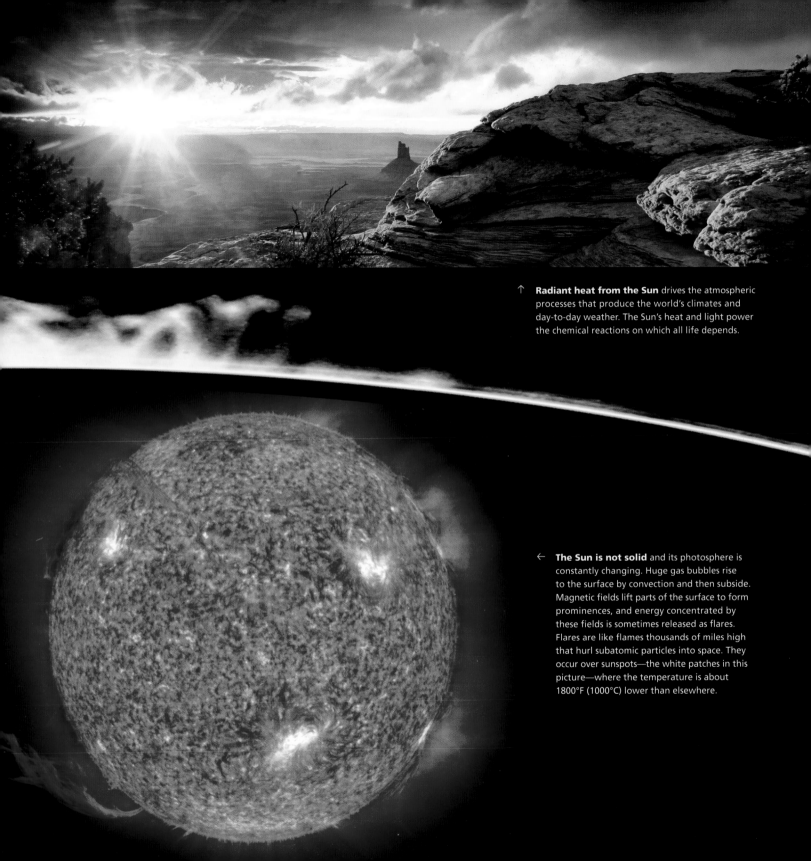

↑ **Radiant heat from the Sun** drives the atmospheric processes that produce the world's climates and day-to-day weather. The Sun's heat and light power the chemical reactions on which all life depends.

← **The Sun is not solid** and its photosphere is constantly changing. Huge gas bubbles rise to the surface by convection and then subside. Magnetic fields lift parts of the surface to form prominences, and energy concentrated by these fields is sometimes released as flares. Flares are like flames thousands of miles high that hurl subatomic particles into space. They occur over sunspots—the white patches in this picture—where the temperature is about 1800°F (1000°C) lower than elsewhere.

Four Seasons

In places close to the equator the difference between daytime and night-time temperatures is greater than the difference between the temperatures in January and July. In most equatorial regions rainfall varies from one time of year to another, but in other ways the weather hardly changes. Seasonal changes become more marked as we move farther from the equator. Summer and winter are very different from each other in the latitudes of Europe and North America, and the seasonal contrast is most extreme in polar regions.

Imagine that Earth's orbital path around the Sun traces out the circumference of a disk. That disk is called the plane of the ecliptic and differing seasons occur because Earth's rotational axis is not perpendicular to this plane. The amount of tilt from the perpendicular varies between 22.1 degrees and 24.5 degrees over a cycle of about 41,000 years. At present the tilt is 23.45 degrees. Because of the tilt, as Earth travels around the Sun, first one hemisphere, then the other, is turned toward the Sun. It is summer in the hemisphere facing the Sun and winter in the opposite hemisphere.

→ **In middle and high latitudes,** differences in temperature distinguish summer from winter. Closer to the equator it is changes in rainfall that differentiate the seasons. Some regions have cool, wet winters and warm, dry summers. Throughout most of the subtropics and tropics more rain falls in summer and winters are relatively dry. Spring and autumn, or fall, are transitional seasons between summer and winter.

EQUINOXES AND SOLSTICES

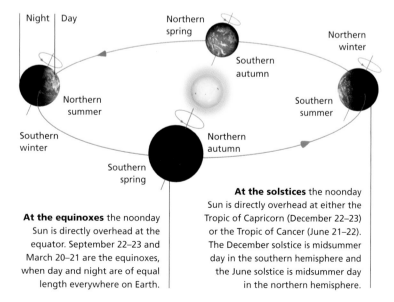

Night | Day

Northern spring

Northern winter

Southern autumn

Northern summer

Southern summer

Southern winter

Northern autumn

Southern spring

At the equinoxes the noonday Sun is directly overhead at the equator. September 22–23 and March 20–21 are the equinoxes, when day and night are of equal length everywhere on Earth.

At the solstices the noonday Sun is directly overhead at either the Tropic of Capricorn (December 22–23) or the Tropic of Cancer (June 21–22). The December solstice is midsummer day in the southern hemisphere and the June solstice is midsummer day in the northern hemisphere.

Solar eclipse

Earth orbits the Sun and the Moon orbits Earth. From time to time, the Moon passes between Earth and the Sun, obscuring the view of the Sun from Earth. That is a solar eclipse. Eclipses are possible because although the Sun is 400 times as wide as the Moon, it is also 400 times as far away.

If the orbits of both Earth and the Moon were circular, all solar eclipses would be the same, but they are not. Earth's elliptical orbit means that, as seen from Earth, the Sun's diameter varies by 2 percent, and the elliptical lunar orbit changes the apparent diameter of the Moon by 8 percent. When the Moon is farthest from Earth it is not big enough to obscure the Sun completely. The result is an annular eclipse.

An eclipse can occur when the new Moon is close to one of the points, called nodes, where its orbit intersects that of Earth. It takes the Moon 27.21 days—a draconic month—to travel from one node back to the same node again. There are 29.53 days—one lunation—between one new Moon and the next. If the new Moon is at a node it takes 242 Draconic months or 223 lunations for the same configuration to recur, during which the Sun passes the node 19 times. If an eclipse happens at the beginning of the cycle, the next eclipse will be about 18 years and 10 days later.

↓ **When an annular eclipse** occurs the Moon moves across the face of the Sun, leaving a circle of bright sunlight around the edge of the Moon's dark shadow. The word "annular" means "ringlike."

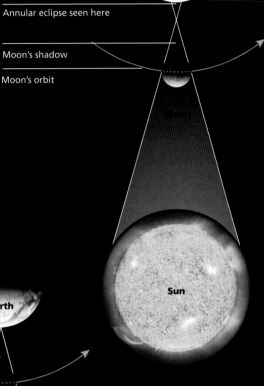

Earth

Annular eclipse seen here

Moon's shadow

Moon's orbit

Sun

Earth

Total eclipse seen here

Moon's shadow

Moon's orbit

Sun

ANNULAR AND TOTAL ECLIPSES
An annular eclipse results when the apparent diameter of the Moon is smaller than that of the Sun (above). When the Moon is closer to Earth it causes a total eclipse (left).

→ **A total eclipse** reveals the Sun's inner and outer corona—outer atmosphere. The inner corona rises to about 47,000 miles (75,000 km); the outer corona extends several million miles into space.

Solar activity

Hot gas, bubbling up by convection, gives the Sun's visible surface, the photosphere, a granular appearance. The grains are in constant motion. Within this granular structure, strong magnetic fields suppress the convection cells carrying heat to the visible surface, which produces sunspots. These sunspots are regions about 31,000 miles (50,000 km) across that are about 2700°F (1500°C) cooler than their surroundings. The number of sunspots increases and then decreases over an 11-year cycle. Above the photosphere lies the chromosphere, which merges with the Sun's outermost layer, the corona. Shock waves travel upward from the photosphere through the chromosphere, making the corona expand outward. This expansion causes the corona to release a mixture of electromagnetically charged particles that stream away at up to 300 miles per second (500 km/s). This stream of particles is known as the "solar wind."

AURORAS

When the solar wind reaches Earth, its particles travel through the upper atmosphere along field lines in Earth's magnetic field, descending at the North and South poles. As they descend, the particles collide with oxygen and nitrogen atoms, imparting energy to them. These atoms emit light as they return to their ground state, visible as curtains, bands or arches of light—the aurora borealis (northern lights) and aurora australis (southern lights). Auroras are most often seen in high latitudes, although sometimes they appear in latitudes as low as 40°.

→ **Photographed in ultraviolet light,** the false colors in the Sun's corona indicate different temperatures. Blue gases are at 1,800,000°F (1,000,000°C); green indicates 2,700,000°F (1,500,000°C); and red indicates 3,600,000°F (2,000,000°C). The corona is too faint to be seen without special instruments.

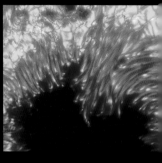

↑ **This sunspot is** about 30,000 miles (50,000 km) across. Sunspots increase and decrease in number over an 11-year period, corresponding to the Sun's cycle of variation in magnetic activity.

↑ **Coronal loops**—bulges, or prominences, in the corona—consist of streams of very hot gas. The loops trace lines in the Sun's magnetic field.

← **The shimmering curtains** or luminous patches of the northern and southern auroras are most often seen inside the Arctic and Antarctic circles.

The Moon

Earth's only natural satellite, the Moon, orbits at an average distance of 239,000 miles (384,500 km). The Moon's diameter is 2160 miles (3476 km). Gravity on the Moon is approximately one-sixth of that on Earth. The Moon has no atmosphere and surface temperatures range from 260°F (127°C) by day to –280°F (–173°C) at night. The entire lunar surface is covered with a layer of dust several inches thick. Seventeenth-century astronomers believed the Moon resembled Earth in its composition, and they called the dark areas of the surface "maria" (seas) and the pale areas "terrae" (continents). The terrae are now called highlands. The low-lying maria are formed from volcanic basalt. The Moon is extremely dry, but scientists are searching for signs of water beneath the surface. There are plans for permanently manned lunar bases and if water is present it will save the cost of transporting it from Earth. Apart from drinking, growing food and washing, water can also be made into rocket fuel. So far none has been found.

BIRTH OF THE MOON

↗ **A full Moon** is seen above the Baltoro glacier in the Karakorum Mountains, Pakistan. The lunar highlands are the pale areas and the maria are the dark shadows visible in the photograph.

→ **American astronaut** James B. Irwin works with the Lunar Roving Vehicle. This photograph was taken in July 1971, at the Apollo 15 landing site in the Hadley–Apennine region of the Moon.

← **About 100 million years after the Solar system formed,** an object approximately the size of Mars struck Earth a glancing blow (top). This shattered the impacting body, as well as Earth's outer layer. As gravity drew the fragments together (center), the cores of the two bodies merged and the remaining material formed two new bodies, Earth and the Moon (bottom). Earth acquired almost all the iron in the impacting body, which is why Earth is rich in iron, but there is little iron on the Moon.

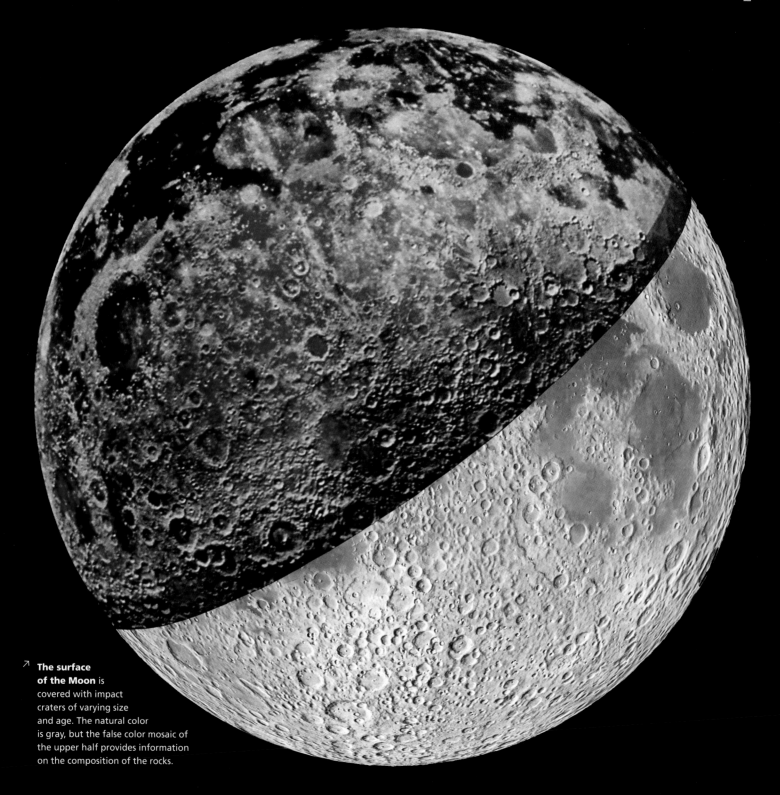

↗ **The surface of the Moon** is covered with impact craters of varying size and age. The natural color is gray, but the false color mosaic of the upper half provides information on the composition of the rocks.

The Earth-Moon system

Earth and the Moon are sometimes thought of as a double-planet system, orbiting their common center of gravity. Earth is 81 times as massive as the Moon, and that center of gravity lies deep inside Earth. The Moon also rotates on its own axis. It takes the Moon 29.53059 days—one synodic month—to complete one orbit and the same time to complete one rotation. Tidal forces due to gravity raise a bulge on both Earth and the Moon. Earth's bulge moves around the planet as the Moon orbits, producing the tides, but the bulge on the much smaller Moon no longer moves. The tides have slowed the Moon's rotation so that it is held in lockstep with Earth—its bulge always facing toward Earth. Because the Moon always presents the same side to Earth little was known about the far side of the Moon until 1959, when it was photographed by the Soviet probe Luna 3.

↓ **The Moon's orbit** is inclined 5 degrees to Earth's orbit, so the two orbits cross repeatedly, altering the amount of the lunar surface that is visible from Earth and producing the phases of the Moon. The New Moon is at the left, with only a sliver of the illuminated side visible. When more than half of the Moon is visible it is said to be "waxing gibbous," then "waning gibbous."

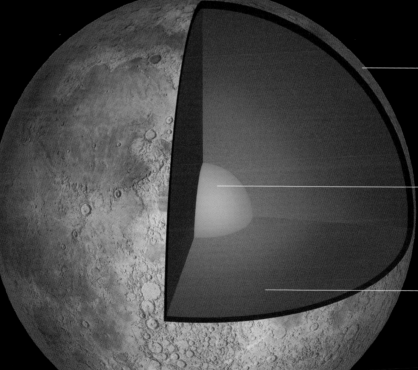

↑ **When Earth lies directly between the Sun** and the Moon its shadow falls across the Moon, causing a lunar eclipse that may be partial or total. The Sun is so bright that during a total eclipse the Moon remains clearly visible. It appears large and is pink in color.

← **Apollo 8 astronaut** William A. Anders took this photograph of Earth rising over the lunar horizon on December 24, 1968. In fact, Anders photographed the scene with the horizon vertical and Earth to its left.

THE MOON'S STRUCTURE

Crust The highland crust is 37–75 miles (60–120 km) thick and is made from feldspar; the thinner crust of the maria is composed of volcanic basalt.

Core The lunar core is believed to be 370–500 miles (600–800 km) across and probably consists of iron.

Mantle The mantle is made from silicate rocks and is 760–860 miles (1220–1380 km) thick. It fills the space between the core and the base of the crust.

Tidal phenomena

Solar and lunar gravity both exert an influence on Earth, but although the Sun is by far the more massive, the proximity of the Moon means its pull is much stronger. The side of Earth that faces the Moon is pulled outward, and as Earth turns on its axis, the bulge travels right around the planet, taking 24 hours 50 minutes—a tidal day—to do so. In fact, there are two bulges: one on the side that faces the Moon; and the other on the opposite side of Earth, where the Moon's attraction reduces Earth's own gravitational force. The bulges produce tides 12 hours 25 minutes apart, although the configuration of some coastlines means that not every place experiences two tides a day. Tides are barely detectable in small seas such as the Mediterranean. When the tidal bulge flows from the ocean and into a partly enclosed sea it tends to follow the coastlines, moving in one or more large circles. But at the still centers of the circular flows—places called amphidromic points—the tides have no effect at all.

There are tides that create movements in Earth's solid crust as well as atmospheric tides that influence movements of air. But the largest and most familiar tides are the ones that affect movements of Earth's oceans and large seas.

↑ **The Bay of Fundy,** between New Brunswick and Nova Scotia, Canada, is 180 miles (290 km) long, 62 miles (100 km) wide at its mouth, and 400–700 feet (120–215 m) deep. It experiences one of the greatest tidal variations on Earth.

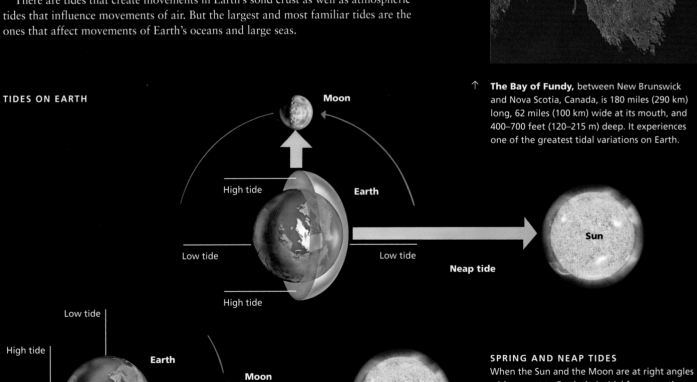

TIDES ON EARTH

Moon

High tide

Earth

Low tide   Low tide

High tide

Neap tide

Sun

Low tide

High tide

Earth

Moon

Sun

Spring tide

High tide

SPRING AND NEAP TIDES

When the Sun and the Moon are at right angles with respect to Earth their tidal forces partly cancel each other out and the range of tidal movement is small. These are neap tides. Spring tides occur when the Sun and the Moon are aligned. When this occurs, their forces act together to produce a large tidal range.

↑ **At the head of the Bay of Fundy,** in Canada, tides rise an incredible 52 feet (16 m). The bay narrows and its floor rises steadily, making it shallower, so it funnels the water entering it. At the same time, the length of the bay means that by the time the rising tide reaches the far end, the next rising tide from the Gulf of Maine is already entering it, so the returning tide meets the incoming tide. In contrast, tides in the Gulf of Maine measure less than 3 feet (1 m).

← **The coastal areas of Greece,** which lie at the eastern end of the Mediterranean basin, experience almost no tidal movement because the sea contains too little water.

Before life

Gravity caused the collapse of the cloud of gas and dust that would become the Solar System. As the cloud collapsed its mass concentrated at the center, where it grew into the Sun. At first, the temperature of the cloud was about 3600°F (2000°C), but as it cooled some of its gases condensed into solid particles. Colliding particles adhered to one another and larger fragments attracted and retained smaller ones. Small stones formed, then rocks.

The orbiting material began to separate out, with the heavier rocks being drawn closer to the center. Their mutual gravitational influences pulled the particles into rings. Within the ring that became Earth, the largest rock attracted others. The young planet grew through collisions with planetismals—rocks up to half a mile (about 1 km) across. This bombardment continued for approximately 700 million years. Gravitational pressure inside Earth, heat from the bombardment, and the radioactive decay of heavy elements melted young Earth. It became a ball of molten rock.

→ **Within molten Earth,** reactions with carbon and sulfur reduced iron silicates to metallic iron. Over about 50 million years, the iron sank to the center, where, mixed with 4 percent nickel and 10 percent oxygen, it became Earth's core.

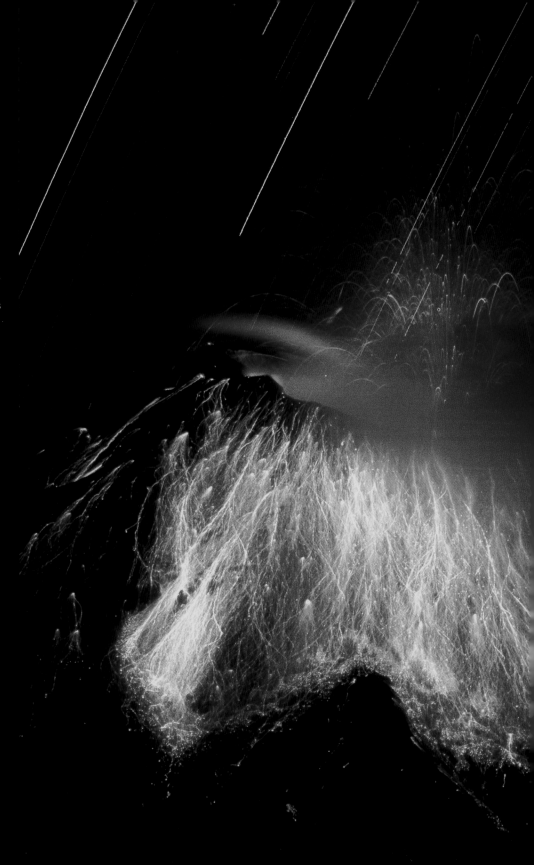

4.6–4.2 BILLION YEARS AGO

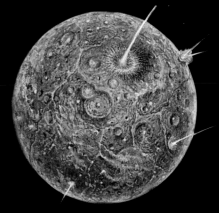

4.2–3.8 BILLION YEARS AGO

↑ **Crustal movements and weathering** have removed the evidence of bombardment from Earth's surface, but these processes have not affected the Moon, where the extent of cratering shows how intense the planetesimal bombardment was. The intense bombardment continued for about 700 million years (top). By about 4.2 billion years ago Earth had an atmosphere and oceans, and collisions were less common (bottom).

← **The heat of the interior** released water that was chemically bound to minerals, and impacting bodies also delivered water. At first the water vaporized, but then it fell in huge storms that cooled the surface and filled depressions.

First life

Rocks in South Africa, and also in Australia, that are known to be about 3.5 billion years old contain traces of carbon and carbonates that may have been produced by living cells. There are rocks in Greenland, estimated to be about 3.8 billion years old, that contain graphite, which may also be an indication of life. The oldest fossil evidence of life is from stromatolites—algal mats—about 3.2 billion years old. Clearly some life forms existed on Earth soon after the planetesimal bombardment ended. Some scientists suggest it may have been "seeded" by material entering from space—perhaps carried on meteorites from Mars. No one knows precisely how life began, but it must have developed from large molecules that were able to reproduce by dividing in two, with each daughter molecule growing to full size by gathering smaller molecules from its surroundings. Then molecules must have appeared that were enclosed in a membrane to protect the chemical reactions taking place inside. At the next stage the protected molecules became living cells.

The first organisms were single cells, simpler than modern bacteria. Oxygen would have poisoned them. They tolerated high temperatures and high concentrations of salts, and obtained their energy and the carbon to construct and maintain themselves from inorganic chemicals in the water around them. Before long, certain organisms would have become predators and hunted other cells for food.

↓ **Fluid at about 680°F (360°C),** rich in sulfur and minerals, rises from a seafloor vent, or "black smoker." This is the Saracen's Head hydrothermal vent, which is at a depth of 10,170 feet (3100 m) on the mid-Atlantic ridge. Archaea, worms and crabs thrive in this environment.

↑ **Fossils first found in 1961** in the Ediacara Hills in the Northern Flinders Range, South Australia, comprise about 30 genera of soft-bodied organisms that became stranded in tidal pools or on mudflats about 640 million years ago.

Proterozoic	542	Cambrian	488	Ordovician	444	S
			Paleozoic era			

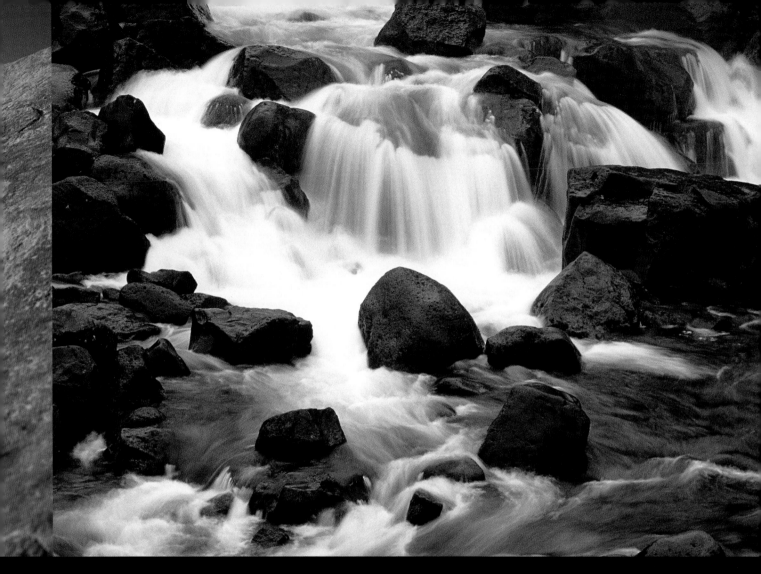

About 550 million years ago there was a dramatic increase in the diversity of life on Earth, known as the "Cambrian Explosion." Since then plants and animal life has become more complex. Humans are latecomers to planet Earth.

Early Earth may have looked like this. At the Oxararfoss waterfall at Thinvellir, Iceland, the Oxara River plunges into the Almannagja fissure, 165 feet (50 m) wide and 100 feet (30 m) deep, at the mid-Atlantic ridge, where the ocean is widening.

| 416 | Devonian | 359 | Carboniferous | 299 | Permian | 251 | Triassic | 200 | Jurassic | 146 | Cretaceous | 65.5 | Paleogene | 2 |

Mesozoic era   Cenozoic era

The Proterozoic eon

Early in the Cambrian period of Earth's geological history there was a veritable explosion of multicellular life. It was at this time that animals with mineralized skeletons, the ancestors of modern animals, first appeared.

The Cambrian period began 542 million years ago—four billion years after the formation of Earth. Before the Cambrian, evolution had been proceeding for a long time, although not as dramatically as it did during the Cambrian. Life was present more than three billion years ago, but it was during the Proterozoic eon, from 2.5 billion years ago until the start of the Cambrian, that evolution took several important steps. The earliest living cells, called prokaryotes, had no nucleus to contain their DNA. The first cells with a nucleus, known as eukaryotes, appeared in the Proterozoic eon and had a much more complex internal structure than prokaryotes. That is also the time when the ancestors of plants, fungi and animals appeared. Photosynthesis began, releasing oxygen into the air. Oxygen, which is reactive, poisoned all those organisms that were unable to adapt to it or that existed in airless environments.

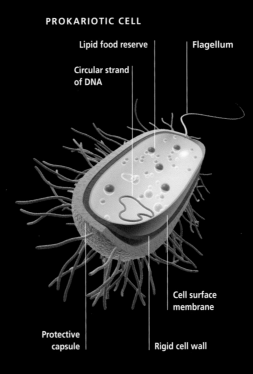

PROKARIOTIC CELL

Lipid food reserve

Flagellum

Circular strand of DNA

Cell surface membrane

Protective capsule

Rigid cell wall

↓ **A mound of yellow** elemental sulfur, an indication of high sulfur content, is precipitated from the water that emerges from this spring at Te Wharkarewarewa, Rotorua, in North Island, New Zealand. Some archaea and bacteria use sulfur compounds rather than oxygen to release energy by anaerobic respiration.

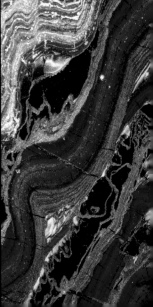

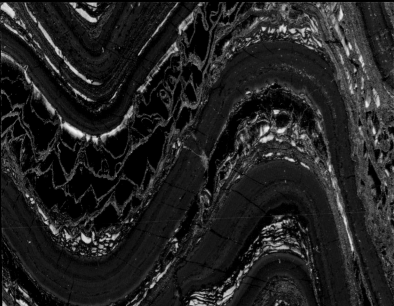

↑ **These living algal mats** in Shark Bay, Western Australia, consist of layers of cyanobacteria and other bacteria. The oldest fossils on Earth are of mats very like these, although in life they would not have been coated in green algae exposed to oxygen-rich air. The fossils are called stromatolites and they date from the Paleoarchaean era, about 3.5 billion years ago. It is not certain that stromatolites contained cyanobacteria.

← **Banded iron formations** are sedimentary rocks that comprise alternate layers of iron oxide (hematite or magnetite) and shale, or, as in this example, jasper and tigereye. The rocks began forming about three billion years ago as oxygen from photosynthesizing cyanobacteria oxidized iron in the water, thus producing insoluble oxides that precipitated out. Crustal movements subsequently deformed the layers. Many banded iron formations are found in Australia.

The Paleozoic era began 542 million years ago with the beginning of the Cambrian period and ended 251 million years ago, with the "Great Dying." The Great Dying, as its name implies, was a huge mass extinction that defines the end of the Permian period. The Paleozoic era, therefore, lasted for 291 million years. During that long time there were two ice ages and the world's great landmasses, or continents, merged to form the supercontinent of Pangaea. The Moon was closer to Earth than it is now, so the tides were stronger, and Earth rotated faster, which meant that the days were shorter.

The era began with a huge and rapid expansion of multicelled organisms. Known as the Cambrian Explosion, this is when the ancestors of most modern animal groups first appeared. Evidence for the Cambrian Explosion was discovered in 1905 in fossils in the Burgess Shale, rocks in British Columbia, Canada. From simple beginnings, life continued to evolve during the Paleozoic. Many types of fish swam in the seas of the Devonian period. The first reptiles emerged, among them the mammal-like reptiles that were ancestors of the present-day mammals. Insects, including giant dragonflies, appeared and the first vascular plants established themselves on land.

↑ **Trilobites** were aquatic arthropods, related insects and spiders, which lived throughout t Paleozoic and were very common. There wer nearly 4000 species, ranging in size from 0.0C inch (0.5 mm) to about 3 feet (90 cm) long. T last trilobites disappeared during the "Great Dying" that occurred at the end of the Permia

← **The footprints pictured at left** were made by *Dimetrodon*, a fierce carnivore that lived i the Permian period. It was the dominant and largest predator of its time. It had a large "sa on its back, supported by long, spiny bones. I is thought that this sail helped it regulate its body temperature. *Dimetrodon* was a mamma like reptile, ancestral to present-day mammal

→ **Cycads are gymnosperms** and are related to coniferous trees. Despite their long palmlike leaves, supported by thick trunks, cycads are not closely related to palms. These evergreen seed plants appeared during the Permian period and about 100 species—commonly referred to as "living fossils"—survive to this day in tropical and subtropical regions of the world. Among present-day examples are these specimens that grow in Carr Boy Range, in the Kimberley region of northern Western Australia.

↓ **Brachiopods, or lampshells,** are shellfish that have two parts to their shells. Most live attached to the seabed by a strong fleshy stalk, called a pedicle, though some rest on the muddy bottom. Brachiopods first appeared early in the Paleozoic era and fossils like this one are fairly common in cold or deep ocean areas.

The Mesozoic era

"Mesozoic" means "middle life," and it was in the Mesozoic era that the immediate ancestors of many modern plants and animals made their first appearance. The Mesozoic was a long era that lasted more than 180 million years. It began 251 million years ago, when life was recovering from the extinction of most invertebrate animals that took place at the end of the Permian period. It ended 65.5 million years ago when an asteroid collided with Earth, causing yet another mass extinction. During the Mesozoic, life expanded on land, where dinosaurs were the dominant animals. Reptiles such as plesiosaurs lived in the oceans, and winged reptiles, the pterosaurs, took to the air. The first lizards and snakes appeared during this era. The pterosaurs were not the only flying animals: *Archaeopteryx*, the first bird, flew during the Jurassic period, in the middle of the Mesozoic. Before long, others followed.

At the beginning of the Mesozoic all the continents were joined in the supercontinent Pangaea, but about 200 million years ago Pangaea began to split in two—Laurasia in the north and Gondwana in the south. By the end of the Mesozoic most of the present continents had separated. In the early part of the era the climate was dry, with large seasonal extremes of temperature. During the Jurassic sea levels rose, flooding large land areas. Temperatures became more moderate and rainfall increased.

→ **The first bird, *Archaeopteryx lithographica*** is known from only five fossils, one of which is shown here. All were found in limestone rocks in the Solnhofen region of Germany. *Archaeopteryx* was probably capable only of weak flight and retained many reptilian features. It had teeth and a long tail, but it was also feathered and had hollow bones that are typical of later birds.

← **The first flowering plants** appeared during the Cretaceous period, near the end of the Mesozoic, and the first flowers resembled those of *Magnolia grandiflora*, which is shown here. There are about 125 species of magnolias, and there are two species of their close relatives, the tulip trees (*Liriodendron*). Most botanists consider this family (Magnoliaceae) the most ancient of all flowering plants that are still in existence.

← **Before the appearance** of flowering plants, gymnosperm forests covered vast areas of land. Today's gymnosperm forests are, like the one shown here, dominated by coniferous trees. The most abundant trees in Mesozoic forests, however, were cycads, bennetitales and ginkgos. Cycads and bennetitales looked rather like palm trees. By the end of the Mesozoic the bennetitales were extinct.

The Pleistogene period

The Pleistogene period began about 1.81 million years ago. It is the period in which we are still living today. It comprises two epochs: the Pleistocene, which ended 11,000 years ago; and the Holocene, which followed it. The Pleistocene epoch is the age of ice. About one million years ago temperatures began to fall and ice sheets began to advance in the first of the ice ages. Sea levels fell as more and more water changed to ice. When the ice age ended and the ice sheets retreated, sea levels rose once more. The Holocene began 11,000 years ago, when the ice sheets that had covered much of the northern hemisphere for the preceding 60,000 years began to retreat. Known as the Wisconsinian in North America, the Weichselian in northern Europe, the Würm in the Alps and the Devensian in Britain, the Holocene was the last of four major Pleistocene ice ages. Today we are living in an interglacial age known as the Flandrian. Scientists predict that one day the ice will return.

The Pleistocene was not only an age of ice; it was also a period of giant mammals. Mammoths, mastodons, giant sloths, cave bears and saber-toothed cats roamed Earth at this time. All of these are now extinct. Neanderthal humans also lived during the Pleistocene, and for a time modern humans (*Homo sapiens*) lived alongside Neanderthal humans (*H. neanderthalensis*). Modern humans began displacing Neanderthals about 45,000 years ago and Neanderthals became extinct about 30,000 years ago.

This saber-toothed cat fossil skull was found in South Dakota. Several groups of animals developed huge teeth like these, which were used to deliver a fatal stab. Smilodon, the best known saber-toothed cat was heavier, but slightly smaller, than a lion and had a short tail.

↑ **No plants can grow** at the center of a thick ice sheet, and without plants there is no food for animals. As well, ice sheets are not easy to cross. Mountains covered in ice and snow project above the level ice of the plains, presenting ice-age landscapes that are found today only in mountain ranges that extend upward beyond the tree line. Plants and animals, however, can thrive in forests close to the edge of the ice.

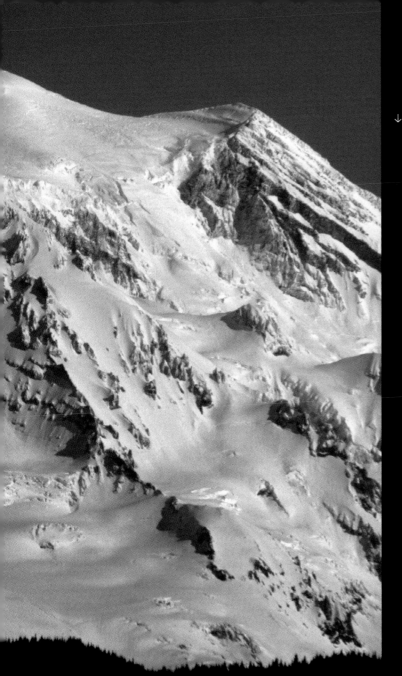

↓ **Mammoth elephants** lived in tundra and on grasslands. This is a skeleton of the Columbian mammoth (*Mammuthus columbi*), found in 1922 in Lincoln County, Nebraska. The largest of all mammoths, it was 13 feet (4 m) tall at the shoulder and weighed 11 tons (10 t).

PLEISTOCENE ICE SHEETS
The map at right shows the maximum extent of ice during the Pleistocene ice ages. In addition to the northern-hemisphere ones shown here, there was also an extensive ice sheet in western South America. Average temperatures in these regions were about 11°F (6°C) lower than those of today.

With rising temperatures and the retreat of the ice, meltwater filled rivers that watered the newly exposed and barren land. Plant seeds from more temperate latitudes, blown by the wind or dropped by birds, germinated, and little by little the landscape turned green. In time, the forests returned—first the dark coniferous forests of northern climates, and later, where conditions were milder, the broad-leaved forests. With the forests came the animals, and following the animals came modern humans.

Modern humans (*Homo sapiens*) appeared in Africa nearly 200,000 years ago, during the Pleistocene. As they expanded their range into Eurasia, the Neanderthals became fewer and by the late Pleistocene they were extinct. *Homo floresiensis* survived until at least 18,000 years ago, but throughout the 11,000 years of the present age, the Holocene, *Homo sapiens* has been the only species of human. During this time humans have occupied much of the world, replacing the natural vegetation with cultivated crops. The Holocene is too short to detect evolutionary trends, although most scientists fear that expanding human influence is driving many species toward extinction.

Coniferous trees tolerate cold winters, short summers and heavy snow. Because they are evergreen, they do not have to grow new leaves each spring before they can commence photosynthesising. They were the first trees to colonize ice-free landscapes.

This is the skull of a three-year-old *Australopithecus afarensis* child, who lived in Ethiopia 3.3 million years ago. She has been nicknamed "Daughter of Lucy" because of the famous fossil of the same species that was found in 1974. Almost three million years of evolution separate her from modern humans.

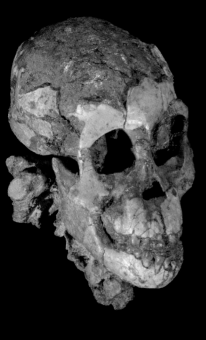

← **At first, the ice** that melted each spring from lakes and around coasts during the Holocene would form again in winter. Eventually, however, water in lower latitudes did not freeze over, but remained open all year.

↑ **Tundra, dominated by lichens,** sedges and low shrubs, was the first vegetation to claim the exposed land. Coniferous forests arrived later, and along their low-latitude edges these eventually gave way to broad-leaved deciduous forest.

The emergence of humans

Scientists classify humans in the subfamily Homininae within the order Primates, which is the order comprising lorises, lemurs, tarsiers and all the monkeys and apes. The hominins are the African great apes—gorillas and chimpanzees—and humans, together with their immediate ancestors. About five million years ago, the evolutionary line that led to the emergence of humans separated from the line that produced our closest relative, the chimpanzee (*Pan troglodytes*). Many species of ancestral humans appeared and then became extinct in the course of those five million years. Out of all those species, only one survives. The first modern human (*Homo sapiens*) lived nearly 200,000 years ago in what is now Kenya, in eastern Africa. Wandering in search of food, perhaps following herds of game, humans gradually spread throughout eastern and southern Africa until, about 100,000 years ago, they moved farther afield. Some went eastward, reaching northern India about 80,000 years ago, China 60,000 years ago, Australia about 40,000 years ago and Siberia 14,000 years ago. Others traveled westward, arriving in central Europe 50,000 years ago.

↑ **The front skull** is of *Homo habilis*, an ancestor of *H. sapiens* (the farthest skull). *H. habilis* lived 1.75 million years ago. The middle skull is of *H. erectus*, an ancestor of Neanderthal humans (*H. neanderthalensis*). *H.erectus* lived between 2 and 0.5 million years ago.

SPREAD OF MODERN HUMANS

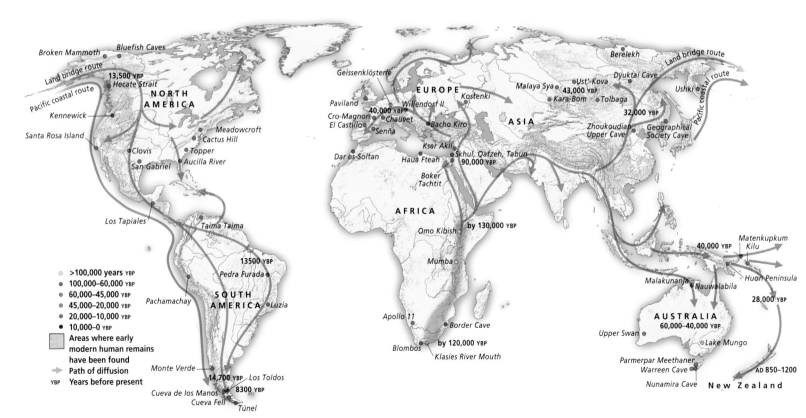

Broken Mammoth
Bluefish Caves
Land bridge route
Pacific coastal route
13,500 YBP
Hecate Strait
NORTH AMERICA
Kennewick
Santa Rosa Island
Meadowcroft
Cactus Hill
Clovis
Topper
San Gabriel
Aucilla River
Los Tapiales
Taima Taima
13500 YBP
Pedra Furada
Pachamachay
SOUTH AMERICA
Luzia
Monte Verde
14,700 YBP
Los Toldos
8300 YBP
Cueva de los Manos
Cueva Fell
Túnel

Geissenklösterle
EUROPE
Paviland
Willendorf II
Kostenki
Malaya Sya
Cro-Magnon
40,000 YBP
Chauvet
El Castillo
Senña
Bacho Kiro
ASIA
Ksar Akil
Dar es-Soltan
Haua Fteah
Skhul, Qafzeh, Tabun
90,000 YBP
Boker Tachtit
AFRICA
by 130,000 YBP
Omo Kibish
Mumba
Apollo 11
Border Cave
Blombos
by 120,000 YBP
Klasies River Mouth
Berelekh
Land bridge route
Dyuktai Cave
Pacific coastal route
Ust'-Kova
43,000 YBP
Kara-Bom
Tolbaga
Ushki
Zhoukoudian
Upper Cave
32,000 YBP
Geographical Society Cave
Matenkupkum
Kilu
40,000 YBP
Malakunanja
Nauwalabila
Huon Peninsula
28,000 YBP
Upper Swan
AUSTRALIA
60,000–40,000 YBP
Lake Mungo
Parmerpar Meethaner
Warreen Cave
AD 850–1200
Nunamira Cave
New Zealand

○ >100,000 years YBP
● 100,000–60,000 YBP
● 60,000–45,000 YBP
● 45,000–20,000 YBP
● 20,000–10,000 YBP
● 10,000–0 YBP
▢ Areas where early modern human remains have been found
→ Path of diffusion
YBP Years before present

← **Modern humans first migrated out of Africa** about 100,000 years ago. As they moved, they settled each new area, but after a time some moved on in search of better living conditions and food. When people reached the tip of the Malayan peninsula they traveled from island to island until they arrived in Australia. Humans probably reached North America about 15,000 years ago, although some scientists believe they may have arrived there earlier.

↑ **Stone Age hunter-gatherers** decorated the walls of caves with depictions of animals and hunting scenes. Cave paintings have been found in several parts of the world. Most European examples date back to the latter part of the last ice age. The paintings shown here, depicting horses, reindeer and an aurochs (an ancestor of domestic cattle), are from a cave at Lascaux, France. They were made between 15,000 and 13,000 years ago.

→ **Human survival** depended on the capacity of game animals to produce offspring year after year and on the growth of plants on which the animals fed. Fertility—of the land, of food animals and of humans—was of vital importance and it featured strongly in religious beliefs and rituals. This fertility symbol was made between 30,000 and 25,000 years ago. It is known as the Venus of Willendorf (the place in present-day Austria where it was found).

Evolution

Over many millions of years, small heritable differences between populations of organisms lead to the emergence of new species. Every individual organism is a little different and occasionally one of those differences allows the organisms carrying it to produce more offspring than those lacking it. The difference becomes more widespread in the population and a point may be reached where organisms with the difference cannot or will not interbreed with organisms that lack it. Alternatively, rising sea level, the growth of a mountain range, or some other insuperable physical barrier may divide a species into two populations. In both cases two groups are reproductively isolated and become separate species. As these species continue to evolve, the outward differences between them may increase, decrease or remain the same. If the differences between related species increase, and the species therefore become increasingly dissimilar, their evolution is said to be divergent. If species that are descended from a common ancestor continue to resemble one another, this is an example of parallel evolution.

It can also happen that unrelated species come to resemble each other, sometimes so closely that it is difficult to tell them apart. That is convergent evolution, and it occurs when organisms adopt similar ways of life in similar environments. Convergent evolution means that some plants and animals in particular types of environment—for example rain forests, deserts or polar regions—closely resemble their counterparts in similar environments in other parts of the world, even though the species are not closely related.

↑ **The emerald tree boa** (*Corallus canina*) (above left) lives in the dim light of the forests of the Amazon Basin, in South America. In this environment the heat sensors in pits above this snake's mouth help it detect prey. The green tree python (*C. hondropython viridis*) (above right) is almost indistinguishable from the emerald tree boa, but it lives in New Guinea and lacks heat sensors. The two snakes, which are not close relatives, are an example of convergent evolution.

THE EVOLUTION OF THE HORSE

From left to right: *Hyracotherium*, the size of a fox terrier, lived about 50 million years ago; *Mesohippus* lived about 30 million years ago; *Merychippus* about 20 million years ago; *Pliohippus* about four million years ago; and *Equus*, the modern horse, appeared about one million years ago. Although these horses are directly linked, there were also many side branches to the evolutionary tree. These led to species that died out.

Hyracotherium   Mesohippus   Merychippus   Pliohippus   Equus

↑ **Armadillos and pangolins** are another
example of convergent evolution. Armadillos
live in North, Central and South America. This
three-banded armadillo (*Tolypeutes tricinctus*)
(above right) lives on the grasslands of Brazil.
It feeds on soil invertebrates, especially ants and
termites, and is armor-plated for protection. The
pangolin (*Manis tricuspis*) (above left), which
closely resembles the three-banded armadillo
but is not related to it, has no teeth. It uses
its long, sticky tongue to feed on ants. It has
scales that protect it from predators, especially
when it rolls into a ball. It lives in Africa.

← **Lady Bird Johnson Grove** in the Redwood
National Park, California, is an example of
the type of forest that was once much more
widespread in western North America, where
the warm, humid climate favors a temperate
rain forest dominated by huge redwood trees.

Adaptation

When people migrate to a foreign country they may need to make adaptations to new and often challenging conditions. They may need to learn a new language, conform to different social conventions, eat unfamiliar food and make many other significant changes to the way they are used to living.

Adaptation also has a related, but more precise, scientific meaning. An organism that possesses a physical feature that gives it an advantage over other members of its species in the particular environment they all inhabit will be more successful than others. It will produce more offspring, and if the offspring inherit that feature they, too, will enjoy the advantages it confers. These offspring will be better adapted to the environment than individuals that lack the feature, and the feature will become fixed in the population. After a number of generations all members of that population will possess it. Small differences among individuals result from genetic mutations. The gradual accumulation of these mutations leads to the appearance of new species.

EYE ADAPTATIONS
All animals' eyes are complex structures. Eyes are so useful—indeed, they are often essential for survival—that they have evolved independently at least 40 times in different animal groups. Insect eyes serve the same general purpose as those of vertebrates and non-vertebrates, but they have evolved differently and have adapted to different uses and conditions.

Dragonflies hunt on the wing. Their multiple eyes are adapted to have a wide range of vision that can detect even very slight movements.

African crocodiles have slit-like pupils that are adapted to protect the eyes from very bright light and allow the crocodile to see in dim light.

Owls, like a number of other birds that hunt at night, have very large, bulging eyes that are adapted to allow optimal vision in dark conditions.

Human eyes, which are more adapted to daylight conditions, are smaller, narrower and less bulging than those of nocturnal hunters.

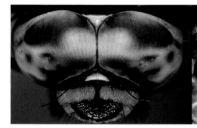

SEXUAL SELECTION

Individuals need to attract mates, and potential mates can often take their pick of several rival suitors. Sexual selection therefore favors the most attractive suitors. This has led to spectacular adornment adaptations in some species, especially among some male birds. The long tail of the male long-tailed widowbird (*Euplectes progne*); symmetric tail streamers in the male barn swallow (*Hirundo rustica*); and asymmetric tail feathers in the male paradise whydah (*Vidua paradisaea*) are striking examples. There is also male–male sexual selection, where males compete for females. Size and strength in elephant seals (*Mirounga* species) and antler size in stags such as red deer (*Cervus elaphus*) are examples of male–male sexual selection.

→ **Many birds** have decorative tail feathers that they display to attract mates, but none are so eye-catching as those of the blue peacock (*Pavo cristatus*). As the male dances, the female he is courting is entranced by a huge curtain filled with eyes, all, seemingly, staring at her.

↓ **These tourists** are enjoying a camel ride in the Moroccan Sahara. The camel is superbly adapted to desert conditions. In summer it can remain healthy without drinking for 17 days, losing 25 percent of its body fluid, until its ribs are clearly visible. Its hump provides insulation and stores fat and its thick coat absorbs heat, preventing it from reaching the skin.

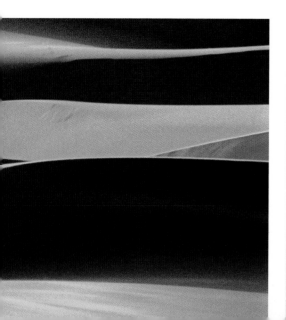

Extinction and speciation

New species emerge when two populations of a species are no longer able to interbreed. There are several ways this can happen. It may be because they find themselves on opposite sides of an impassable barrier, such as a mountain range or sea. Or their reproductive cycles may cease to be synchronized, so that the groups are fertile at different times. Behavior may change, and the two groups may respond to different courtship strategies. Once the two groups are reproductively isolated, gradual genetic changes within each group will enhance the differences between them. Eventually they will be different species. They will be known as "daughter" species of the original species, and "sibling" species in relation to each other.

Species do not last forever. For example, mammal species exist on average for one million years and invertebrate species for 11 million years. Speciation and extinction happen all the time, but there have been episodes when some event has caused large numbers of species to disappear over a short period. There is evidence of several such mass extinction events and many scientists suspect we may be entering one now, in this case resulting mainly from human alteration of habitats. Following a mass extinction, abundant resources are available to the survivors. As the survivors adapt to exploit those resources they divide into new species in a process called adaptive radiation. A burst of speciation follows extinctions and speciation eventually ends in extinction.

→ **The pallid squill (_Scilla morrisii_)** seems to be on the verge of extinction. Fewer than 600 individual plants are known to exist, in three locations in Cyprus. At present its numbers are not declining, but it lives in old oak forest, much of which has already disappeared as a result of logging, road construction and conversion to farmland. In 2006 the plant entered the IUCN Red List of Threatened Species, where it is described as critically endangered.

MASS EXTINCTIONS

The graph shows the rate at which genera have become extinct as a percentage of all genera that existed at different times. The spikes mark mass extinction events. The dinosaurs disappeared in an event at the end of the Cretaceous. The greatest extinction of all, at the end of the Permian, is known as the Great Dying.

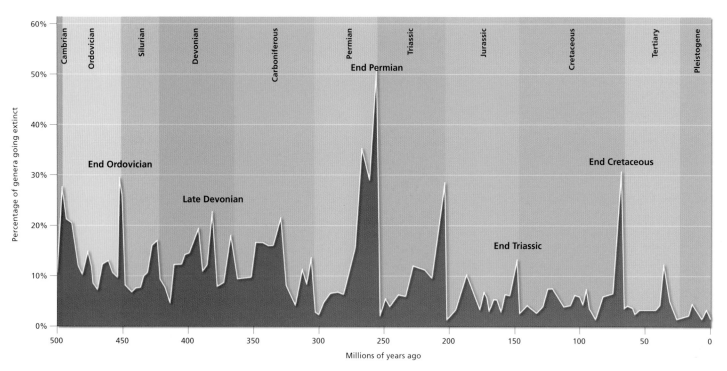

Cambrian · Ordovician · Silurian · Devonian · Carboniferous · Permian · Triassic · Jurassic · Cretaceous · Tertiary · Pleistogene

End Permian

End Ordovician

Late Devonian

End Cretaceous

End Triassic

Percentage of genera going extinct

Millions of years ago

Sickle-billed Vanga
(*Falculea polleni*)

← **The aurochs** (*Bos primigenius*) was the ancestor of all domestic cattle. At one time it ranged across Europe, the Middle East, central Asia, India and Africa. Gradually its numbers declined and the last aurochs died in 1627, in the Jaktorów Forest, Poland. In the 1920s the brothers Heinz and Lutz Heck attempted to breed back to the aurochs from domestic cattle. Herds of recreated aurochs are now kept in several zoological parks. This one lives in Rambouillet Forest, France.

Pollen's Vanga
(*Xenopirostris polleni*)

→ **Animals are sometimes carried**—by the wind or drifting on plant material—away from continental coasts to distant islands. If a small population of such accidental voyagers should become established on an island they may evolve to live in different ways. These vangas, descended from one African species, live on Madagascar in habitats with a latitudinal range equal to that of California.

Helmet Vanga
(*Euryceros polleni*)

Red-shouldered Vanga
(*Calicalicus rufocarpalis*)

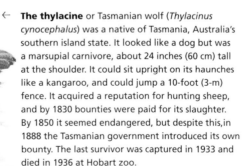

← **The thylacine** or Tasmanian wolf (*Thylacinus cynocephalus*) was a native of Tasmania, Australia's southern island state. It looked like a dog but was a marsupial carnivore, about 24 inches (60 cm) tall at the shoulder. It could sit upright on its haunches like a kangaroo, and could jump a 10-foot (3-m) fence. It acquired a reputation for hunting sheep, and by 1830 bounties were paid for its slaughter. By 1850 it seemed endangered, but despite this, in 1888 the Tasmanian government introduced its own bounty. The last survivor was captured in 1933 and died in 1936 at Hobart zoo.

Blue Vanga
(*Cyanolanius madagascarinus*)

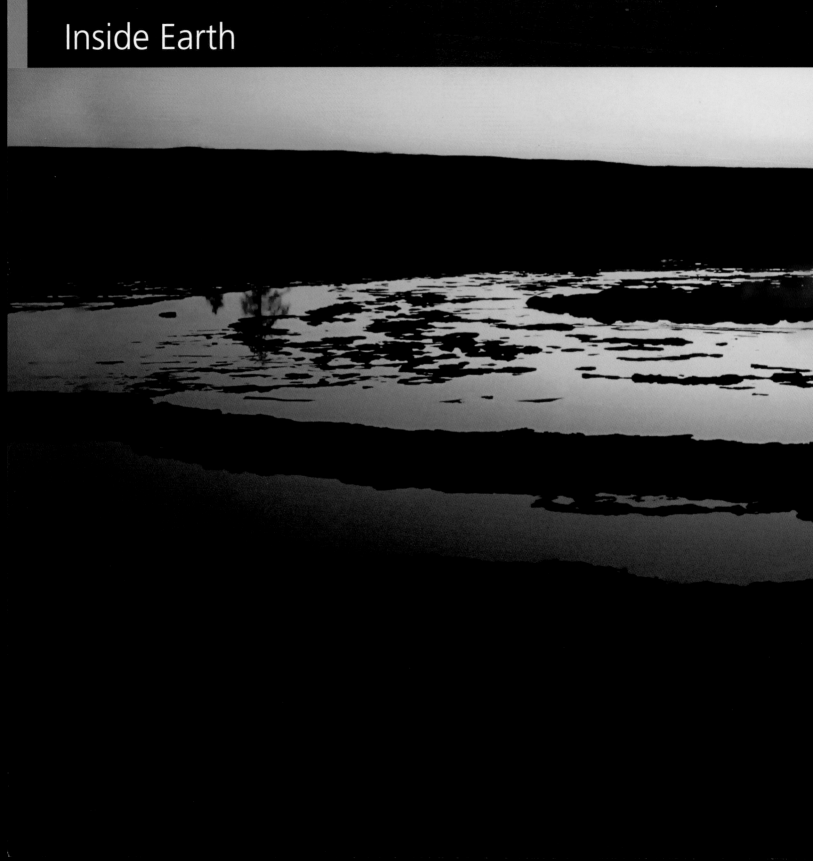

Inside Earth

Earth has a solid iron core, a thick mantle and a thin and fragile crust that supports all plant and animal life. This crust is composed of rocks, formed from minerals and created in different ways. Plant and animal fossils give clues to past life, and fossil fuels drawn from below the surface provide energy to sustain human life.

The interior

Earth formed by the accretion of material from a ring of gas and dust that orbited the young Sun. It was a violent process, because dust collected to form rocks and these rocks bombarded the new planet. Some of the material was radioactive, comprising heavy elements that formed during the violent collapse and a supernova explosion of an earlier star. Radioactive elements emit energy as they decay and that radioactive energy is still the principal source of Earth's internal heat: Earth is in effect a thermal nuclear reactor. Gravitational and kinetic energy were also converted to heat during the bombardment. The total release of energy—radioactive, gravitational and kinetic— melted all of Earth's rocks and formed a worldwide ocean of magma with a temperature of 2300°F (1260°C) or more. As the fiery ball cooled and its rocks solidified, the densest material sank toward the center and Earth acquired a layered structure. This is why the composition of the planet's exterior crust is different from that of its deep interior.

→ **Earth's outermost crust** accounts for less than 1 percent of the planet's volume. It is extremely thin. About 32 percent of Earth's mass is concentrated in the inner and outer cores. The mantle contains the remaining two-thirds. Above the solid surface, the oceans and atmosphere comprise only a thin skin.

↓ **Convective movements** in the iron–nickel alloy of the outer core generate electrical currents that produce Earth's magnetic field, which is much like the field of a simple bar magnet. This magnetic field extends, as the magnetosphere, far beyond Earth. The magnetosphere deflects the electrically charged particles of the solar wind, but is compressed by them.

→ **A bar magnet** is surrounded by a magnetic field that much smaller than the Earth's but is otherwise very similar. Scatter dry iron filings on a sheet of card, lay the card over a magnet and tap it gently with a pencil. The iron filings will align themselves with the magnetic field, revealing its field lines.

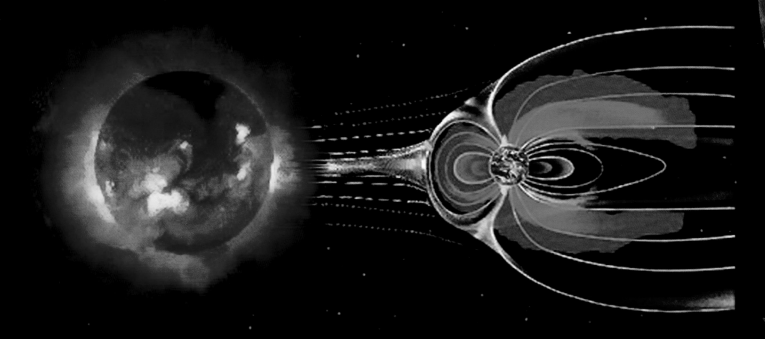

EARTH'S STRUCTURE

Crust Earth's crust is made from cold, solid rock. It is about 3 miles (5 km) thick beneath the ocean basins and up to 37 miles (60 km) thick beneath mountain chains.

Mantle Beneath the crust, the mantle is about 1430 miles (2300 km) thick. Although it is denser than the crust, its high temperature and pressure make it plastic, so it flows like a thick liquid.

Outer core The outer core is about 770 miles (1240 km) thick and consists of molten iron–nickel alloy at a temperature of about 11,000°F (6000°C). Convection currents generate Earth's magnetic field.

Inner core At Earth's center, the inner part of the core has a radius of about 760 miles (1220 km). It consists of iron and a little nickel, and it is solid.

If we shrunk Earth to the size of an orange, its surface, from the deepest ocean floor to the top of the atmosphere, would comprise a layer no thicker than a film of moisture on the skin. Yet that layer is home to every living thing.

Core and mantle

Most scientists believe that Earth's mantle consists of silicate minerals. Basalts and peridotite are the predominant rocks in the upper 186 miles (300 km) of the mantle and peridotite may also be present at lower levels. Many geologists believe the mantle comprises upper and lower layers separated by a transition zone between 250 and 400 miles (400–650 km) below Earth's surface. High pressure in the transition zone transforms olivine, a mineral constituent of peridotite and some basalts, into wadsleyite, a denser mineral. At a depth of about 320 miles (520 km), wadsleyite changes into the still denser ringwoodite. The inner mantle, below 370 miles (600 km), consists of perovskite and magnesiowüstite. The inner core is made mainly from solid, metallic iron alloyed with between 5 and 15 percent nickel. The outer core also contains lighter elements—probably oxygen and sulfur.

LAYERS OF THE MANTLE
The mantle accounts for the largest part of the Earth's interior. It forms two principal layers, and at the top of the upper mantle a third layer, the asthenosphere, is able to bend slowly, like an extremely viscous liquid.

SEISMIC TOMOGRAMS

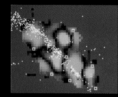 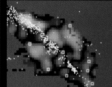 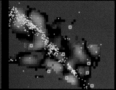 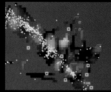

Layer 1
1.5–2 miles (2.5–3.5 km)

Layer 2
2–3.7 miles (3.5–6 km)

Layer 3
3.7–5.5 miles (6–9 km)

Layer 4
5.5–9 miles (9–15 km)

⬉ **These four diagrams, called seismic tomograms,** show a 15.5x12.5-mile (25x20-km) horizontal cross-section at different depths of the rocks beneath Parkfield, California. Red and blue indicate different types of rock structure. The green and blue squares show the location of seismometers. The yellow and white dots are where microquakes have been recorded. The movement of crustal rocks on either side of the fault that occurs in these small earthquakes relieves strain that has built up beneath Earth's surface. The San Andreas Fault is part of a complex system of faults along the boundary between two tectonic plates that are moving past each other, driven by convectional movements in the asthenosphere, which is the uppermost part of the mantle.

⇉ **Lava from the eruption** of Mt Kilauea, Hawaii, raises clouds of steam as it flows into the ocean. Incandescent gases, condensing into hot, volcanic ash, accompany the lava flow.

→ **The eruption** of the volcano Yasur, on Tana Island in the Vanuatu archipelago, creates a spectacular fire fountain that surges skyward.

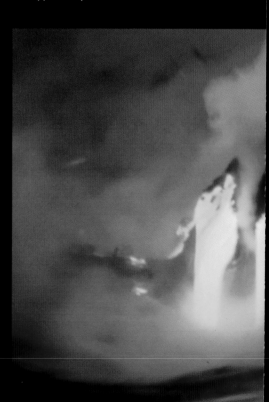

Mantle plume carries hot material upward by convection to the asthenosphere, where the material spreads to the sides, cools, and sinks once more.

Mantle, made from hot and dense rock similar to peridotite, accounts for about 84 percent of Earth's volume and 68 percent of its mass.

The outer core is a layer of liquid with 5 percent of the mass of the inner core; it is made principally from iron mixed with a lighter element, probably oxygen or sulfur.

Mohorovičić disontinuity marks the abrupt boundary separating the crust from the denser material of the mantle.

New crust forms at a spreading ridge, where two plates are moving apart and mantle material rises between them, forming volcanoes.

The crust

The outermost layer of the solid part of Earth consists of large blocks of rock that rest on the mantle. Between the base of the crust and the top of the mantle there is a boundary. This boundary is marked by a change in the velocity of seismic waves, known as the Mohorovičić discontinuity, often abbreviated to Moho.

There are two types of crust: oceanic and continental. Both consist principally of silica and alumina, but differ in the minerals their rocks contain and therefore in the types of rock that constitute them. Oceanic crust is comprised of basalt rock overlain in most of its extent by sediment. It is between 3 and 9 miles (5–15 km) thick and covers about 59 percent of Earth's surface. Continental crust covers about 41 percent, but because it is much thicker—between 19 and 50 miles (30–80 km)—it accounts for 79 percent of the total volume of crustal rock. Granodiorite is the most abundant rock in continental crust. In some areas continental crust, like oceanic crust, is covered by sediment. Oceanic crust forms three layers. All three are of basaltic rock, but they differ in structure. Where sediment covers the rock, it forms a fourth, uppermost layer. In some places the continental crust forms upper and lower layers separated by a boundary known as the Conrad discontinuity.

↓ **The crust and upper mantle** comprise the lithosphere, shown below in cross-section. The oceanic crust is interrupted in three places: by thicker continental crust that projects above the sea surface; by an island arc formed by volcanoes associated with a trench; and by a volcanic island. The base of the continental crust lies lower in the lithosphere than the base of the oceanic crust. The trench occurs where oceanic crust is subducted into the mantle at a margin between two lithospheric plates.

→ **Cerro Torre,** rising to 10,260 feet (3128 m), is the highest of four Andean peaks in the Patagonian Ice Field, in a region claimed by both Chile and Argentina. The Andes formed during the last 50 million years as a result of the collision between the South American, Nazca and Pacific plates. Their height has increased markedly in the last 10 million years. Erosion will eventually smooth the spike of Cerro Torre.

THE LITHOSPHERE

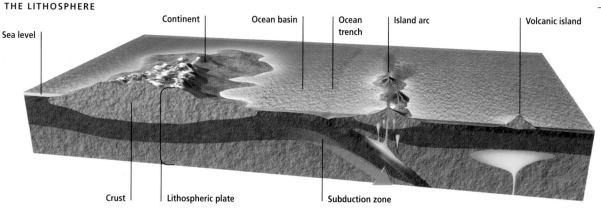

Sea level | Continent | Ocean basin | Ocean trench | Island arc | Volcanic island

Crust | Lithospheric plate | Subduction zone

→ **This false-color photograph,** taken by a Landsat satellite, shows part of northern Saskatchewan and Northwest Territories, Canada. It is part of the Canadian (Laurentian) Shield and its rocks are about 600 million years old. The landscape is of low hills, forests (red) and many lakes (black). The lake at the extreme left is Lake Athabasca.

The Devil's Postpile, in the eastern Sierra Nevada, California, is a national monument, famed for its regular basalt columns up to 60 feet (18 m) high. Viscous basalt lava shrinks as it cools. Vertical contraction makes the layer thinner, but horizontal contraction produces vertical cracks, which result in a hexagonal (and occasionally pentagonal) pattern throughout the layers, producing the columns.

This bedrock in Killbear Provincial Park, near Nobel, Ontario, Canada, is part of the Canadian Shield that formed from continental crust, which has been undisturbed by tectonic activity for at least 600 million years. During that long time, weathering smoothed the mountains that may once have existed. Only continental crust can be this old. Oceanic crust is recycled more quickly.

Used loosely, the word "mineral" refers to any organic substance that is mined below ground. To an Earth scientist, however, the word has a more precise meaning. In the scientific sense, a mineral is a substance, usually inorganic, that occurs naturally and that typically has a crystalline structure. Rocks are composed of minerals and some minerals, such as quartz, mica and feldspar, help define the rocks in which they occur. These are known as rock-forming minerals. Mineral names end in "-ite."

Certain characteristics are used to define a mineral. Each mineral has a distinctive chemical composition, specific gravity and hardness when compared with other minerals. It has a typical color; a way of reflecting light, called its luster; and, when rubbed against an unglazed porcelain plate, it makes a colored mark, called its streak. The way it cleaves along lines of weakness in its crystal lattice is also a defining characteristic, as is the way it fractures.

Some minerals occur in more than one form, called polymorphs. Each form has the same chemical composition but differs because of the arrangement of its atoms. Calcite and aragonite, for example, are polymorphs of calcium carbonate, and graphite and diamond are polymorphs of pure carbon. Impurities can alter the appearance of a mineral. Quartz is made from silica. It can be colorless or pink (rose quartz), purple (amethyst), dark brown (cairngorm) or light brown (citrine).

BROOKITE

Brookite, anatase and rutile are polymorphs—minerals with the same chemical composition but with varying crystal structures—of titanium dioxide. Brookite is reddish-brown to brownish-black in color and has a white streak. It has a metallic luster. Its crystals are orthorhombic. It has a hardness of 5.5–6.0 and a specific gravity of 4.1. Brookite occurs in igneous and metamorphic rocks and in hydrothermal veins. This specimen is from Tremadoc, Wales.

HARDNESS

One of the simplest ways to begin identifying a mineral is to test its hardness by trying to scratch other minerals with it. In 1812 the German mineralogist Friedrich Mohs (1773–1839) used this process to develop a scale of hardness that is still used. Mohs's scale lists 10 minerals in order of their hardness. Each mineral is significantly harder than the one that precedes it on the scale.

MOHS'S SCALE OF HARDNESS

Talc	1
Gypsum	2
Calcite	3
Fluorite	4
Apatite	5
Orthoclase	6
Quartz	7
Topaz	8
Corundum	9
Diamond	10

MALACHITE

Malachite, or hydrated copper carbonate, is a bright green mineral with a pale green streak, seen here in a thin and polished section. It has a specific gravity of 3.9–4.0 and a hardness of 3.5–4.0. When, as often, it is fibrous, it has a silky luster; in crystal form its luster is adamantine (brilliant) or vitreous (glasslike). It is an ore mineral for copper and is often used to make ornaments. It was formerly a source of a green pigment.

CALCITE CRYSTAL

A common, rock-forming mineral, calcite, along with aragonite, is a polymorph of calcium carbonate. It has a specific gravity of 2.7, and a hardness of 3. It is usually colorless or white, but impurities produce a wide variety of colors. The example shown here is reflecting a blue sky. It has a white streak and vitreous luster. Its crystals are trigonal (rhombohedral) and are prized for their beauty. Calcite also has industrial uses.

VANADINITE

A mineral found near sulfide-ore lead deposits, vanadinite can be used as a source of vanadium. It has a specific gravity of 6.88–6.93 and a hardness of 2.5–3.0. Vanadinite crystals are usually sharp hexagonal prisms, although sometimes they are rounded. Its color is orange-red to yellow and its streak is white to yellowish. It has a resinous luster. It is used in metal alloys and in making dyes and mordants. This specimen is from Morocco.

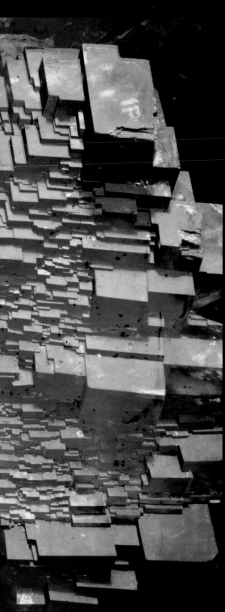

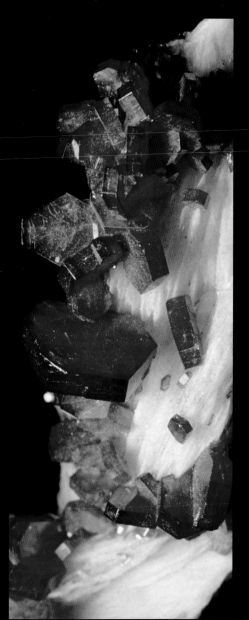

Types of minerals

The study of minerals is called mineralogy. Mineralogists examine the physical properties of minerals—a branch of the discipline called determinative mineralogy—as well as their crystallography and chemistry. Mineralogists also evaluate minerals from an economic standpoint.

Chemical analysis involves crushing the mineral and subjecting it to a number of tests. A mineral's optical properties can also reveal a great deal about that mineral. These properties can be observed by examining a thin section of the mineral under a polarizing microscope. A slice cut from a specimen is stuck to a slide using a resin with a particular refractive index. It is then ground in stages to a thickness of 0.0012 inch (0.03 mm), and covered with a cover slip, which is fixed with the same resin. A thin section is semi-transparent. The microscope polarizer (a piece of polaroid) allows light vibrating in a single plane to pass through. Rotating the polarizer allows the passage of light polarized in two planes at right angles.

GOLD

Throughout history, gold has been prized for its beauty, rarity and purity. Its purity is the reason that this metal does not tarnish. Other metals tarnish because they react with chemicals that are present in the air. Gold is reluctant to form compounds, and this is why it remains unaffected by those chemicals. Gold can be found in its pure, or native, state or in a form in which it is alloyed with other metals.

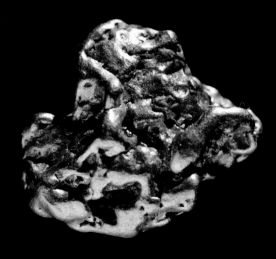

APATITE

A common phosphate mineral, apatite has a specific gravity of 3.1–3.3 and a hardness of 5. It forms hexagonal prismatic crystals. It is usually green or gray-green, but is sometimes white, yellow, brown, blue or red. It is the principal ingredient in fossil bones. This pink apatite crystal is growing on albite, one of the plagioclase feldspars—a group of rock-forming minerals with a range of compositions from apatite to anorthite.

COMMON ROCK-FORMING MINERALS

Rock	Mineral	Composition
Olivine	olivine	magnesium, iron, silicon, oxygen
Feldspar	orthoclase	potassium, aluminum, silicon, oxygen
	albite	sodium, aluminum, silicon, oxygen
	anorthite	calcium, aluminum, silicon, oxygen
Pyroxene	enstatite	magnesium, silicon, oxygen
	hypersthene	magnesium, iron, silicon, oxygen
	diopside	calcium, magnesium, silicon, oxygen
	heldenbergite	magnesium, iron, silicon, oxygen
	augite	calcium, sodium, magnesium, iron aluminium, silicon, oxygen
Serpentine	serpentine	magnesium, iron, silicon, oxygen hydrogen
Mica	muscovite	sodium, aluminum, silicon, oxygen hydrogen
	biotite	sodium, magnesium, iron, aluminum silicon, oxygen, hydrogen
	chlorite	magnesium, iron, silicon, aluminum oxygen, hydrogen
Graphite	graphite	carbon

DOLOMITE

A rock-forming mineral that is also known as pearlspar, dolomite is used as a building stone and in making bricks for furnaces. Its specific gravity is 2.8–2.9 and its hardness 3.5–4.0. Its crystals are trigonal (rhombohedral) with curved faces, but dolomite also occurs in massive (noncrystalline) and granular forms. It is usually white or colorless but can be yellow or brown. It has a white streak, and its luster is vitreous.

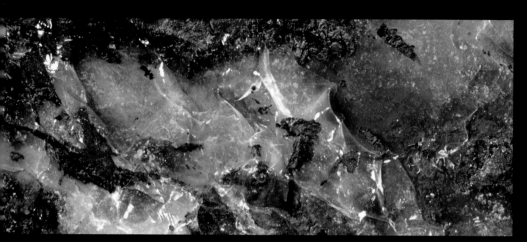

OPAL

Opal, or hydrous silica, consists of between 6 and 10 percent water. It has a layer of water molecules trapped near its mineral surface and this layer causes the iridescence, or opalescence, that is one of its diagnostic properties. The specific gravity of opal is 1.99–2.25 and its hardness 5.5–6.5. It is amorphous (does not form crystals). It can be colorless, milky-white to gray, red, brown, blue or green. It forms from silica-rich water and often fills fissures in rocks.

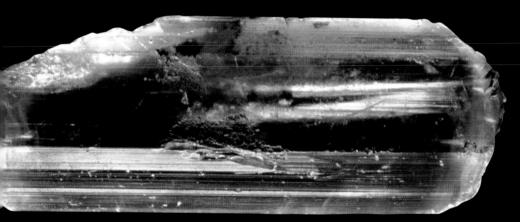

GYPSUM

Gypsum, or hydrated calcium sulfate, is the first mineral to be precipitated from evaporating seawater. In volcanic areas it can result from the reaction between sulfuric acid and limestone. It has a specific gravity of 2.3 and a hardness of 1.5–2.0. It usually forms clear tabular crystals, often with curved surfaces, and it has a white streak and vitreous luster. Alabaster is a fine-grained variety of gypsum that can be carved.

HEMATITE

Hematite is also known as iron glance and red iron ore. It is called specularite when it occurs as a gray mass, or aggregate, of tabular or trigonal (rhombohedral) crystals. It is named kidney ore in the mamillated form seen here. It is one of the most important ores for iron . It has a specific gravity of 4.9–5.3 and a hardness of 5.0–6.0. It is often dull or bright red with a red to reddish-brown streak and metallic luster.

SAPPHIRE

Sapphire is the blue variety of the mineral corundum. Red corundum is ruby and the green variety is emerald. The specific gravity of sapphire is 3.9–4.1 and its hardness 9. It forms rough, often barrel-shaped, trigonal (rhombohedral) crystals. It is transparent and has a vitreous luster. Gem varieties of this mineral are highly prized, but corundum is used mainly for commercial purposes: grinding wheels and disks, emery paper and grinding and polishing powders.

GARNET

Garnets are an important group of rock-forming minerals with a range of chemical compositions based on X, Y, SiO_{12}, where X is calcium, magnesium or iron, and Y is aluminum, iron or chromium. Their specific gravity is 3.6–4.3 and their hardness 7.0–7.5. Their color varies with chemical composition from deep red to almost black, green, yellow, brown or white. Garnets form cubic crystals (commonly dodecahedra). Transparent forms are gemstones, but garnets are used mainly as abrasives.

FLUORITE

Calcium fluorite is used as a flux in iron smelting and also has uses in the ceramics and chemical industries. It has a specific gravity of 3.2, and a hardness of 4.0. It forms cubic crystals. Fluorite is usually yellow, green, blue or purple, with a white streak, but it can also be red, pink, black or colorless, and it is often banded. The deep-purple banded form is known as Blue John.

ARAGONITE

A polymorph of calcite, aragonite occurs in veins and rock cavities, and in hot springs, sometimes together with gypsum. Pearls and mollusk shells are formed from it, but in fossil shells aragonite is converted to the more stable calcite or replaced by some other mineral. Its specific gravity is 2.9 and its hardness 3.5–4.0. It forms colorless, white, gray or yellow orthorhombic crystals with a white streak.

PYRITE

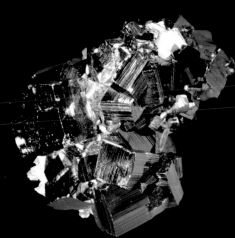

Pyrite is also known as fool's gold because of its pale, yellow color, the metallic luster of its cubic crystals and the fact that it does not tarnish. Iron sulfide is its chemical name and it was formerly used to make sulfuric acid. It has a specific gravity of 4.9–5.2, a hardness of 6.0–6.5, and it has a black streak. Pyrite occurs in many types of rock in a wide variety of environments. It sometimes forms nodules in rocks.

COPPER SULFATE CRYSTAL

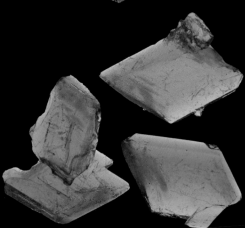

In its hydrated form, copper sulfate occurs naturally as the mineral chalcanthite in the oxidized zones of copper deposits. It forms blue triclinic crystals, but these crystals form only rarely. The specific gravity of copper sulfate is 2.12–2.3 and its hardness 2.5. It has a vitreous luster and is transparent to translucent, with a white streak. Chalcanthite is soluble in water, so the mineral, which is poisonous, is most often found in arid environments.

CRYSTAL SYSTEMS

Cubic Crystals in the cubic or isometric system have three axes of equal length that are perpendicular to each other. The crystals form symmetrical cubes.

Tetragonal Crystals in this system are oblong and have three axes that are perpendicular to each other, but not of equal length. The vertical axis is either longer or shorter than the other axes.

Orthorhombic Crystals in the orthorhombic system are, like tetragonal ones, also oblong. They have three axes, which are all perpendicular to each other, but are of different lengths.

Monoclinic The three axes of crystals in the monoclinic system are of unequal length. Two intersect at an oblique angle and the third is perpendicular to the plane of the other two.

Triclinic Crystals in the triclinic system are completely asymmetrical. Their three axes are of different lengths and they all meet at oblique angles.

Hexagonal and trigonal A hexagonal crystal has six vertical faces; a trigonal crystal has three faces. In these closely related systems three lateral axes, of equal length, intersect at 60 degrees and a vertical axis, of a different length, is perpendicular to them.

Rocks

Most people think of rock as the solid, unyielding surface that lies below the soft surface layer of soil. They understand that when the physical forces of freezing, wind, rain or geological disturbances fracture the rock, pieces, known as "rocks," become detached. As a useful scientific definition, however, this is somewhat too vague.

Geologists define rock as any consolidated or unconsolidated aggregate of mineral or organic material. Though they look and feel dissimilar, sand on a beach, soil in which crops grow and the clay a potter uses are all, in a geological sense, classed as forms of rock. There is a reason for this inclusiveness. All rock begins as magma, in Earth's mantle. When it enters the crust this magma cools and solidifies to form "igneous" rock. Weathering processes then begin to work on this igneous rock, steadily grinding it into ever smaller fragments, until it is reduced to grains of sand or soil particles such as clay. Those particles may then be compressed to form "sedimentary" rock—one of the numerous forms of hard rock that covers three-quarters of Earth's surface. Or they may be heated to form a third type, "metamorphic" rock. Slate and marble are types of metamorphic rock.

↓ **The types and ages of rocks** in the Grand Canyon, Arizona, are shown in this cross-section. Rocks in this canyon date back more than two billion years.

ROCKS IN THE GRAND CANYON

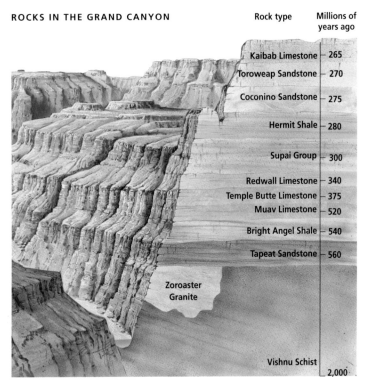

Rock type	Millions of years ago
Kaibab Limestone	265
Toroweap Sandstone	270
Coconino Sandstone	275
Hermit Shale	280
Supai Group	300
Redwall Limestone	340
Temple Butte Limestone	375
Muav Limestone	520
Bright Angel Shale	540
Tapeat Sandstone	560
Zoroaster Granite	
Vishnu Schist	2,000

↑ **Autunite, shown here in crystalline form**, is hydrated calcium uranyl phosphate, a secondary mineral that forms when a previous (primary) mineral melts and recrystallizes. Autunite is radioactive and fluorescent. It is an ore mineral for uranium and was used in the development of the atomic bomb during World War II.

↑ **Pitchblende is an impure form** of uraninite, the most important ore mineral for uranium. Impurities include thallium, cerium, lead, polonium and radium. In 1898 Marie Curie (1867–1934) and her husband Pierre Curie (1859–1906) extracted polonium (named after Marie's native Poland) from pitchblende, and later extracted 0.1 gram of radium chloride from several tons of ore.

→ **Where stone with a commercial value** lies close to the surface the soil is cleared away and the stone cut from the body of rock. The result is a quarry, which can be vast like the one seen here.

↓ **This micrograph** shows a thin section of quartz porphyry in plane-polarized light. The large crystals are called phenocrysts and a rock containing them is said to be porphyritic. Phenocrysts are of quartz and feldspar in a matrix of quartz, alkali feldspar and biotite—a type of mica. Quartz porphyry, also known as elvan, is used for building, road construction and in the manufacture of glazed tiles.

The rock cycle

Crustal rocks originate in the mantle and rise through fissures to cool and solidify close to the surface. Rocks that were once molten are described as igneous—from ignis, the Latin word for "fire." As igneous rocks solidify, their ingredients crystallize to form the range of minerals that define the rock. Because crystals grow, their size indicates the rate at which the rock cooled: rapid cooling produces small crystals and imparts a fine texture to the rock. Chemicals react with ingredients in the rock and rain, ice and wind assault the rock once it is exposed to air. These weathering forces combine to reduce the hard, igneous rock to fragments and grains. As the grains gradually become compacted and heated, they form sedimentary rocks. Further heating and intense pressure may partially melt and recrystallize the rock. This process is called metamorphism. Finally, plate movements carry all surface rocks to a subduction zone, where one plate is sinking beneath another. There the rocks descend into the mantle, whence they originally came.

↓ **Material from Earth's mantle** intrudes into the crust, some of it as a result of volcanic eruptions. Physical and chemical weathering remove softer rock from around this material, leaving the igneous rock exposed. As this igneous rock weathers, it forms sediments that may change into sedimentary rock. Sedimentary rock may eventually change into metamorphic rock. The world's highest rates of erosion are found in young mountain chains such as the Himalayas and Andes. Shield areas, such as the north of Canada, consist of extremely ancient rock. Once mountainous, long periods of weathering and erosion have reduced shield areas to plains and low hills.

↑ **Dartmoor** is in southwest England. The moor, a place of rugged, windswept beauty, and a national park, rises 1000 feet (300 m) above sea level. Beneath the surface, there is a large quantity of granite that has intruded from Earth's mantle. In many places weathering has worn away the softer overlying material to leave large blocks of granite—called tors on Dartmoor—protruding dramatically above the surface. This one is Saddle Tor.

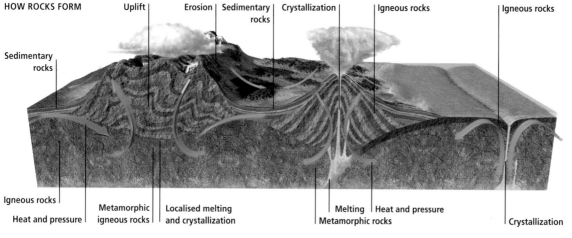

HOW ROCKS FORM — Sedimentary rocks · Uplift · Erosion · Sedimentary rocks · Crystallization · Igneous rocks · Igneous rocks · Igneous rocks · Heat and pressure · Metamorphic igneous rocks · Localised melting and crystallization · Melting · Metamorphic rocks · Heat and pressure · Crystallization

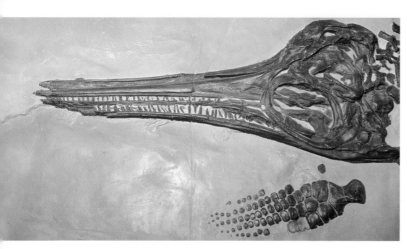

← **Granite is the most widespread** igneous rock of the continental crust. It is light in color, hard and coarse-grained. It consists of at least 20 percent quartz. Granite forms by the local replacement of continental crust; by the melting and recrystallization of old continental crust; by the depletion of basalt magma during cooling; or by a combination of these processes.

←← **If dying plants** or animals fall into soft mud that buries them, the hard parts of their remains may be preserved as fossils, as heat and pressure change the mud into sedimentary rock. This is the fossilized skull and limb of *Ichthyosaurus quadriscissus*, an ichthyosaur, or "fish-reptile," that lived during the Jurassic period, between 199.6 and 65.5 million years ago.

Sedimentary rocks

Sediment forms as a result of a number of processes. Erosion reduces hard, igneous rocks to small particles, some no bigger than specks of dust. Raindrops wash airborne particles to the ground, and rainwater flowing across the surface washes particles into rivers that carry them to the sea. Here they settle on the seabed. After a period of heavy rain, when rivers are in spate, their waters are usually muddy with the suspended material they are carrying. Sandy beaches and beach dunes form from grains that are washed into the sea. Other particles accumulate on land. Sand grains, about 0.04 inch (1 mm) thick and consisting mainly of quartz, form desert dunes. In some parts of the world, smaller, silt-sized particles that average 0.001 inch (0.03 mm) across settle to form a type of deposit called loess. Other types of sediment include evaporite, which forms when an enclosed body of seawater evaporates and the salts that are dissolved in it are precipitated. Many microscopic marine organisms have skeletons, shells or plates of silica or calcium carbonate. When the organisms die, these hard parts sink to the floor of shallow seas to form a calcareous ooze. Volcanic ash also settles to form a sediment.

All sediments consist of loose particles, but if those particles become cemented or compacted together the sediment is transformed into sedimentary rock. Aragonite can cement sand grains together to form beach rock. Pressure from the weight of overlying material can also compress sediments into rock.

→ **Tiny mineral grains** are not the only material that can cement together to form solid sedimentary rock. When larger, rounded particles, more than 0.08 inch (2 mm) across—and called "clasts," regardless of their size—become cemented in this way they form a type of rock called a conglomerate or puddingstone. The cemented clasts are often the size of pebbles, as in this example from England; they can be as large as cobbles or boulders. The clasts are set in a fine-textured matrix of sand or silt and held together by a cement of calcium carbonate, silica, iron oxide or clay.

SALT FLATS

Evaporites consist of salts that have been precipitated onto the bed of a shallow lagoon or arm of the sea. As a result, salt flats are level and, because they consist of salt, they are brilliantly white. Bonneville Salt Flats, Utah, cover 30,000 acres (12,100 ha). In 1914, the first, unofficial, land speed record of 141.73 miles per hour (228 km/h) was set at Bonneville Salt Flats. It is still the principal venue for land speed record attempts.

SANDSTONE

Sediments are deposited in horizontal layers and interruptions in the rate at which they are deposited produce distinct layers of sediment, which settle one above the other. When the sediment is compressed and cemented to form rock, the stratification is preserved. Subsequent movements of Earth's crust may bend and fold the layers, and erosion may, over time, expose them to view. This is a dramatic exposure of sandstones that once lay on the seabed.

SILT AND CLAY

About 170 million years ago this landscape in Utah, in southwestern USA, was a sandy desert. Then, for a brief period, floodwaters deposited red mud on top of the sand dunes. After that, the desert climate returned. Today, a thin layer of silt and clay covers the surface, producing red and tan streaks that stain the white Navajo Sandstone that is typical of the area. This view shows part of the West and East temples, two prominent features of Zion National Park.

RESISTANCE TO EROSION

Sedimentary rocks, even those in close proximity to each other, often vary in the degree to which they are resistant to erosion. If the sediment layers are horizontal, erosion of the weaker rocks leaves the more resistant rocks standing as isolated, flat-topped hills called mesas, or similar, but smaller, hills called buttes. If the layers slope gently, asymmetric erosion produces a ridge called a cuesta, with one steep side and one that slopes gently. If the angle is 40 degrees or more, the resulting ridge is more symmetrical; it is called a hogback or hog's back.

→ **Where vertical fractures** exist in a coastal cliff with horizontal bedding, erosion by the sea will widen them. Waves then isolate sections of the cliff, wearing back the cliff face and leaving more resistant sections standing as towers called stacks. These stacks are known as the Twelve Apostles. They are in Port Campbell National Park, Victoria, Australia.

↓ **Sedimentary rocks** sometimes contain a glasslike form of silica called chert, and chalk contains nodules of a type of chert called flint. Flint, because of its hardness, has long been used to make sharp-edged tools and weapons. These flint tools were made by humans during the Upper Paleolithic (Stone Age) period, between 37,000 and 12,000 years ago.

↓ **Occasional wetting** by slightly acidic rain dissolves some of the compounds among the grains of desert sand. When the rain ceases and the sun dries the sand, those compounds crystallize. The crystals sometimes radiate into beautiful forms such as this desert rose—formed from crystals of gypsum or calcite.

↓ **When calcium sulfate** crystallizes the crystals usually form in irregular shapes. Gypsum is an evaporite mineral with a specific gravity of 2.3 and a hardness of 1.5–2.0. In its colorless transparent form it is called selenite; the fine-grained variety of gypsum is alabaster. The fibrous gypsum shown here is called satin spar. It is formed when anhydrite dissolves and then recrystallizes.

← **Crocidolite, or blue asbestos,** is a fibrous form of the mineral riebeckite. If quartz infiltrates the crocidolite fibers the result is the formation of a semi-precious stone known as tigereye, or cat's eye. These names arise from the stone's "chatoyancy"—the vertical luminescent band is thought to resemble the pupil of a cat's, or tiger's, eye. Soldiers in ancient Roman times wore this stone because they believed it provided protection in battle.

←← **Red Rock Canyon State Park,** on the northwestern edge of the Mojave Desert, California, has long been a favorite with movie-makers. A number of westerns, as well as part of the movie Jurassic Park, were filmed here. It is also a source of many important paleontological finds. The cliffs exposed in its canyons are famed for their white, pink, red and brown layers. The ones shown here are formed from mudstone covered by a caprock layer of harder lava.

Igneous rocks

Magma, the material of Earth's mantle, is hot and is contained under high pressure. Although it is denser than crustal rock, magma has little structure. It contains dissolved volatiles—substances that vaporize when the pressure decreases—and suspended crystals. Silicate magma, by far the most common type, consists of silicon and oxygen in various arrangements of crystals and large molecules, with atoms of other elements between them. When magma penetrates fissures in the crust, or when it erupts above the surface, it enters a region of lower temperature and pressure. Its volatiles enter the atmosphere and as the remainder cools some of its ingredients crystallize into minerals. Igneous rock is the solidified, crystalline magma that is formed by this process.

Igneous rocks are classified in a number of ways. One system takes account of the amount of silica a rock contains. Rocks with less than 45 percent silica by weight are called "ultrabasic," those with between 45 and 52 percent are "basic," those with between 52 and 66 percent are "intermediate" and rocks that contain more than 66 percent silica are "acid." Most acid rocks are pale in color or "leucocratic;" basic rocks are dark, or "melanocratic." Igneous rocks are also classified according to grain size. Those with grains that are invisible to the naked eye are deemed to be fine-grained; those with grains that are visible but are up to only 0.04 inch (1 mm) thick are medium- to fine-grained; those whose grains are 0.04 inch (1 mm) or more thick are coarse- to medium-grained. The CIPW norm classification, developed in 1902 by the American petrologists W. Cross, J.P. Iddings, L.V. Pirrson and H.W. Washington, compares rocks on the basis of their chemistry.

← **When molten lava** cools very quickly there may not be sufficient time for its constituent minerals to grow into crystals. Instead it forms a shiny, amorphous solid—a type of glass. This picture is of obsidian, a black volcanic glass that is more than 70 percent silica by weight. Obsidian was highly valued in Paleolithic times because it can be chipped to produce sharp-edged tools. Obsidian blades, with edges up to five times as sharp as a steel scalpel, are still used in cardiac surgery.

← **The rays of the setting Sun** strike Half Dome, a cliff in Yosemite National Park, California, that rises more than 4700 feet (1435 m) above the floor of the Yosemite Valley. The most famous feature of the valley, the dome has challenged climbers at least since it was declared unclimbable in the 1870s. There are now several trails that lead to the top. The Half Dome is a granite ridge that is equally steep on both sides, except near the summit. Despite its "half-dome" appearance, the dome has probably lost little material by erosion. In the language of the local Native Americans, the dome is called tis-sa-ack, meaning "cleft rock."

←← **About 30 million years ago** a volcano erupted in the Four Corners area of Shiprock, in northwestern New Mexico. Basalt magma rose up a central pipe that led to a number of smaller vents. The volcano exploded, producing a crater at the summit that filled with water, but some of the magma solidified inside the central pipe, or neck, and has remained there ever since. It is formed from breccia—fragments that have cemented together. Gradually the surrounding rocks have eroded away, leaving behind the lava spire, which rises 1700 feet (520 m) above the Colorado Plateau. Navajo people call it Tse Bi dahi, the "winged rock," and consider it sacred.

→ **According to legend,** the giant Fionn MacComhal built the Giant's Causeway, in County Antrim, Northern Ireland, in order to reach his rival, Fingal, who lived in a cave on his island of Staffa. More realistically, lava once formed a pond here, at the lower end of a tunnel. It shrank as it cooled, and shrinkage produced vertical cracks, which divided the lava into hexagonal columns.

↑ **Pillow-shaped piles** of basalt lava are seldom more than three feet (1 m) across, but can be hundreds of feet thick. A skin of fine-grained lava surrounds each pillow. Pillow lava forms when a volcano erupts beneath water. The exterior of the lava cools rapidly, but the central part remains plastic for much longer.

→ **The Devil's Marbles,** in Australia's Northern Territory, are granite boulders 13 feet (4 m) high and 43 to 108 feet (13–33 m) wide. They formed about 1.6 billion years ago as a solid granite mass that split into blocks as it cooled.

↑ **This statue of the standing Buddha** is 23 feet (7 m) tall. It is one of three Buddhas that were carved from granite at Gal Vihara, a UNESCO World Heritage Site a few miles north of Polonnaruwa, Sri Lanka. It depicts the Buddha standing on a lotus plinth, his arms folded and eyes half closed, and was the first of the three to be made. Granite is a hard stone and is difficult to carve, but fine-grained granite can be smoothed and polished.

← **Eucrite, seen here as a polished thin section** viewed through a microscope in plane-polarized light, did not originate on Earth. It is a basaltic rock from the crust of the asteroid Vesta that reached Earth as a meteorite. Eucrite consists mainly of low-calcium pyroxene (called pigeonite) and plagioclase feldspar, with some metallic iron, troilite, and one or more silicates. More than a hundred meteorites of this type have been found.

Metamorphic rocks

Earth's crust is seldom still and its rocks are subject to change within the igneous or sedimentary environments they occupy. Those alterations are the result of changes in the fluids to which the rocks are exposed or in the temperature and pressure to which they are subjected. The process of change is called metamorphism, and the altered rocks are said to be metamorphic. Metamorphism commonly involves the breakdown and recrystallization of minerals. Chemical reactions during metamorphism may also produce minerals that are entirely new to the rock composition. Extreme metamorphism may partially melt the rock, but most metamorphism takes place when the rock is in a nearly solid state.

Metamorphism usually occurs after sedimentary rocks have been buried and heated near subduction zones or igneous intrusions. Regional metamorphism affects rocks over a wide area. Contact metamorphism, also known as thermal metamorphism, is a more local phenomenon. Prolonged contact with hot flowing water produces hydrothermal metamorphism, and energy released by the impact of meteorites causes impact metamorphism. Geologists can determine the conditions under which metamorphic rocks formed. Because particular minerals form at certain temperatures, the mineral composition of the rock reveals the temperature at which it formed. Temperature increases with greater depth, so the temperature at which rock formed reveals the depth it was buried. Some metamorphic rocks were buried 60 miles (100 km) below the surface. As metamorphism proceeds, the pressures to which the rock is subjected align its crystals in particular ways that reveal the direction and strength of the forces involved. The length of the process can sometimes be measured in tens of millions of years. Often, though, metamorphism occurs over hundreds of millions of years.

← **Phyllite is a fine-grained metamorphic rock**—its grains are less than 0.004 inch (0.1 mm) across—intermediate between slate and schist. It is rich in aluminum and often has a silky sheen because of the alignment of its phyllosilicate, or sheet, minerals. These include chlorite, muscovite and sericite—a white variety of muscovite that gives phyllite its silvery color. Phyllosilicates form at low temperatures through the alteration of igneous rocks by weathering. The metamorphism that results in phyllite is classed as low grade. This means that it does not involve intense heat and pressure.

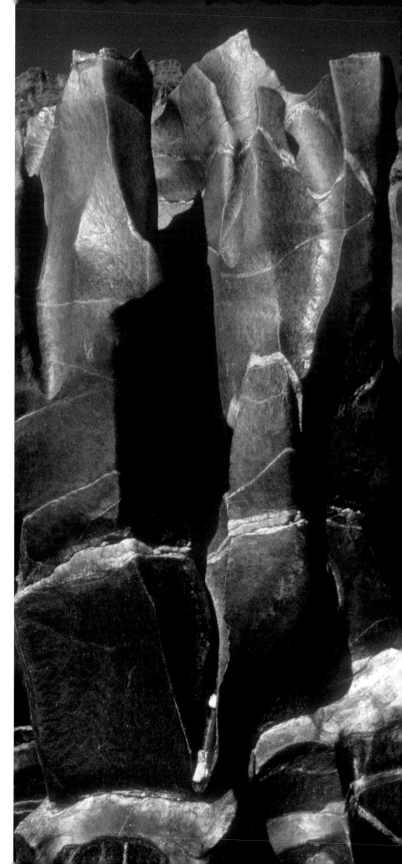

← **Schist, such as this example from the Colorado River Canyon**, Arizona, is formed from plates of micas and amphiboles (silicate tetrahedra) that are aligned. The alignment, which can be seen clearly in this magnified image, occurs either by the rotation of the plates as a result of shear stress or by the growth of new minerals whose plate axes are aligned to the principal direction of stress. Schist is a regional metamorphic rock with grains more than 0.04 inch (1 mm) across.

↑ **These gneiss boulders** lie in a river in the Maggia Valley, at Ponte Brolla, Switzerland. Gneiss is a general term that applies to any coarse-grained, banded rock that forms through high-grade regional metamorphism. During the process of metamorphism the dark minerals, such as biotite, hornblende and pyroxenes, separate from the light-colored minerals, such as quartz and feldspar. It is this separation process, known as gneissosity, that produces the light and dark bands that are characteristic of gneissose rocks.

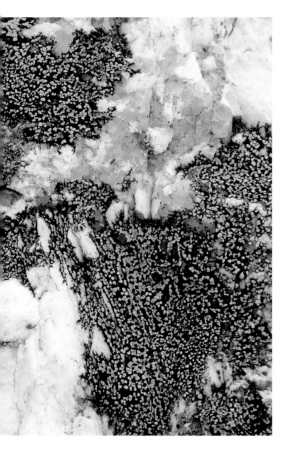

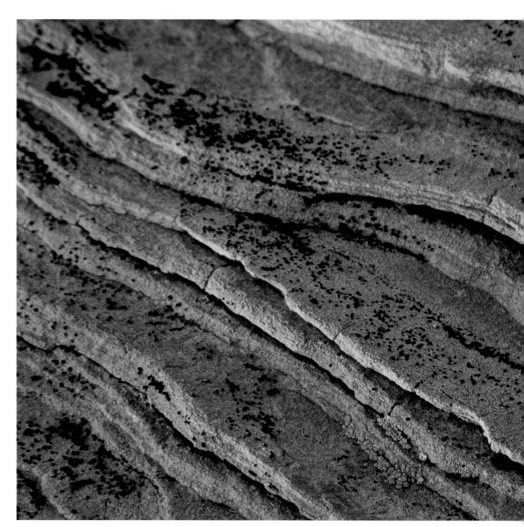

↑   **Quartzite is a metamorphic rock** that is formed mainly of quartz, usually by the alteration of quartz sandstones. This is a metaquartzite from British Columbia, Canada. The prefix "meta" indicates its metamorphic origin. Unmetamorphosed sandstones held together by a quartz cement are called orthoquartzites. The quartzite seen here is covered with lichen, a composite organism comprising a fungus that lives symbiotically with an alga or cyanobacterium.

→   **Once cut and dressed, many metamorphic rocks** are beautiful and architects often choose them for important public buildings. This building is made from sandstone. Limestone is also popular. Portland stone, from Dorset, England, is an oolitic limestone (containing spherical particles called ooids). It is used in some of London's famous buildings, including St. Paul's Cathedral.

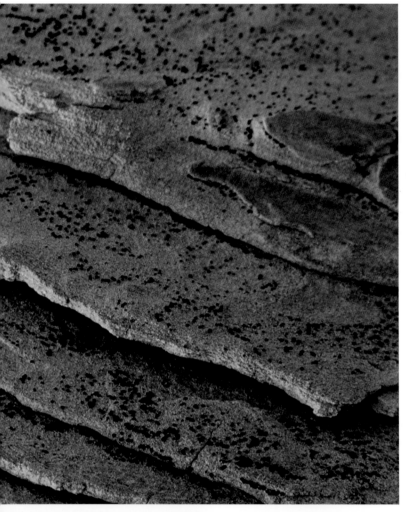

← **Slate seen here in its natural state in southeastern Utah**, is a low-grade, regional metamorphic rock that is used for roofing tiles and for floor and wall cladding. Tectonic movements in the crust align the plates of this rock's phyllosilicate minerals. This gives slate its tendency to break into flat sheets.

↓ **Skarn is the product of contact metamorphism**. Large amounts of silicon, iron, aluminum and magnesium enter limestone or dolomite rocks from a nearby igneous intrusion, usually of granite. This process is called metasomatism. The resulting metamorphic rock is formed from calcium, magnesium and iron silicates, with or without iron, copper and manganese oxides and sulfides. Skarns often contain limited deposits of magnetite (iron oxide) and copper sulfide ores. This example, from Dachang tin mine, in China, contains garnets.

← **Marble is a metamorphosed limestone** in which the calcite or, less commonly, dolomite has recrystallized. Recrystallization destroys any fossils the rock might once have contained—so a rock with fossils cannot be genuine marble—but yields a rock that is hard enough to be polished. Marble may be white, colored or banded, depending on its chemical and mineralogical composition. The most attractive varieties have been used since antiquity for making statues and ornaments. This marble carving is from an archaeological site at Eva, Greece. Michelangelo used white marble from the Carrara quarry in Tuscany, Italy; Tuscan marble from Siena has red mottling. Both Carrara and Siena marble are still quarried today. Marble for the statue of Abraham Lincoln at the Lincoln Memorial in Washington, D.C., came from Georgia.

Meteorites

As well as its planets and their satellites, the Solar System contains countless millions of smaller bodies. Asteroids are rocky or iron-rich bodies that orbit in the Asteroid Belt between Mars and Jupiter. Ceres, the largest asteroid, with a diameter of 605 miles (974 km), is now classed as a dwarf planet. The smallest asteroids are no bigger than small pebbles. Comets are formed from ices—including water ice, but also with many others—mixed with dust and soot. The American astronomer Edwin Hubble (1889¬1953) described them as "dirty snowballs." They orbit in the outermost regions of the Solar System.

From time to time, an asteroid's orbit may bring it close to Earth. If it enters Earth's atmosphere, friction will heat it and cause it to shine brightly. It is then termed an "atmospheric phenomenon," or meteor. Friction vaporizes most meteors, but a few fall to the surface. These are meteorites.

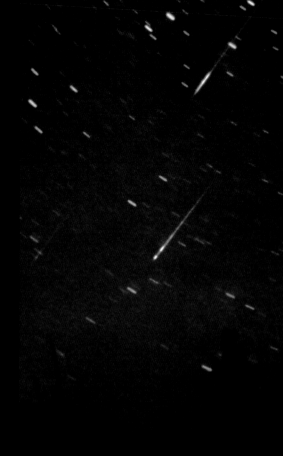

→ **The Leonid meteor shower lights up the November sky** as friction with the atmosphere heats fast-moving "space pebbles"—most of which are no bigger than peas—until they vaporize.

↓ **This image of the Manicouagan impact crater,** in Québec, Canada, came from the Landsat 1 satellite. Sixty miles (100 km) across, and surrounded by a graben—a depression in the crust—this crater is now used as a reservoir.

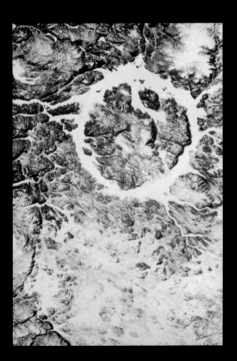

TORINO SCALE	
Possibility of impact	
0	Zero or minimal chance of impact
1	Impact extremely unlikely
2	Close but not unusual encounter; collision likely
3	Close encounter, 1 percent or more chance of collision causing local damage
4	Close encounter, 1 percent or more chance of collision causing regional destruction
5	Close encounter, significant threat of collision causing regional distruction
6	Close encounter, extremely significant threat of collision causing regional destruction
7	Collision able to cause localized destruction
8	Such events occur every 50 to 1000 years Collision able to cause regional devastation
9	Likely to occur every 1000 to 100, 000 years
10	Collision able to cause global devastation and major climate change. Likely to occur less than every 100,000 years

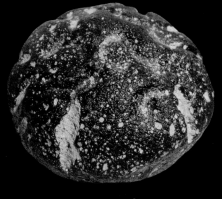

↑ **Tektites are small pieces of black glass** that are rich in silica. They are formed when a meteorite impact melts sand or silicate rock and hurls droplets high into the air, where they rapidly solidify. This example is from the Philippines.

↑ **This fragment came to Earth** as a result of the explosion in the atmosphere of the Sikhote-Alin iron meteorite, which fell over eastern Russia one morning in February 1947. The meteorite arrived as a fireball brighter than the Sun and it made 106 craters in Earth's surface.

← **Meteor Crater, near Flagstaff,** northern Arizona, is also known as Barringer Crater. It is 0.74 mile (1.2 km) across and 550 feet (168 m) deep. It was made 49,000 years ago by a meteorite—not, as its name suggests, by a meteor—about 80 feet (24 m) in diameter. This is the best-preserved impact crater on Earth.

The fossil record

When plants and animals die their tissues decompose and before long no evidence is left to show that they ever existed. Very occasionally, though, a dying plant or animal may be buried by fine mud or volcanic ash before it decomposes. If the sediment is then compressed into sedimentary rock, the remains of the once-living organisms trapped inside it may be preserved for millions of years, as fossils. Most fossils are of the hard parts of organisms such as wood, bones and teeth. Fossils allow paleontologists to discover the size and general appearance–although not the color or soft texture–of organisms that have long been extinct. Our knowledge of evolutionary history is derived very largely from this fossil record. The record is very incomplete, but occasional discoveries of previously unknown fossils help to fill some of the gaps.

↗ **Related to the modern nautilus,** ammonites first appeared in the Devonian, about 400 million years ago, and became extinct 65.5 million years ago at the end of the Cretaceous. *Hoploscaphites nebrascensis* is an ammonite that measures 5.5 inches (14 cm) across.

→ **Measuring about 14 inches (35 cm) long,** *Bothriolepis* was the most successful of the many placoderm (armored) fish that swam in later Devonian seas some 370 million years ago. *Bothriolepis* possessed jaws, and bony plates protected the front part of its body.

↠ **About 350 million years ago,** during the Carboniferous, *Lepidodendron*, a species of lycopods—plants related to club mosses but growing up to 6.5 feet (2 m) across and 130 feet (40 m) tall—formed forests. This is a piece of fossilized bark.

← When soft mud is compressed to form shale, plant leaves that are decomposing inside the mud may leave impressions. These fern fronds, from the Potomac Museum Group, in Minneapolis, have left clear fossil imprints. Ferns first appeared in the Devonian period between 416 and 359 million years ago.

← About 350 million years ago, rugose (rough-textured) corals like the ones shown here inhabited the Carboniferous seas. This is a polished section of *Lonsdaleia caledonia*, which was found in Scotland. All the rugose corals died out during the Permian period.

← Crinoids, or sea lilies, are echinoderms—animals related to sea urchins. The arms, or "fronds" that surround these animals' mouths are used to filter food from the water. This crinoid lived about 160 million years ago. It is 8 inches (20 cm) across and is from the Solnhofen limestone in Bavaria, Germany.

Fossil formation

Fossilization is the process by which plant and animal remains are converted to fossils. It begins as soon as the remains of a plant or animal come to rest on the surface of fine-grained mud. Scavengers feed on dead material and if fossilization is to proceed, the remains must be buried quickly in more mud. This mud must be waterlogged to exclude air and to keep the remains beyond the reach of air-breathing, burrowing scavengers.

Usually, the soft parts of the remains decay, but chemical reactions may leave a thin film of carbon to show where they once lay—a process called carbonization. Water moving through porous structures, such as bones and shells, may deposit minerals that strengthen them. Aragonite shells may dissolve and recrystallize as calcite. Shells may also dissolve and be replaced by entirely different minerals. This sometimes happens molecule by molecule, which helps to preserve the original shape and structure in fine detail. In some cases remains survive as an impression in the mud. This impression then becomes a mold, which is filled by minerals. Animal tracks and burrows may also be filled, to become ichnofossils—also known as trace fossils.

↑ **Soft tissues rarely escape complete decomposition.** However, a world heritage site at Messel, near Darmstadt, Germany, contains fossils of many animals, including *Messelobatrachus*, the frog shown here, with some soft tissues preserved. The fossilized animals at Messel lived 49 million years ago. They died suddenly, possibly as a result of poisoning by cyanobacteria.

↓ ***Neoasaphus kowalewskii*** was a trilobite of the Ordovician period, between 488.3 and 460.9 million years ago. Its compound eyes are visible on the end of long stalks. The mouth is on the underside.

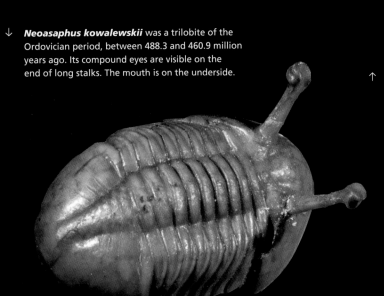

FOSSILIZATION STILL CONTINUES

Fossils are the remains of organisms that lived in the distant past and it is tempting to think of fossilization as a process that came to an end long ago. This is wrong. Where suitable conditions exist, organic remains will always have a chance of becoming fossils. The process is a very slow one and, inevitably, occurs in inaccessible places. It is, therefore, usually impossible to observe. Fossilization that is occurring right now may not be completed or exposed to view for many millennia.

→ **Where a river meets the sea,** the chemical reaction between fresh and salt water makes fine particles stick together and sink to the bottom. That is how mudflats, like the ones shown here, form. The heavily waterlogged mud of mudflats provides ideal conditions for fossilization to begin.

The process of fossilization begins when plant or animal remains are buried in sediment. Inside the sediment, chemical processes slowly convert the remains to fossils. Rock movements may then bring the fossils close to the surface, where weathering of the rock may eventually expose them to view.

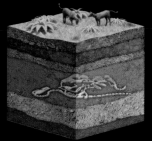

Types of fossils

Until relatively recently, anything ancient was called a fossil, especially if it was dug out of the ground. We still refer to substances obtained by mining as fossil fuels. Since the seventeenth century, however, "fossil" has been used in a more precise sense—to describe the remains of anything that was once a living organism, regardless of its age. A fossil may be a skeleton or shell, but microorganisms can also be preserved as microfossils. The hard parts of an organism sometimes remain as impressions that record the shape, but not the material, of the original organism. Ancient footprints, trails made by animals that crawl, burrows and other holes bored by animals are called trace fossils, or ichnofossils. Fossils are usually found in rock, but they are also preserved in amber, or even in frozen earth. The entire bodies of woolly mammoths have been recovered from frozen ground in Siberia.

→ **When plants die,** occasionally fine sediment retains impressions of leaves or flowers. More commonly it is the wood that is preserved, like this tree trunk in which it is still possible to count the annual growth rings. Minerals have replaced the original wood, petrifying it.

→→ **During the Triassic period,** between 251 and 199.6 million years ago, northeastern Arizona lay on a tropical coast. Trees that died there were buried in sediment and petrified: their tissues dissolved and were replaced by minerals. This tree grew at that time in what is now part of the Petrified Forest National Park. The park contains one of the world's most extensive collections of petrified wood.

← **Amber is fossilized resin.** Resin is a sticky substance that is exuded by coniferous trees. Leaves and insects that fall or alight on the resin as it seeps out are held by it. As more resin envelopes them, the leaves or insects become immersed in it. These minute flies (family Sciaridae), are held in amber from the Baltic. They lived 40 million years ago, in the Eocene epoch.

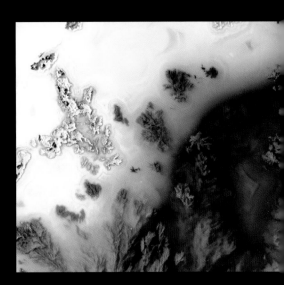

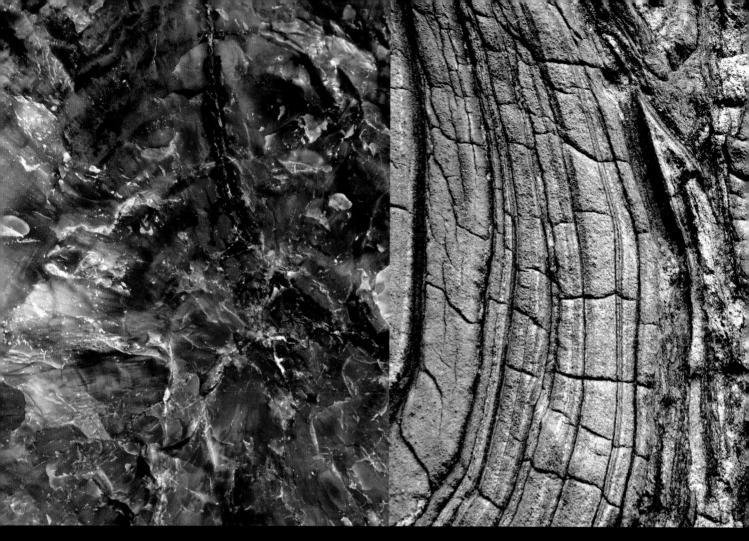

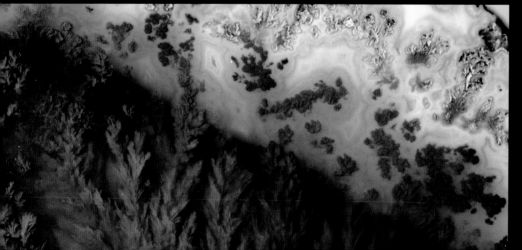

PSEUDOFOSSILS

The pattern to the left resembles scale leaves or fern fronds and suggests that these could be fossilized remains. But this is not a fossil: it is a semi-precious stone known as moss agate. Agate is a glasslike form of silica that contains iron and manganese, which give it its color. In moss agate these impurities move through the silica as it is solidifying and form delicate patterns. Minerals that look like fossils, and are often mistaken for them, are called pseudofossils.

Trace fossils

When invertebrate animals die, their soft bodies decay, but in rare incidences their burrows, holes or tracks do survive as records of aspects of their lives. Such indirect evidence of the activity and life conditions of a wide range of animals, both vertebrate and invertebrate, from the distant past is preserved in the form of trace fossils, or ichnofossils—from the Greek ikhnos meaning "track."

There are six main categories of trace fossils: Domichnia—dwelling structures—are burrows in which animals once lived; Fodinichnia—mining structures—are burrows that animals dug while feeding in the sediment; Pascichnia—grazing traces—are traces made by animals that fed on the surface; Cubichnia—resting traces—are holes made by animals that buried themselves in the sediment; Repichnia—locomotion traces—are traces made by animals as they moved around; Fugichnia—escape burrows—are tunnels dug by animals that moved upward through sediment that had recently buried them. Larger vertebrate animals have also left trace fossils in the form of footprints or fossilized dung. Examples of fossilized dung are called coprolites.

← Trace fossils have names that refer to the appearance of the fossils, rather than to the organisms that made them. This type of fossilized track—under the general classification Repichnia, or crawling fossil—is called Cruziana. Cruziana are tracks with two lobes separated by a groove, and with fine, chevron-like grooves along each lobe made by the animal's limb as it walked. Trilobites made Cruziana trace fossils.

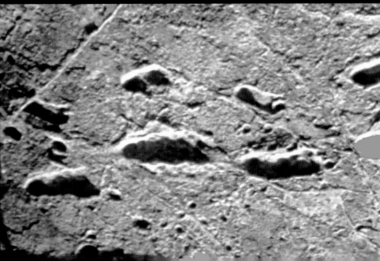

TRACE FOSSIL

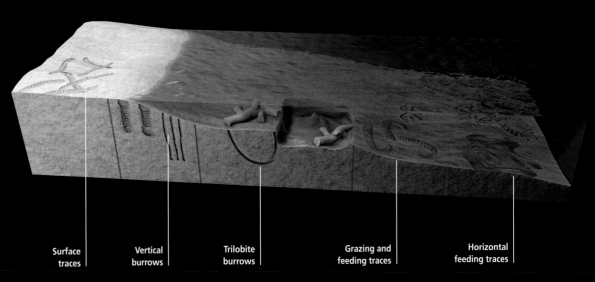

Surface traces

Vertical burrows

Trilobite burrows

Grazing and feeding traces

Horizontal feeding traces

THE LAETOLI FOOTPRINTS

In 1976, paleoanthropologist Andrew Hill, a member of the team led by Mary Leakey, came across a set of footprints at Laetoli, Tanzania. Most of the footprint site was excavated in 1978 and it proved to be one of the most important of all finds that relate to the evolution of humans. The footprints were made about 3.6 million years ago by two adults, and possibly a child—a family group—who were walking across a layer of fine volcanic ash. Soon after they passed, light rain turned the ash into a kind of cement, which set hard, preserving these footprints. Many birds and mammals also walked across the ash and their footprints were preserved, too.

← **These fossils,** in vertical formations in sandstone in Kalbarri National Park, Western Australia, are called Skolithos. They are U-shaped burrows in which animals lived permanently (Domichnia), filtering food from the water above them. The animals lived below the tide line in the bed of a shallow sea.

↓ **The Laetoli footprints** have a well-developed arch and the great toe does not diverge. The *Australopithecus afarensis* individuals who made them were bipedal and walked like modern humans. Scientists believe *A. afarensis* was a direct ancestor of modern humans. The prints at the extreme right belong to *Hipparion*, a three-toed horse that is now extinct.

↓ **These dinosaur coprolites,** from a variety of species, were collected by Karen Chin, who was then at the University of California, Santa Barbara. Coprolites—fossil dung—record the size and shape of the animal's alimentary tract. Dissection of coprolites can disclose plant and animal remains and thus reveal details of the animal's diet.

Microfossils

Microfossils are tiny fossils that can be examined only with the aid of a microscope. Micropaleontology is the study of microfossils. Most sedimentary rocks contain microfossils in such abundance that micropaleontologists need only a small rock sample in order to examine a range of specimens. The communities of organisms represented by microfossils reveal a great deal about the sediment and the way it formed. This information is of particular value in geological investigations.

Before a scientist can study the microfossils, the rock that contains them must be broken up gently in order to extract them. This usually involves soaking the rock in water, washing soda or water softener. Limestones are treated with diluted acetic or formic acid. The resulting sludge is then sieved or decanted or treated with special chemicals to separate the fossils from the mineral particles. If the fossils are too delicate to be treated in this way the rock is cut into thin sections or the fossils peeled from a smooth rock surface onto acetate sheets.

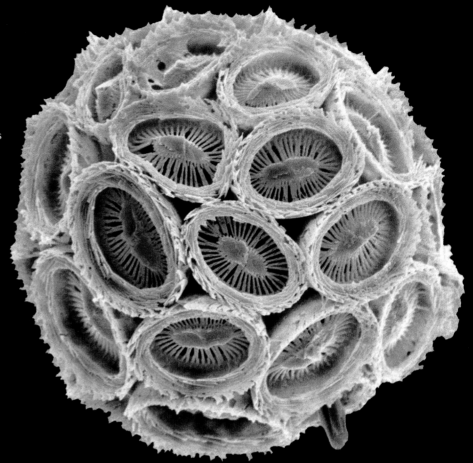

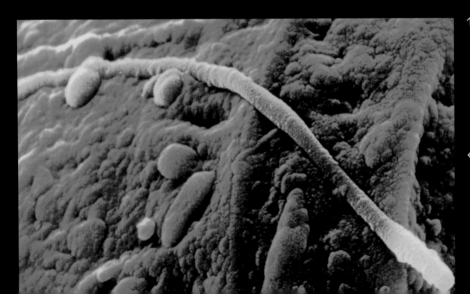

↑ **The marine alga** *Coronosphaera mediterranea* forms part of the plankton that drifts near the ocean surface. This alga, called a coccolithophore, is enclosed in calcium carbonate plates, or coccoliths. When the alga dies the coccoliths sink to the seafloor and may eventually form chalk rock. The White Cliffs of Dover, in England, are formed largely from coccoliths.

← **In this scanning electron micrograph** of a fossil bacterium, the bacterial cell appears as yellow. It was isolated from a sample of seafloor sediment. Its study provides important information about the way bacteria affect sediments. Fossil bacteria are usually difficult to identify. Under certain conditions, bacterial cells may be replaced by minerals—usually pyrite or siderite—to form pseudomorphs. Fossil cyanobacteria (formerly known as blue-green algae) that were found in sediment in the Bay of Borgneuf, Nantes, France, are about 3.5 billion years old.

→ **These fossilized radiolarians** belong to several species. A radiolarian is a single-celled organism. It is enclosed in a shell that comprises a perforated, membraneous capsule and a silica skeleton ornamented with bars or spines. When radiolarians die their skeletons form a sediment called radiolarian ooze.

↓ **This single-celled organism,** or protozoon, is *Paramecium*. It uses the hairlike structures that surround it—called cilia—to propel itself through the water. It feeds mainly on bacteria. Paramecium species range in length from less than 0.0004 inch to more than 0.0012 inch (0.01–0.03 mm)

→ **This scanning electron micrograph** is of fossil foraminiferan shells. These shells are known as "tests." Forams are amoeba-like, marine protozoa. They live inside tests that have one or more chambers. There are many types of tests. These ones are formed from calcium carbonate in the form of aragonite or calcite and are less than 0.04 inch (1 mm) across.

Soils

As soon as rocks are exposed to the effects of wind, rain, freezing and thawing, as well as to a range of chemical solutions that dissolve compounds within them, they begin to erode. Small fissures that appear fill up with mineral grains and rainwater. These fissures provide sites in which seeds or spores can germinate and where the resultant small plants can find secure anchorage and the nutrients they need. When these plants die, their tissues decompose and mix with the minerals. That is the beginning of soil formation. The scientific term for this process is pedogenesis. As years pass, the ever-growing accumulation of minerals and plant material creates conditions in which bigger plants can establish themselves. The soil gradually matures until it reaches a point of optimum fertility. After that it ages and eventually becomes infertile.

↓ **In southern Asia,** rice is the most important and widely grown crop. Like wheat, rice can be grown on dry land but it is generally grown from seedlings that are planted out in flooded fields. Both the rice and the field in which it grows are called a paddy. These paddy fields are on the island of Bali, Indonesia.

↓ **In cool climates,** waterlogged soil becomes acid and infertile. Plant remains decompose slowly in this soil, and the partly decayed material accumulates to form peat. Peat can be cut from the ground, dried and burned, either as a domestic fuel or for power generation. This peat bog is in Ireland.

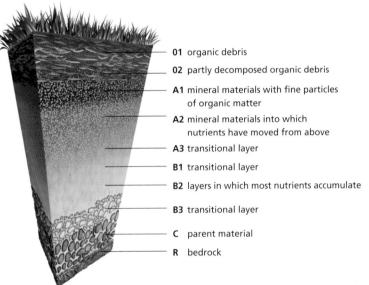

Wind and rain erode bare soil naturally. Soil erosion becomes serious if the rate of erosion exceeds the rate of soil formation. Farmers cultivate the land in ways that minimize erosion. One technique, seen here in Washington State, is to plow parallel to the contours of the land. Plowing across the contours makes channels that can grow into gullies.

A vertical section, known as a profile, reveals distinct layers, or soil horizons. These horizons vary; not every soil has all the horizons shown here.

01 organic debris

02 partly decomposed organic debris

A1 mineral materials with fine particles of organic matter

A2 mineral materials into which nutrients have moved from above

A3 transitional layer

B1 transitional layer

B2 layers in which most nutrients accumulate

B3 transitional layer

C parent material

R bedrock

This lava field is formed from blocky lava that has a high silica content. Nothing grows here yet, but provided the field is not buried beneath another lava flow, plants will eventually appear in the sheltered hollows and a richly fertile soil will develop.

A fertile soil teems with animal life, but most of its inhabitants are minute. This is *Caenorhabditis elegans*, a nematode, or eelworm, about 0.04 inch (1 mm) long. It is abundant in soils and is a subject of intense scientific study. Biologists have published its entire genetic constitution.

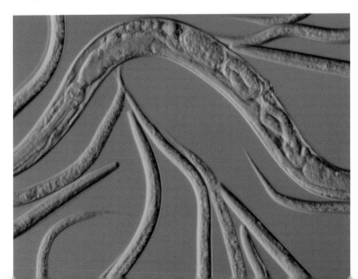

Earth's resources

All living organisms survive by exploiting the resources that surround them. There are many needs that all plants, fungi, animals, and even microorganisms, have in common. We humans share all these needs, but the way we satisfy them gives rise to further needs. We need materials to construct our dwellings and to make the tools we rely on. And we need fuels. Without fuel for cooking, the human diet would be extremely restricted. Many of the foods we eat require cooking to render them palatable and to make their nutrients more easily digestible. Without fuel for heating we would find life very difficult in high latitudes. Without fuel for industry we would have to do without most of the objects and substances that make life comfortable and safe. Throughout most of human history, wood has been the primary fuel. It is still widely used, but burning it releases far less energy than burning an equivalent weight or volume of peat, coal, natural gas or oil. These are fossil fuels—using "fossil" in its general, popular sense of anything dug out of the ground. Apart from wood—and charcoal made from it—we take most of our fuel from below ground or beneath the seabed.

→ **Oil is formed** from the remains of marine organisms that have been heated in airless conditions. It is held, beneath a cap of impervious rock, under great pressure in porous rocks such as sandstones. Drilling through the cap releases the pressure and allows the oil to rush to the surface. These workers are sealing a leaking well in the Greater Burhan oil field, Kuwait.

DEPOSITS OF METHANE HYDRATES
Methane hydrates have been found in sedimentary rocks on the margins of most continents and in some permafrost regions inside continents. Red dots on this map show known offshore deposits; purple dots show known inland permafrost deposits.

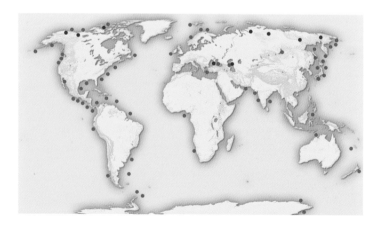

→ **Methane hydrates** are made up of ice crystals with molecules of methane inside them. The material looks like slushy ice and it can block gas pipelines. Methane is the principal constituent of natural gas, and geologists estimate that the amount of methane in these hydrates is equal to more than twice the world's total reserves of all other fossil fuels. Recovering methane, however, may prove both difficult and expensive.

← **Coal is** Earth's most widely used fossil fuel. In 2003 the world's coalmines produced about 5.65 billion tons (5.13 billion t) of coal. Of this, about 80 percent was bituminous coal used to fuel most domestic fires. These railcars filled with coal are at Hampton Roads, Virginia. The United States is the second largest coal producer. It produces 1 billion tons (973 million t) annually. China produces 1.7 billion tons (1.5 billion t).

→ **When dead vegetation** falls onto cold, acidic, waterlogged ground the material fails to decompose completely. Over time it becomes peat—a dark, fibrous substance in which plant remains are clearly visible. Peat is a traditional fuel, especially in Ireland and Scotland. This Irish man is cutting brick-shaped peat turfs, an arduous summer task. In winter they will be dry enough to burn.

Energy from Earth

Wherever there is a marked difference in temperature between two bodies, it is possible, at least in principle, to extract useful energy from that difference. It is also possible to harness kinetic energy, the energy of motion—for example of wind or falling water. Below Earth's surface the temperature of the rocks increases with depth. This is called the geothermal gradient and it results mainly from the energy that is released by the decay of radioactive elements in the rocks. The ordinary geothermal gradient is too shallow to be of use for energy generation, but in some places it is much steeper. There are subterranean reservoirs of rock or water that are at extremely high temperatures. These can be exploited to provide geothermal energy.

Heat from the Sun drives the air movements that produce our weather. Wind is the product of solar energy, which is the heating of Earth's surface as it absorbs solar radiation. For centuries, wind was used to power mills and other machines and was the driving force for ships. Today wind power is used mainly to generate electrical power. Sunshine can also be employed directly as a source of energy. Solar cells convert sunlight into electricity. Solar panels capture solar warmth and use it to heat water or provide space heating. Sunshine can also be harnessed on an industrial scale. Mirrors can focus sunlight onto a target to produce extremely high temperatures in a solar furnace. The High-Flux Solar Furnace, near Golden, Colorado, has been in operation since 1998. It focuses solar radiation to produce temperatures high enough to generate 10 megawatts (MW) of electrical power. A 500-megawatt plant is currently being built in Israel.

→ **White vapor erupts** from Pohutu Geyser, in New Zealand. A geyser has a central shaft with rock fissures that allow water to drain into it at different levels. Rock near the bottom of the shaft is at an extremely high temperature. While this rock heats water at the base of the shaft, cold water flows into the shaft nearer the surface. The expanding hot water pushes some of the cold water out of the shaft, thus reducing the weight of cold water on top. As the hot water boils explosively underneath, water and steam surge spectacularly into the air.

→→ **New Zealand is famous for its geysers,** hot springs and boiling mud, all of which are signs of hot water or hot rock deep below ground. These pipes are serving a geothermal power station in North Island. Hot water may be piped directly into a power station from a subterranean heat reservoir. Sometimes, however, cold water first needs to be pumped from the surface through dry hot rock that has been shattered by explosives. The hot water from below ground helps heat the water that boils to drive the generating turbines.

↑ **This power plant** is driven by a solar furnace. The array of mirrors, called heliostats, tracks the Sun across the sky. The mirrors focus the reflected solar radiation onto a target, heating it to thousands of degrees. The target heats water, which generates the steam that drives the station's turbines.

← **Champagne Pool** at Wai-o Tapu Thermal Wonderland, New Zealand, is heated by magma in a magma chamber deep below ground. The yellow color comes from sulfur, which is precipitated from the hot water. Steam that rises from the pool shows how warm the water is. Hot pools and springs occur in volcanically active areas.

↑ **A wind farm** at Altamont Pass, California, stretches away to the horizon. The generating capacity is proportional to three factors: the square of the area that is swept by the blades; the air density; and the cube of the wind speed. Wind turbines are efficient mechanically, but because wind is not dependable, over a year the turbines rarely generate more than 35 percent of their rated capacity. This compares with 90 percent for a conventional power station. Many wind farms are being built in coastal waters, where they are less visually intrusive and where the wind is stronger and more constant. Although wind energy currently provides less than 1 percent of global electricity, the amount of this electricity more than quadrupled between 1999 and 2005.

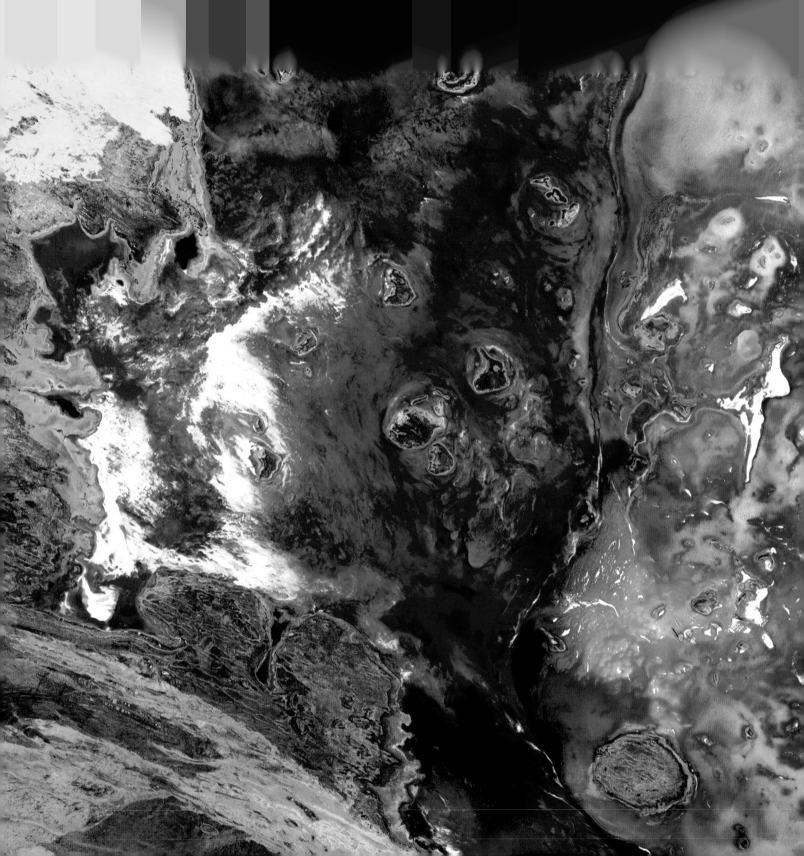

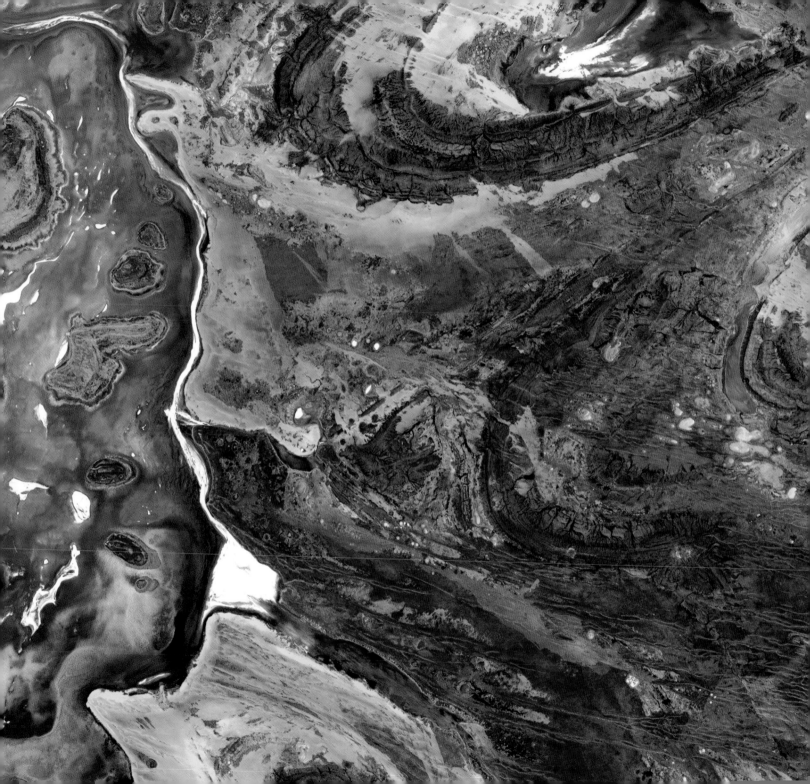

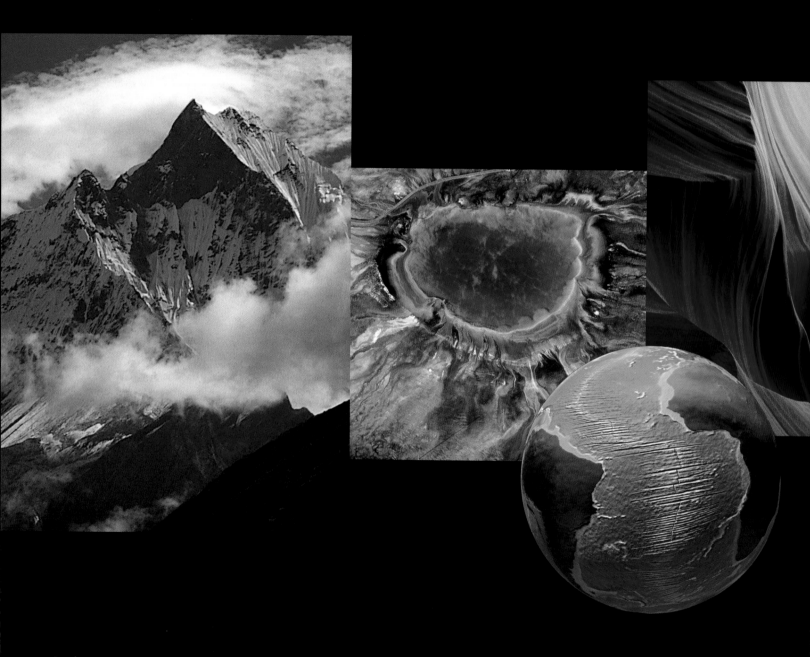

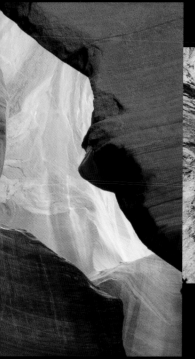

Shaping the surface

Earth is a dynamic planet whose surface is in constant flux. Below the surface massive tectonic forces create earthquakes and volcanoes, land and sea, mountains and valleys. Ice caps and glaciers advance and retreat with changing climate. The relentless power of rain and wind erodes the landscape into ever-changing forms.

Shifting Earth

Earth's crust is in constant motion and over time all surface features are erased and replaced. That is why Earth is not covered with impact craters like the Moon, even though it has collided with as many asteroids and comets. The action of wind, rain and ice erodes mountains until eventually they become level plains. But movements of the crust itself are what raise mountains. The solid crust is broken into sections called plates. These plates move in relation to each other, and where moving continents collide the plates crumple like a tablecloth pushed together from two sides. When an ocean basin collides with a continent, sedimentary rocks on the seabed are thrust upward. The map below shows the seven major plates and several minor plates and their boundaries.

PLATE TECTONICS

▨	Earthquake zone	—	Transform fault
●	Prominent hot spot	·····	Diffuse or uncertain
▲▲	Convergent margin	➡	Movement direction
—	Divergent margin	▲	Volcanic zone

↑ **In 1963 an underwater volcano** erupted on the mid-Atlantic ridge where the North American and Eurasian plates are moving apart. It produced the volcanic island of Surtsey, 20 miles (33 km) south of Iceland.

← **Malamala Island** is a coral atoll in the Mamanuca Group, in Fiji. When a submarine volcano erupts and empties its magma chamber, the unsupported roof of the empty chamber often collapses, producing a crater called a caldera. Corals may then colonize the rim of the caldera to form a reef. A later fall in sea level will leave the top of the reef exposed.

THE 2004 ASIAN EARTHQUAKE AND TSUNAMI

The left satellite image shows Thailand's southwestern coast on January 1, 2003. The right image was taken on December 29, 2004. On December 26 , 745 miles (1,200 km) of the boundary between the India and Burma plates to the west of Sumatra shifted about 50 feet (15 m) sideways and the seabed rose several feet. The earthquake sent a shock wave across the ocean. When the wave entered shallow water it slowed and water behind it piled up into a huge and destructive tsunami.

Continental drift

For centuries scientists puzzled over the fact that Africa looks as though it would fit neatly against Central and South America. Some suggested these landmasses had once been joined but had been torn apart. Then, in 1912, Alfred Wegener (1880¬1930), a German meteorologist, proposed that the continents had once been joined and had drifted slowly to their present positions. He called the process "continental displacement." In support of his theory, he produced evidence of the existence of similar rocks, fossils and modern species on lands separated by vast oceans. Wegener's book was not translated into English until 1924. Even then, most geologists opposed his idea because they believed Earth to be solid and could think of no way that continents could move.

The discovery that Earth's mantle is hot and slightly plastic finally led to the realization that continents can and do move. Scientists have tracked their movements into the distant past and have drawn maps that show the former arrangement of continents.

The Chile pine or monkey puzzle (*Araucaria araucana*), at top, grows naturally only in Chile and western Argentina. It is closely related to the bunya bunya (*Araucaria bidwillii*), below, which is native to some Pacific islands, New Guinea and coastal Queensland, Australia. Their distribution is evidence that South America and Australia were once joined. Long ago, all the southern continents formed a supercontinent, Gondwana.

DISJUNCT DISTRIBUTION

These maps shows where the Chile pine and bunya bunya occur naturally—in parts of the world separated by an ocean that their common ancestor could not possibly have crossed. Such examples of disjunct distribution provide compelling evidence of continental drift.

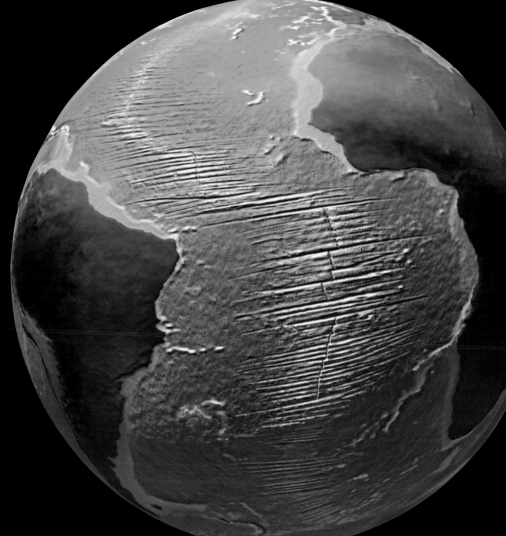

↖ **The koala** (*Phascolarctos cinereus*), a marsupial mammal, occurs naturally only in eastern Australia, south of latitude 17°S. About 55 million years ago Australia, South America and Antarctica were joined. When Australia broke away, between 46 million and 35 million years ago, its marsupials became isolated from those in South America.

← **The Virginia opossom** (*Didelphis virginiana*) is one of almost 100 species of American marsupials. When South America became joined to North America, between two and five million years ago, many South American marsupials became extinct, but the opossums moved north.

SEAFLOOR SPREADING
The wavy line that runs down the center of the Atlantic Ocean is a mid-ocean ridge. Submarine mountains on either side of the ridge are moving apart at the rate of about 1 inch (2.5 cm) a year, as the North and South American plates move westward and the Eurasian and African plates move eastward. Magma rises to fill the space between them, then solidifies to form new oceanic crust. A system of mid-ocean ridges encircles Earth.

Tectonic plates

Earth's uppermost solid layer is broken into strong, rigid plates that move over the surface. There are 12 major plates and a number of smaller ones. The plates consist of the crustal rocks together with the uppermost part of the mantle. Together these comprise the lithosphere, which is, on average, about 60 miles (100 km) thick. The lithospheric plates rest on a layer called the asthenosphere, which separates them from the underlying mantle. The mechanism that drives plate motion derives largely from the fact that water that is chemically bound to mineral compounds makes the material of the asthenosphere malleable. This allows it to move in response to heat that rises by convection from the mantle. It is this movement that carries the plates.

The boundaries of adjacent plates are divergent where plates are moving apart; they are convergent where plates are colliding; and transform where plates are moving past one another.

COLLISION AND SUBDUCTION

Convergent plate boundaries are destructive. Where two ocean plates collide, one is subducted beneath the other at a deep-ocean trench. The bottom of the trench marks the boundary between the plates. Because oceanic crust is denser than continental crust, at an ocean-to-continent boundary the oceanic crust is subducted beneath the continental crust. At a continent-to-continent boundary both plates are of equal density and neither is subducted. Instead, the rocks crumple upward, forming a mountain range.

OCEAN-TO-OCEAN SUBDUCTION

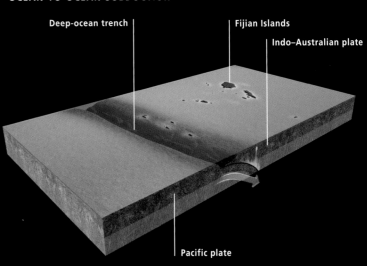

Deep-ocean trench | Fijian Islands

Indo–Australian plate

Pacific plate

OCEAN-TO-CONTINENT BOUNDARY

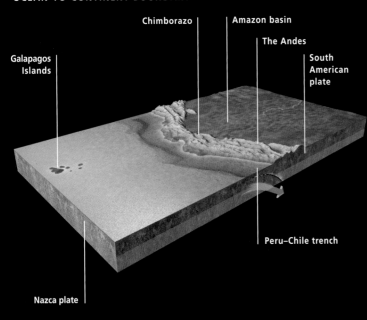

Chimborazo | Amazon basin

The Andes

South American plate

Galapagos Islands

Nazca plate

Peru–Chile trench

CONTINENT-TO-CONTINENT BOUNDARY

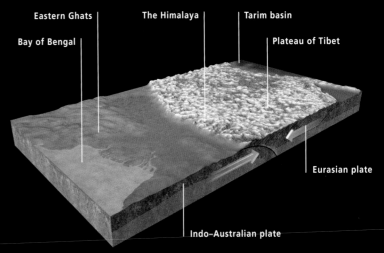

Eastern Ghats | The Himalaya | Tarim basin

Bay of Bengal | Plateau of Tibet

Eurasian plate

Indo–Australian plate

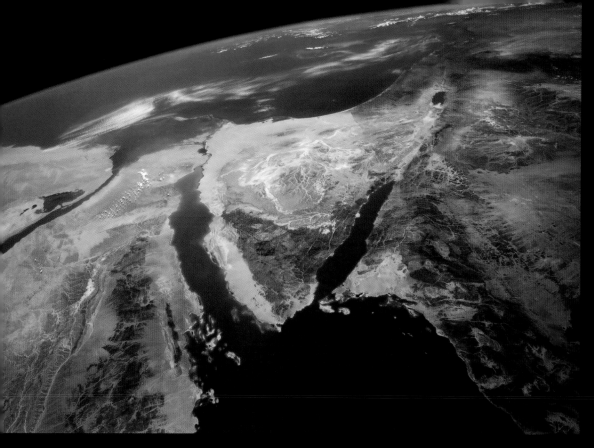

← **The Sinai Peninsula,** seen here from an orbiting spacecraft, is the triangular wedge of land between the Gulfs of Suez and Aqaba, at the northern end of the Red Sea. The Red Sea is one of three places where the African and Eurasian plates are moving apart. The others are the East African Rift and the Gulf of Aden. The Red Sea is growing wider. It may eventually become an ocean the size of the Atlantic.

← **This scene, near Pingvellir,** Iceland, shows part of the Atlantic fault, where the North American and Eurasian plates meet. The land to the left of the ravine is geologically part of North America, and the land to the right is part of Eurasia. The fault, which crosses Iceland from the northeast to southwest, makes that country intensely active seismically and volcanically. The last major earthquake at Pingvellir was in 1789, when the ground sank 19 inches (50 cm).

Faulting

At the boundary between lithospheric plates, the tendency of the plates to move in relation to one another generates stresses that are transmitted throughout the plates. These stresses accumulate in the rocks within the plates. There are zones of weakness within sedimentary rocks and eventually the stresses within the plate overcome the resistance of the rocks. The rocks fracture where they are weakest and they move on one or both sides of the fracture. A rock fracture that involves the movement of the rock is called a fault. Once a fault has formed it remains as a permanent feature.

Sediments usually settle in horizontal layers, but crustal movements shift sedimentary rocks, so these are usually inclined. The angle of a rock layer from the horizontal is called the dip. The geometry of faults falls into two main categories: in a dip-slip fault the rocks have moved in a direction parallel to the dip of the layers; in a strike-slip fault the movement is almost horizontal.

FOUR TYPES OF FAULT
A normal fault is a dip-slip fault in which the rock on the upper side of the fault plane (called the hanging wall) moves downward over the underlying rock (called the footwall). A reverse fault is a dip-slip fault in which the hanging wall rocks move upward over the footwall. A thrust fault is a low-angle dip-slip fault in which the hanging wall overhangs the footwall. In a transcurrent (strike-slip) fault the rocks move horizontally. The fault is called dextral if it moves a marker to the right, and sinistral if the marker moves to the left.

NORMAL FAULT

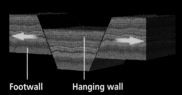

Footwall   Hanging wall

REVERSE FAULT

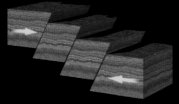

THRUST FAULT

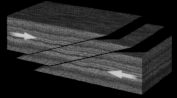

TRANSCURRENT FAULT

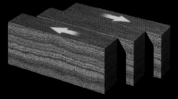

↑ **The San Andreas fault,** seen here on the Carrizo Plains in southern California, is a dextral transcurrent fault system that forms a small part of a much bigger fault system along the boundary between the Pacific and North American lithospheric plates. The Pacific plate is moving northward relative to North America, and this makes the entire region seismically and volcanically active.

→ **Lakeside houses** along the shore near Pingvellir, Iceland, sit at the foot of a steep slope with a cliff behind. This landform is called a scarp, in this case a fault-scarp. The fault, linked to the mid-Atlantic ridge, has caused the ground on one side to stand higher than the ground on the other side.

Earthquakes

When forces in the asthenosphere push lithospheric plates, the plates never move smoothly. Stress builds up along the fault lines that mark the plate margins. Eventually the stress overcomes the strength of the rocks and they fracture, moving with a jerk. That jerk shakes the ground, which quakes. Volcanic activity can also cause earthquakes. The point at which the rocks move is called the hypocenter of the earthquake. The epicenter is the point on the surface directly above the hypocenter. If the hypocenter is less than 44 miles (70 km) below the surface the earthquake is described as shallow. An intermediate earthquake occurs at a depth of between 44 and 186 miles (70–300 km) and a deep earthquake at below 186 miles (300 km). Small foreshocks often precede an earthquake and aftershocks follow the main event. The magnitude of an earthquake depends on the extent of the rock displacement and on the area affected.

AN ASIAN EARTHQUAKE AND TSUNAMI

The Richter magnitude 9.2 or 9.3 earthquake that occurred on December 26, 2004 caused movement along a fault to the west of Sumatra. The sudden displacement in the sea floor sent a shock wave racing across the ocean. This map shows the hour-by-hour progress of the wave over 11 hours. When the wave reached shallow water it piled up into a devastating tsunami.

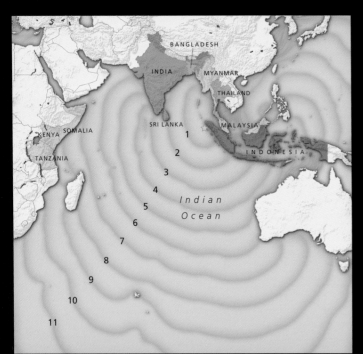

KEY TO DEATH TOLL

- >100 000
- 10 000–100 000
- 1 000–10 000
- <1 000
- insufficient data

↑ **Early in the morning** of October 8, 2005 an earthquake of Richter magnitude 7.6 caused widespread damage in Kashmir and Pakistan. Here workers struggle to rescue people trapped by the collapse of the Margala Tower apartment complex in Islamabad, Pakistan.

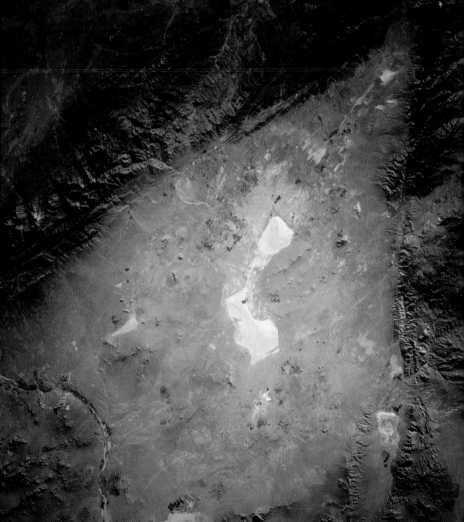

↗ **The record of an earthquake** is called a seismogram. It traces the movements of the ground caused by seismic waves that travel to instruments called seismometers. A seismogram is created by the movement of a pen across paper held on a rotating drum. It reveals the magnitude, depth and location of the earthquake.

→ **Two or more faults** often occur in the same area. Two intersecting fault lines that produce earthquakes are visible in the top right of this view of Edwards Air Force Base in the Mojave Desert, California. It was taken by the crew of the space shuttle *Discovery*. Edwards AFB is a shuttle landing field.

Folding

When movements within the crust stress rocks, the rocks do not necessarily fracture. Rocks that have formed from layers of sediment, metamorphic rocks derived from sedimentary rocks or igneous rocks formed from successive flows of molten rock all have a series of parallel surfaces within them. Such layered rocks may respond to stress by folding. The effects of folding can vary from barely perceptible tremors to movements that determine the shapes of landscapes.

Folding can occur when forces compress rock layers of differing strengths from opposite directions, and so cause the rocks to buckle. Pressure from below can make rocks deform upward into a dome. Rocks can also deform passively, when forces twist them into a different shape. Folding can affect rocks repeatedly, building up patterns that are sometimes highly complex. The center of a fold is called the hinge zone and the sides of the fold are the limbs.

↓ **Sandstone is a sedimentary rock** that forms from layers of sand that have been compressed and cemented together. The layers are clearly visible in this photograph. Sandstone responds to stress by deforming. Although the folds are gentle, they form complex patterns that show how the rock has been twisted in different directions.

Folds are visible in this aerial photo of the Himalayas, which were formed when sedimentary rock was thrust upward from the bed of the sea that separated the Indian and Eurasian plates before they collided. The collision, which still continues, has greatly deformed Himalayan rocks.

→ **The European Alps** were thrust upward when the African and Eurasian plates collided. They contain schists that the collision folded into intricate shapes. The geometry of the folds in alpine metamorphic rocks shows that they were pushed northward by the advance of Italy, on the African plate.

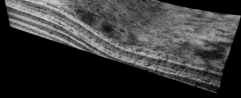

A monocline is the simplest type of fold, in which the dip increases in rock layers that are almost horizontal. The rocks are not so much folded as bent in a region from where they are inclined downward.

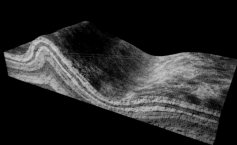

An anticline fold arches upward, with the youngest rock layer on top of the arch. A fold that bends downward to form a basin, with the youngest rocks on top of the bend, is a syncline.

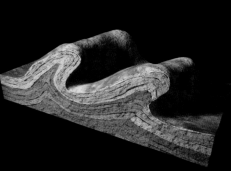

A recumbent fold is one in which the two limbs are almost parallel to each other. The fold is tight and lies on its side, almost horizontally. Some geologists restrict the term to folds that dip no more than 10 degrees.

Volcanoes

A volcano is a naturally occurring vent at Earth's surface through which gases, ash, molten rock and other materials erupt from time to time. The molten rock is magma that rises from deep in the crust or upper mantle; it is called lava once it leaves the vent. Magma may reach the surface through one or more vents. The viscosity of the magma depends on its composition. This viscosity, the amount of gas held in the magma and the rate of the eruption all determine the shape of the mountain that develops as lava cools and solidifies. Many very high volcanoes, including Japan's Mount Fuji, are composite volcanoes, or strato-volcanoes, formed from alternate layers of lava and ash that emerge from a central vent.

↓ **Klychevskaya,** seen here in a false-color satellite image, is a composite volcano, 15,863 feet (4835 m) high, on the Kamchatka Peninsula, in the Russian far east. The most active of the volcanoes in the region, Klychevskaya erupted in 1994, 2004 and 2005. This has led scientists to fear it is growing more violent.

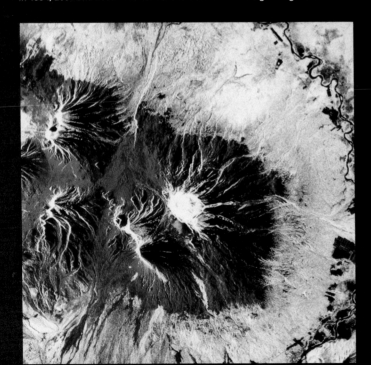

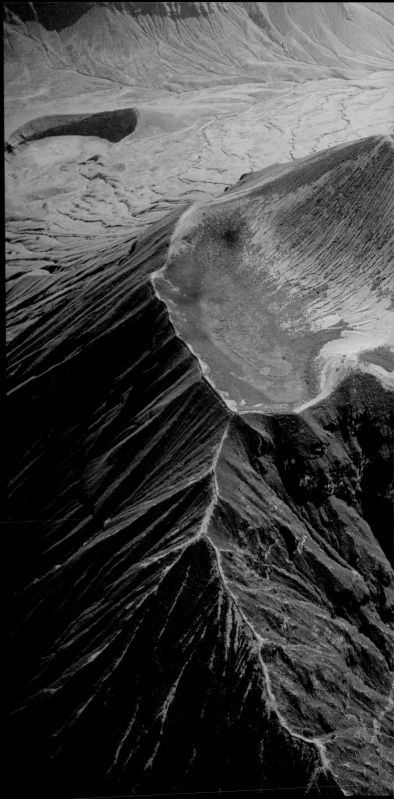

↑ **Mount Etna,** in eastern Sicily, is Europe's biggest active volcano, 10,910 feet (3326 m) high and 87 miles (140 km) in circumference at the base. It is almost constantly erupting. Occasionally its eruptions are destructive; over two days in 1928 it destroyed every building in the town of Mascali. Usually, however, it is harmless and many people live close to it.

← **Ol Doinyo Lengai,** or Mountain of God, is an active volcano, 9500 feet (2890 m) high, in the African Rift valley in Tanzania. It is the only volcano in the world that erupts natrocarbonatite—"white in the cone"—lava, which contains almost no silicon, is nearly as fluid as water and is the coolest of all lavas. Vegetation thrives on this volcano's flanks.

Mountain building

Mountains form when part of a lithospheric plate is thrust upward. This may result directly from a collision between two plates, or from volcanic activity associated with this collision. In scientific terms, mountain building is known as "orogenesis." When a collision between plates creates a mountain chain, the event is called an "orogeny" and the mountain range is an "orogenic belt." Plateaus and basins can also form through the vertical movement of crust in the interior of continental plates, far from the plate boundaries. This type of process is known as "epeirogenesis." The Himalayan orogenic belt is the result of a collision between two continental plates. The Indian plate is still advancing into the Eurasian plate and the mountains are still rising—but they are also being reduced by weathering. The Indian plate is thrusting beneath the Eurasian, but as both plates are of similar density, the Indian plate cannot sink. Instead the crust crumples upward. Where an ocean plate is being subducted, a trench forms between the plates. Magma rising from the trench at intervals along the subduction zone thickens the crust, producing a series of mountains. These may project above the surface as an island arc, or develop onshore as a coastal mountain range.

→ **The summit of Machupachare,** in the Annapurna Region of Nepal, is a Himalayan mountain that has never been climbed. The Himalayas are still rising, but the severe climate means the mountains are subject to the world's fastest rate of erosion.

↘ **The Aleutian Islands** are the tops of mountains and form an island arc. They consist of magma that has risen at intervals along a subduction zone and thickened the crust where the Pacific plate is sinking beneath the North American plate.

→ **The Andes are aligned** parallel to the South American coast. This section, photographed from the space shuttle *Challenger,* is in Chile. The Chilean capital, Santiago, is to the left of the snow-capped mountains. Magma rising from the subduction zone between the Nazca and South American plates has thickened the crust, thrusting the Andean mountain chain upward.

The Himalayan mountain range was produced about 30 million years ago when India, traveling northward, collided with the southern edge of the Eurasian plate. The main episode of mountain building occurred about 20 million years ago, but the plate collision has not ended and the mountains are still growing taller. The Indo-Australian plate broke away from the supercontinent of Gondwana about 145 million years ago. As it moved northward, the section of the Tethys Sea between India and Eurasia disappeared. When the plates collided, India thrust beneath Eurasia. Seabed sediments were compressed and pushed upward and the plates crumpled, raising the Himalayas.

WHEN CONTINENTS COLLIDE

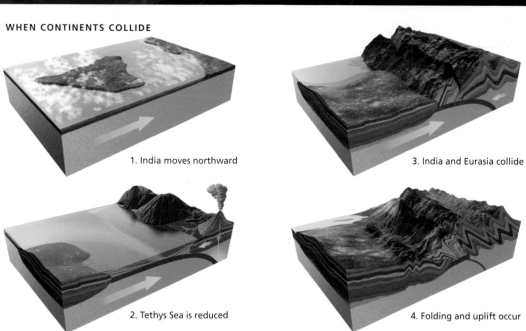

1. India moves northward

2. Tethys Sea is reduced

3. India and Eurasia collide

4. Folding and uplift occur

Erosion and weathering

Rocks come under attack when they are exposed to air and water. While they are still below the surface, water, made acidic by carbon dioxide and other dissolved substances, trickles across them. The acid reacts with compounds in the rock, altering its composition and leaving pits and crevices where soluble reaction products have been removed. The rock that is affected by this chemical weathering—which is not the kind of weathering we associate with wind, rain, heat and cold—becomes the mineral ingredient of soil. Closer to the surface, plant roots penetrate cracks in the rock. When the roots die they decompose, releasing more compounds that react with rock ingredients. In regions that experience extreme temperature changes, rocks expand when warm and contract when cool. This causes flakes to break from the rock surface. Where winters are cold, films of water move along gaps to places where the water freezes. As the ice accumulates, its crystallization weakens the adjacent rocks, which eventually break. Above ground, the wind picks up small fragments and smashes them against bigger rocks. In dry climates blown particles sandblast exposed rock surfaces. Temperature, water and wind produce physical weathering. If rock particles or soil are transported by wind or flowing water, the process is called erosion.

↗ **The Old Man of Hoy,** Orkney, Scotland, is a stack 450 feet (137 m) tall. It consists of resistant rock left behind when waves, and air compressed by them, attacked weaknesses in the sea cliff and caused the cliff face to retreat.

→ **Limestone pavement** is an almost horizontal bed of limestone that was scoured by ice during the last ice age. After the ice melted a layer of peat or wind-blown soil covered the limestone and acids from the surface dissolved material from joints in the rock, making vertical cracks, called grikes, between the blocks, called clints.

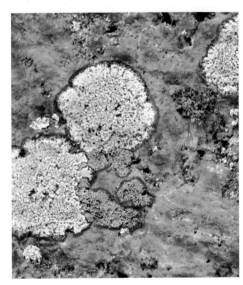

↟ **A relief on St. Bartholomew's Church,** New York, has suffered from erosion by airborne acid. Emissions from factories that burn coal and oil, as well as vehicle exhaust gases, react in the air to form sulfuric and nitric acids. Particles of acid—either dry or dissolved in mist, rain and snow—dissolve limestone.

↑ **Lichen** that grows on bare rock releases acids that erode the rock and expose substances from which plants can eventually obtain nutrients. This biological erosion is a first step in soil formation.

← **Tree roots** that have penetrated rock crevices die and release acids that dissolve more rock and further widen the crevices. This example of biological erosion is made visible by physical erosion that has removed the soil and exposed the roots.

Sedimentary processes

Wind and water can transport rock particles long distances. When finally they sink, the particles form sedimentary deposits. Sediment is deposited when moving air or water slows down, thereby losing some of its energy. When wind blows across an uneven surface friction will slow it. If the wind is carrying particles—or snow—the loss of energy will reduce its capacity to transport material and some or all of this material will settle. Wind-blown soil that settles in this way is called loess, and there are vast deposits of loess in some places. As rivers approach the sea they cross almost flat land. They slow down here and deposit silt that covers the surface of their floodplains.

When a river meets the sea, fresh water, with its load of fine silt mixed with organic matter, meets salt water. The resultant chemical reactions make the material suspended in the fresh water flocculate—form clumps—and settle to the bottom to create mudflats. Offshore, as the river pushes against sea currents, it slows and drops its larger particles. These form sandbars.

↙ **Estuarine mudflats,** such as these in Germany, are often extensive. Despite their drab appearance, they support large invertebrate populations that provide food for wading birds. Flocks arrive to feed at low tide, when the surface is exposed. Sheltered mudflats may be colonized by salt-tolerant plants and develop into salt marshes.

↓ **Sand ripples** form where the wind blows sand grains, a few at a time, up a gentle slope and drops them when it can carry them no farther. Ripples can form on the surface of sand dunes. These ripples are on dunes at the White Sands National Monument, New Mexico.

↘ **Beach ripples** are created by the gentle to and fro of tides on a sheltered coast. The ripples are usually up to 8 inches (20 cm) high and 20 inches (50 cm) apart. These ripples are on a beach on the Isle of Harris, in the Outer Hebrides, Scotland.

The Mississippi Delta is seen here from space in a false-color image that shows where the sediment—the white, cloudy material—is being deposited. The green areas are where silt was deposited in the past to form an earlier delta. The picture covers an area about 112 miles (180 km) wide. Processes in the Mississippi Delta are dominated by the river flow, rather than by tides or waves.

Mass movement

Under certain conditions soil, rocks, snow and other materials that cover hillsides move unless they are securely bonded to the underlying bedrock. Depending on the material involved, this mass movement takes different forms, but the condition necessary for the displacement is the same. It centers on two factors: the shear stress—the force of gravity that pushes the material downhill; and the shear strength—the effect of friction that resists movement. If shear strength exceeds shear stress the slope is stable. If shear stress exceeds shear strength, the slope is unstable and material will slowly and constantly creep down. Sudden rock falls, landslides, mudslides and avalanches happen on slopes that are conditionally unstable. Conditionally unstable slopes are stable until something, such as water, lubricates the boundary between the bedrock and overlying material and destabilizes them.

→ **Heavy rain linked to El Niño** has lubricated this hillside in Del Puerto Canyon, California, causing a type of landslide called an earth flow. This movement happens very fast and the displaced earth is very wet.

TYPES OF MASS MOVEMENT

There are many forms of mass movement. Creep happens slowly. Flow can also be slow, but it is sometimes rapid. A snow avalanche is a type of flow. Creep and flow involve the movement of all the loose material above the bedrock. Rocks and soil sometimes slide across the surface, leaving the lower layers intact. Three types of earth and rock movement are below.

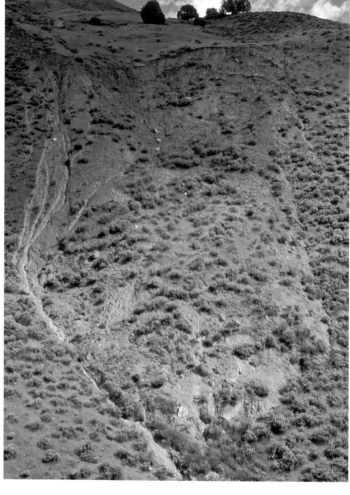

ROCK FALL

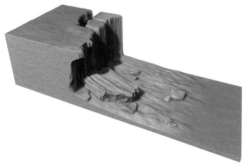

EARTH FLOW

SOIL FLOW

↑ **This is a debris avalanche** on a slope above Emerald Bay, on Lake Tahoe, California. The debris was fairly dry. The flow probably began with a big rock fall that destabilized the slope and sent rock, soil and the trees growing in the soil hurtling down the hillside at tremendous speed.

→ **A slab avalanche**—the most dangerous type—has sent snow, rocks and uprooted trees rushing down this slope near Molas Pass in San Juan National Forest, Colorado. Avalanches happen on slopes of between 30 and 40 degrees when the shear stress caused by the weight of snow exceeds the shear strength.

The meteorite effect

The planets, including Earth, are formed from material that was drawn together by gravity. Much of the material was in the form of large blocks of solid rock, and after the planets and their moons reached their present shapes and sizes some of these blocks were left over. Most orbit in the Asteroid Belt, between Mars and Jupiter, but they can be perturbed and move into orbits that carry them out of the Asteroid Belt. Asteroids that come close to Earth are called Near Earth Objects. Astronomers have identified more than 4000 Near Earth Objects, and about 750 of them are more than half a mile (1 km) across.

Asteroids travel at about 14 miles per second (22 km/s). When one collides with a planet it creates a crater, the size of which depends on the mass of the impacting body. All of the inner planets—Mercury, Venus, Earth and Mars—and their moons have been struck countless millions of times. The Moon's heavily cratered surface bears testimony to the huge number of impacts it has suffered. It has no atmosphere or plate tectonics to erase them. Earth, because it is much bigger, has suffered an even greater number of impacts, but crustal movements and weathering have removed most of the impact craters.

→ **This impact crater** on the Moon's surface, photographed by the Apollo 11 crew, is 50 miles (80 km) across. The smaller craters visible inside it and along its rim must have been made later, indicating that this was an ancient impact.

↓ **At the Moon's South Pole,** the Aitken Basin, inside the broken line, is more than 1550 miles (2500 km) across and 8 miles (13 km) deep. It is the largest impact crater so far discovered anywhere in the Solar System.

IMPACT OF A METEORITE

An approaching asteroid is heated to incandescence by friction with the atmosphere and partially melts. As the meteor travels at about 60 times the speed of sound, friction slows the front of the object more than the remainder, which distorts its shape.

The ball of fire takes about four seconds to descend from a height of 50 miles (80 km). By the time it strikes the surface it is white hot. It blasts surface rocks aside, vaporizing them as it does so.

The impact sends a cloud of vaporized rock into the air. Because it is so hot it is very buoyant and shoots upward to a great height. Some of the material may leave the planet entirely and go into orbit.

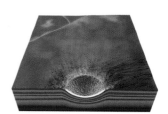

As the vapor cools it condenses into minerals, including fragments of black glass called tektites, that fall over a wide area. Superheated rocks below ground explode upward, forming a hill at the center of the crater.

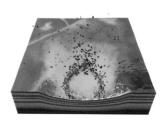

The impact crater is circular, regardless of the angle of the asteroid strike. This is because it results from the explosion that occurs as the asteroid meets crustal rock and both are vaporized. Most craters have a central mound and raised rim.

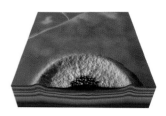

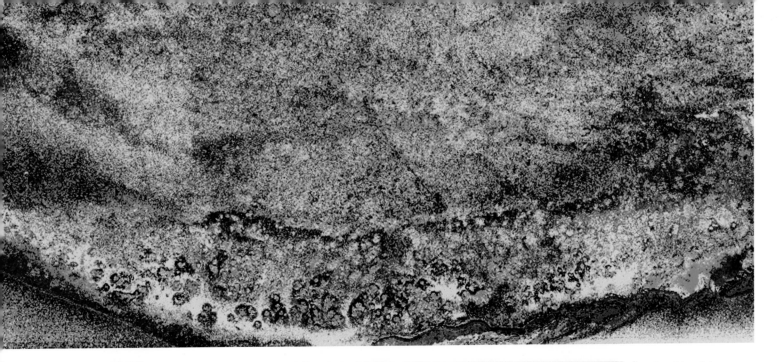

↑ **The Chicxulub crater** on the Yucatán Pensinsula, Mexico, seen here in a false-color radar image taken by the Space Shuttle *Endeavour*, was made about 65 million years ago by an asteroid about 6 miles (10 km) across. Originally the impact crater was approximately 60 miles (100 km) in diameter.

← **The Shoemaker crater** near Wiluna, Western Australia—the semicircular feature in this satellite image—is the oldest impact site in Australia. The crater is about 18 miles (30 km) across and was made by an impact 1.7 million years ago. It was formerly known as the Teague Ring.

Rivers at work

One cubic foot of water weighs about 60 pounds (1 m³ weighs 1 t). Water is heavy and when it moves across the land it can exert tremendous force. Rivers cut their channels through solid rock, in some places carving deep canyons. In order to carve channels the rivers must remove the material that once filled them. Large rivers also acquire water from tributaries. The tributaries collect water that has flowed over and beneath the surrounding land, and that water, as well as the tributaries themselves, also excavates channels through which it flows. It is a slow but persistent process that continues for millions of years. Rivers scour mineral particles and grains from the land that they drain and transport all of these to their lowland flood plains, and eventually to the sea. A major river moves a staggering quantity of sediment. The Mississippi River, for example, delivers more than 200 million tons (203 million t) into the sea each year and the Ganges transports 1125 million tons (1143 million t). The sand and mud that cover the seafloor came originally from the land.

The water that rivers carry originally came from the sea; its return closes the hydrological, or water, cycle. Every year approximately 77,000 cubic miles (321,000 km³) of water evaporate from the oceans and 15,000 cubic miles (62,500 km³) from land; about 21,000 cubic miles (87,500 km³) fall over land. The balance, of 6,000 cubic miles (25,000 km³), is the amount of water rivers return to the sea annually.

→ **The Grand Canyon,** 277 miles (446 km) long and an average 4000 feet (1220 m) deep, was carved by the Colorado River. The process began 10 million years ago, following the uplift of the Colorado Plateau. The canyon was well developed three million years ago.

↓ **A river slows** as it crosses the almost level ground near its mouth and slows again when it enters the sea. This loss of speed depletes the energy needed to transport sediment. Sand grains settle where the river flows most slowly, forming sandbanks and sandbars.

← **Yosemite waterfalls** deliver water into deep valleys that were carved by glaciers during the last ice age. When the glaciers disappeared, valleys that once fed into the glacier surfaces were marooned, as hanging valleys, high above the glacial valley floor. The biggest waterfall in Yosemite National Park, USA, is 1400 feet (427 m) high.

MEANDERING RIVERS

As a river flows along its channel, friction with the banks and bed causes local eddies, where the water flows in horizontal or vertical circles. This motion deposits sediment on the side of the river where the water moves more slowly. Water now flows around the sediment, accelerating its flow against the opposite bank and eroding it. As the eroded bank recedes and the opposite bank advances, the bend in the channel becomes sharper. The diagram at right illustrates how meanders develop; the cross-sections below show the water eddies.

EDDY MOVING CLOCKWISE

EDDY MOVING COUNTERCLOCKWISE

Ice caps and glaciers

In Antarctica, the high Arctic and on the tops of the world's highest mountains conditions are so cold that even in summer the temperature never remains above freezing for long enough to melt the snow that fell during the preceding winter. Each year's snowfall lies on top of earlier falls and the weight of accumulating snow compresses the lower layers until the snow turns into ice. That is how an ice cap or ice sheet forms. An ice cap covers an area of less than 20,000 square miles (50,000 km²); if the ice covers a larger area it is called an ice sheet.

The weight of snow and ice forces ice outward at the base, so an ice sheet lies on top of moving ice. The ice sheet is domed and where the moving ice crosses the coast it may extend over the sea as an ice shelf. Part of an ice shelf is grounded—firmly attached to solid rock—but the outer parts may lie on the surface of water. Tidal and wave movements weaken it and from time to time sections break away—or "calve"—to form icebergs. A mass of moving ice is called a glacier. Valley glaciers that flow down mountainsides are fed from ice made from compacted snow in small ice caps called ice fields.

HOW A GLACIER FLOWS

A valley glacier is fed from above with ice, water, rock and other debris. Geothermal heat warms the base of the glacier, causing it to flow by gravity. At the upper levels snow continues to accumulate in the net accumulation zone, but water is also lost by evaporation, sublimation and wind (deflation). In the net ablation zone below the equilibrium line the glacier loses mass faster than it receives it.

GLACIER EROSION

↑ **Fiordland National Park,** New Zealand, is seen here in twilight. A fjord is the seaward end of a glacial valley. The glacier has melted and seawater has flooded the deep valley carved by the glacier. The existence of fjords indicates that the climate was once much colder than it is now.

→ **Glaciers transport rock** and debris, depositing it as moraine at the foot and along the sides of the glacier. The tiny figures in this picture are a team of climbers and porters crossing moraine near the Gore Urdukas-Boltoro Glacier, Pakistan.

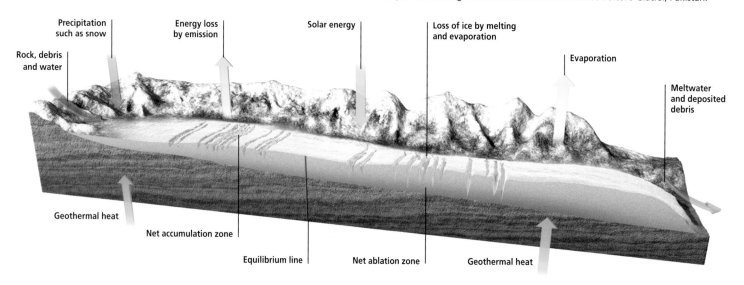

Precipitation such as snow | Energy loss by emission | Solar energy | Loss of ice by melting and evaporation | Evaporation

Rock, debris and water

Meltwater and deposited debris

Geothermal heat

Net accumulation zone

Equilibrium line

Net ablation zone

Geothermal heat

↑ **Moving ice sheets** push clay and stones into oval piles, rounded at one end and streamlined at the other. These piles lie beneath the ice and when the ice melts they are exposed as small hills, called drumlins. This drumlin field, or swarm, is in the Lake District, Cumbria, England.

↑ **Because the surface** of a frozen lake is smooth, it is easy to assume that a valley glacier is smooth. Slow movement, though, breaks up the ice and gives a glacier a very rugged surface. This is the Moreno Glacier, Argentina.

Hot springs and geysers

Among the dangers and discomforts that miners endure working underground, high temperature is one that no safety procedure can reduce. Mines are hot and the deeper the miners dig the hotter they become. That is because the temperature increases with depth by an average of between 12°F and 24°F for every 100 feet (20°–40°C/km). This is known as the geothermal gradient. In some places, however, the gradient is much steeper, and hot rock or pools of superheated water lie close to the surface. These places are found in areas that are, or were, volcanically active and magma is the source of underground heat. Cool water flows into the heated area from the sides, moving beneath the hot water and pushing it upward, only to be heated and displaced in its turn. The heated water may then rise all the way to the surface as a hot spring, or mix with soil to form boiling mud. Under certain conditions the water will shoot skyward at regular intervals from a geyser. Hot water dissolves brightly colored chemical compounds from the rocks below ground. These compounds are often deposited at the surface as the water evaporates.

THE PLUMBING IN A GEYSER
A geyser has a central duct through solid rock, but a fault has displaced the rock that contains the duct and shattered rock along the fault plane. Shattered sedimentary or volcanic rock, called breccia, extends to the base of the duct and immediately above a mass of very hot rock. Water trickles downward through the breccia and is heated at the bottom. The hot water expands upward and some overflows from the top. This releases the pressure on the water below, which suddenly boils, turning the water in the duct into a column of steam that shoots up.

↓ **This boiling mud** is in Champagne Pool, in the Wai-O-Tapu geothermal area of New Zealand. Champagne Pool is a large hot spring, roughly circular and 213 feet (65 m) across. The water temperature is 165°F (74°C) and carbon dioxide that bubbles up through the water gives the pool its name.

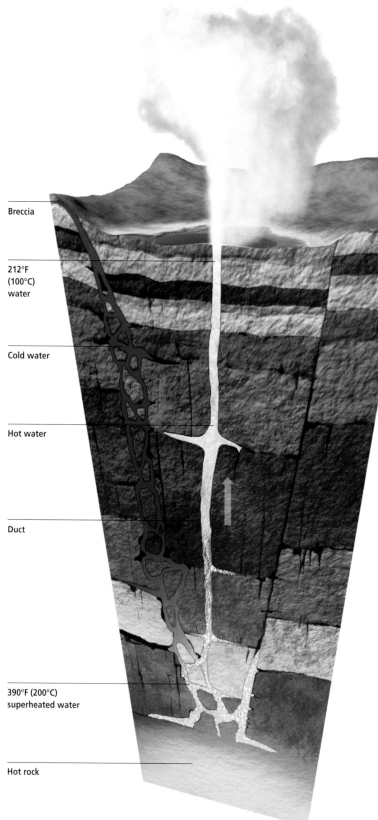

Breccia

212°F (100°C) water

Cold water

Hot water

Duct

390°F (200°C) superheated water

Hot rock

← **Strokkur Geyser,** one of the most famous geysers in Iceland, erupts regularly every five to ten minutes, throwing water up to 70 feet (21 m) into the air. Strokkur is only a short distance from the Stóri Geysir, which no longer erupts, but which gave the word "geyser" to the English language.

↓ **Grand Prismatic Spring** is the largest hot spring in the Yellowstone National Park, Wyoming. Bacterial mats provide the bright colors, and the deep blue at the center of the pool results from the great depth and purity of the water. The spring discharges steaming water into the nearby Excelsior Geyser Crater.

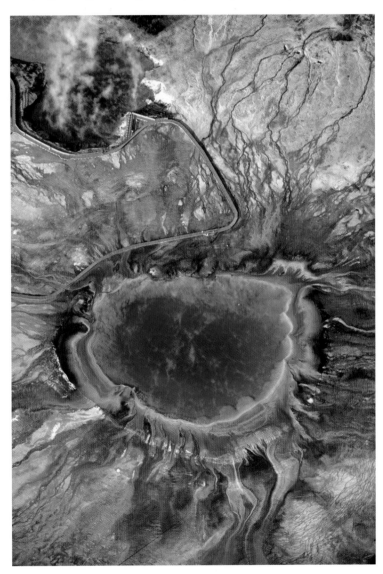

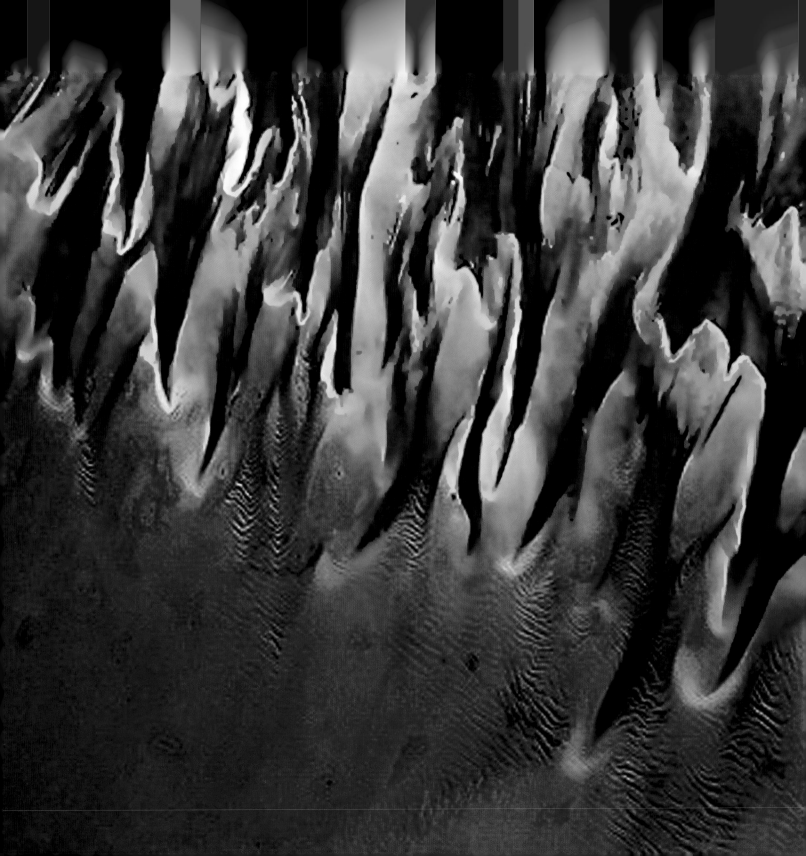

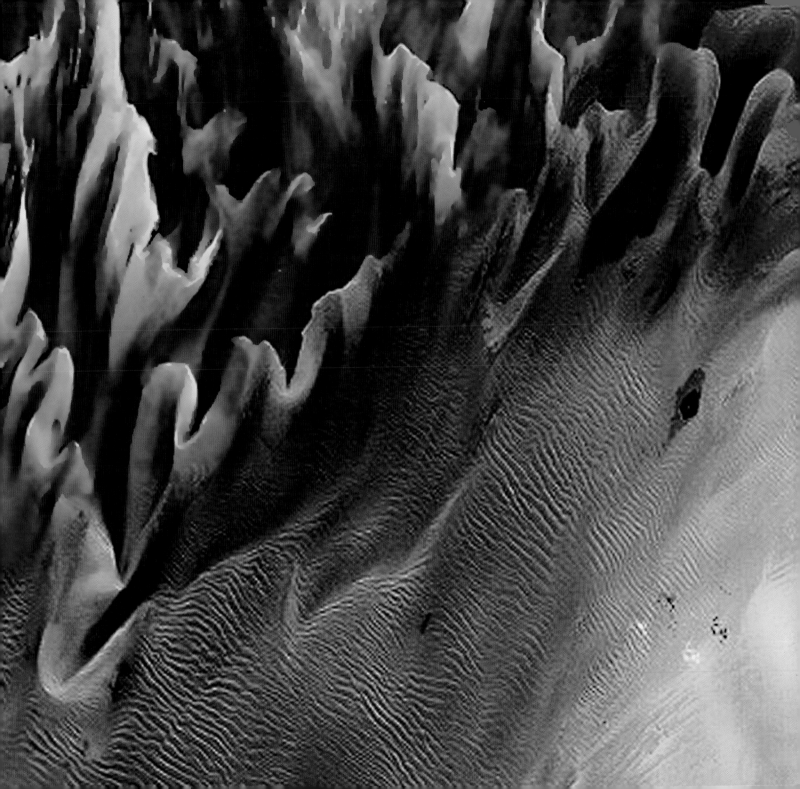

Previous page A satellite view of the sands and seaweed
beds in the Bahamas shows the effect of tides and currents.

Seas and oceans

Earth is indeed the blue planet, with more than 70 percent of its surface covered by water. The formation of the oceans changed our planet from a barren wilderness to one capable of sustaining plant, animal and human life. Oceans control weather patterns and impact on global environmental cycles. Their currents, tides and waves are among Earth's elemental forces.

The blue planet

Oceans and seas cover 70 percent of Earth's surface. Their average depth is 12,240 feet (3730 m) and they hold 530 million cubic miles (1370 km³) of water. When seawater evaporates, some of the vapor condenses to form clouds over land. Water from these clouds falls as precipitation, and rivers carry it back to the sea. As water flows across the land and below the surface as groundwater, substances from rocks and soil dissolve into it. Water that returns to the ocean is a solution of many substances and seawater contains dissolved substances that have been accumulating for billions of years. When water evaporates, however, only water molecules escape into the air; substances dissolved in the water are left behind. That is why the sea is salty. Sodium chloride—common salt—is what gives the sea its taste. Seawater also contains, in descending order of quantity, sulfate, magnesium, calcium, potassium, bicarbonate, bromide, borate, strontium and fluoride. These substances make up 99.9 percent of the dissolved material.

← **The endless sea** extends to the horizon, beneath clouds formed from water that evaporated from the surface. Because seawater is alkaline, reactions that send calcium carbonate and aluminum and iron oxides to join the seabed sediment can take place.

← **Salt flats** are deposits that form as a result of evaporation after an area of sea becomes cut off or, as in this case, water ceases to flow into a salt lake. These flats are in Death Valley National Park, California.

← **A mountain stream** tumbles rapidly over and around rocks at the start of its journey to the sea, the original source of its water. Along the way the water will gather soluble substances that will later recycle back to the land.

THE BLUE PLANET
Seen from space, Earth is
clearly a watery planet. Oceans,
beneath scattered clouds that are
also formed from water, cover more
than two-thirds of the surface and
the clouds extend over much of the
land. This picture shows the Pacific Ocean.

Ocean currents

Seas may be calm, but the surface waters of the world's oceans are never still, because the air is never still. Warm air rises and cool air subsides, forming a complex system of air movements that produce surface winds: easterly winds in high latitudes and near the equator; westerly winds in middle latitudes. Winds push the surface water along and so generate the ocean currents. Ocean currents move warm water away from the equator and cold water away from polar regions. Marine plankton drifts with the currents and larger organisms feed on the plankton.

Currents flow in circles, called gyres, in all the oceans. Where they flow parallel to continental coasts they are called boundary currents. Eastern boundary currents carry cold water and western boundary currents carry warm water. Boundary currents chill or warm air that passes across them. The gyres turn because of the Coriolis effect, which deflects moving air or water to the right in the northern hemisphere and to the left in the southern hemisphere. It is caused by Earth's rotation and its strength increases with distance from the equator. As the water moves farther from the equator it is deflected even more; at the same time it moves from the easterly tropical winds to the midlatitude westerlies, then back again. Eventually it turns in a circle.

OCEAN GYRES

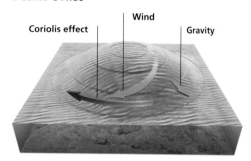

SURFACE CURRENTS

■ Above 86°F (30°C)	□ 41–50°F (5–10°C)
■ 77–86°F (25–30°C)	□ Under 41°F (5°C)
■ 68–77°F (20–25°C)	→ Warm current
■ 59–68°F (15–20°C)	→ Cool current
■ 50–59°F (10–15°C)	

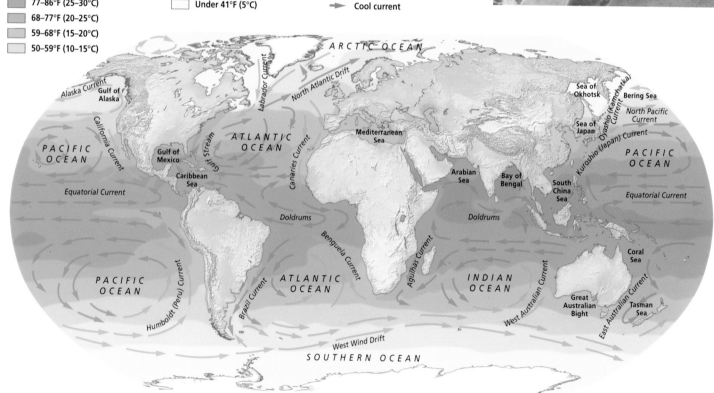

The Gulf Stream flows parallel to the North American coast, seen in this false-color satellite image as the pink band in the bottom right. It is between 60 and 90 miles (100–150 km) wide and its flow is about 20 times greater than all the fresh water in the world that flows into oceans.

Leatherback turtles swim thousands of miles through the Atlantic Ocean, carried by the Gulf Stream. They come ashore to lay their eggs on land.

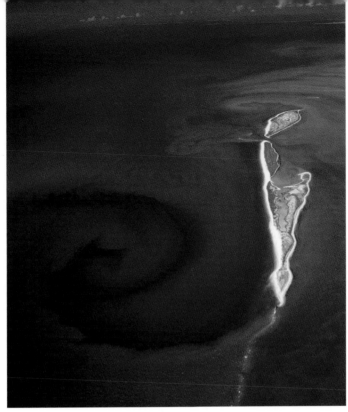

A gentle whirlpool in the Indian Ocean is visible to the left of the Lacepede Islands, Western Australia. Whirlpools occur where tidal flows are deflected, often by seafloor features, and the currents circle.

Ocean eddies form in the Gulf Stream. In this satellite image an eddy appears white. The Gulf Stream flows at varying speeds, up to about 6 miles per hour (10 km/h). The differing speeds produce eddies.

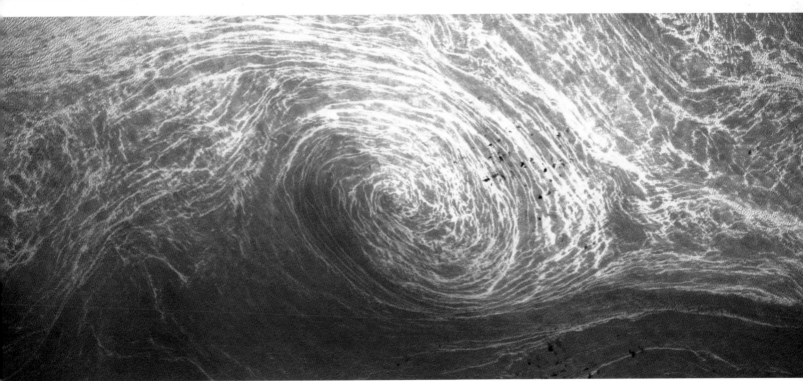

Waves

Winds blowing across the ocean produce waves. The height of a wave depends on the force of the wind and on the fetch, which is the distance over which the wind blows without interruption. The biggest waves are found in the largest oceans and the Southern Ocean is the most violent of all. With no large landmass to check them, Southern Ocean winds are the world's strongest and can blow all the way around the planet. It is for good reason that the southern latitudes are nicknamed the roaring forties, furious fifties and screaming sixties.

The distance between one wave crest and the next is called the wavelength and the time it takes for successive crests to pass a stationary point is the wave period. The speed at which waves travel is equal to the wavelength divided by the period. Sea storms generate waves of varying periods. The short-period waves tend to dissipate soon after leaving the storm area, but long-period waves sometimes have enough energy to cross the ocean in the form of swell. Storms off New Zealand have produced swell that reached Alaska. A wave transmits energy through the water, but the water itself moves in small circles. The effect is felt to a depth equal to about half the wavelength. When the depth of water is less than half the wavelength the bottom of the wave slows. This reduces the wavelength but does not alter the period, so the waves grow higher.

← **Breakers develop** as waves enter shallow water. Friction between the water and the seabed slows the waves, but water continues to arrive at the same speed. As a result, the wavelength decreases, the height increases and the waves grow steeper until they become unstable and tumble forward.

↓ **Wavelength is the distance** between succeeding crests. Wave height is the vertical distance between a trough and a crest. Amplitude is half the wave height. Steepness is the angle to the horizontal of a line drawn from the bottom of a trough to the top of the adjacent crest.

PARTS OF A WAVE

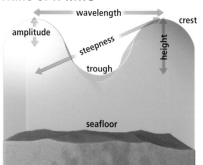

wavelength
crest
amplitude
steepness
height
trough
seafloor

Waves during a violent storm off Baja California, Mexico, are breaking because the tops of the waves, blown by the fierce wind, are moving faster than the water below them. A storm off the Washington coast once produced waves 48 feet (15 m) high. Waves up to 90 feet (27 m) high have been reported from the open ocean.

These waves near Maui, Hawaii, are affecting only the water near the surface. The circular movement of water is drawing in air and creating lots of bubbles that make the water look white. The effect of the waves, however, extends only to a depth equal to half the wavelength, leaving the water below and the gravel on the seabed undisturbed.

The ocean floor

Close to the shore, the seabed slopes gently. This is the continental shelf and it ends on average at 45 miles (72 km) from the shore, where the water is about 500 feet (152 m) deep. From that point the seabed slopes more steeply down the continental slope. Sediment slides slowly down the continental shelf, in many places along deep canyons that end in fan-shaped deposits. It then falls more rapidly down the continental slope onto the continental rise, which extends for several hundred miles. Beyond the continental rise lies the bathyal zone, where the ocean depth is from 650 to 6500 feet (200–2000 m). This part of the ocean floor includes deep trenches associated with subduction zones, and submarine canyons where erosion triggers submarine landslides. The deepest part of the ocean, below 6500 feet (2000 m), is called the abyssal zone. This accounts for 75 percent of the total ocean floor. It is cold, totally dark and animals that live there are black or gray. Not a glimmer of sunlight penetrates here. Water currents move at a few inches per second. There are hills in the abyss, and volcanic mountain ranges at mid-ocean ridges where crustal plates are moving apart and the sea floor is spreading.

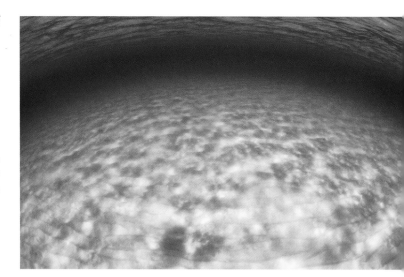

↗ **The surface of the continental shelf** seabed off Okinawa, Japan, is covered with ripples that resemble small dunes—somewhat distorted here by the fisheye lens. The surface consists of sediment—mud, sand and organic material—eroded from the land. It is moving very slowly toward the edge of the shelf, from where it will slide into much deeper water. It contains nutrients that sustain marine life.

→ **Scuba divers cannot swim** below about 150 feet (45 m). Submersibles like this one have arms that hold tools. Manned by up to three people and equipped with lights and cameras, they allow scientists to explore at great depths. In 1960 Jacques Piccard and Don Walsh, in the *Trieste*, descended to the bottom of the Challenger Deep, in the Pacific Ocean, at 37,800 feet (11,530 m).

↠ **Part of the Indian Ocean,** seen from the air, reveals some features of the ocean floor, but only in fairly shallow water, because the deep ocean floor is invisible from above. Enough light for photosynthesis penetrates to about 500 feet (150 m) in the clearest water and some light is detectable at 3000 feet (1000 m). Below about 4000 feet (1200 m), however, total darkness reigns.

OCEAN FLOOR FEATURES

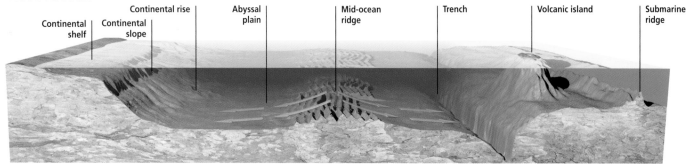

Continental shelf · Continental slope · Continental rise · Abyssal plain · Mid-ocean ridge · Trench · Volcanic island · Submarine ridge

Tsunamis

Tsunami is a Japanese word that means "harbor wave." Most tsunamis are harmless and few rise to more than 30 feet (9 m). But occasionally there is a much bigger megatsunami. On July 10, 1958 an earthquake in Crillon Inlet, at the head of Lituya Bay, Alaska, generated a tsunami 1719 feet (524 m) high. Remarkably, it killed only two people.

A tsunami is triggered by a displacement of rocks or sediment on the ocean floor. It may be an earthquake that suddenly raises or lowers the rocks on either side of a fault, or a submarine landslide that releases millions of tons of sediment. The displacement produces a shock wave that propagates outward throughout the entire depth of water. The wavelength is more than 100 miles (160 km); the period can be minutes, or even hours; and the wave height is less than three feet (90 cm). The wave travels at between 400 and 500 miles per hour (640–800 km/h). When it reaches shallow water near a coast, the wave slows, but as water continues to arrive from offshore its height increases. The tsunami moves ashore quickly, more like a rising tide rather than a breaker.

TEN WORST TSUNAMIS			
	Year	Place	Deaths (approx.)
1.	2004	Indian Ocean	300,000
2.	1883	Krakatau, Indonesia	36,000
3.	1896	Sanriku Coast, Japan	20,000
4.	1771	Okinawa, Japan	12,000
5.	1792	Kyushu, Japan	5000
6.	1976	Mindanau, Philippines	5000
7.	1933	Sanriku Coast, Japan	3000
8.	1960	Chile	2000
9.	1998	Papua New Guinea	2000
10.	1944	Tonankai, Japan	1200

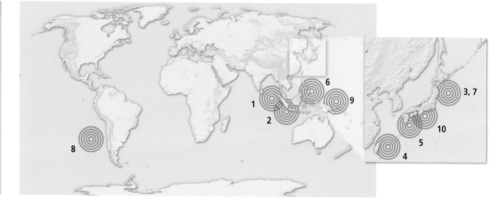

MECHANICS OF A TSUNAMI
A submarine earthquake suddenly raises a section of crustal rock. This produces a series of shock waves (shown here in red) that propagate outward. Because they are hundreds of miles apart and travel fast, ships may not notice them. As the waves enter shallower water they slow down and grow higher. If a wave trough reaches the shore first, the water will recede. Then the crest arrives, like a rising tide.

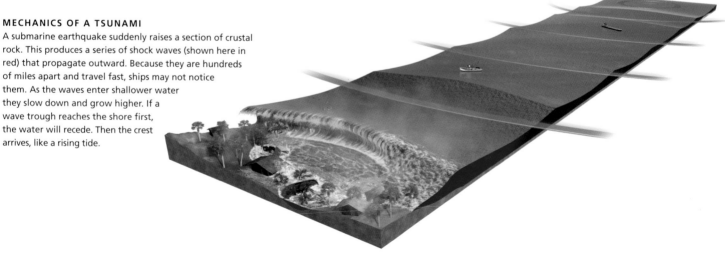

← **On December 26, 2004** a magnitude 9.1–9.3 earthquake off Sumatra, Indonesia, caused an estimated 750 miles (1200 km) of fault line to slip along the subduction zone between the Indian and Burma plates. The seabed rose, displacing an estimated 7 cubic miles (30 km^3) of water and triggering tsunamis that spread across the ocean. Aceh, Indonesia, was affected worst. This picture shows the scene at Banda Aceh on January 9, 2005.

← **Children from Aceh** play between the tents at a flooded refugee camp in July 2005. The tsunamis that made landfall around the Indian Ocean following the earthquake of December 26, 2004 killed an estimated 300,000 people. They also demolished entire villages and devastated communities throughout the region. In addition to the fatalities, approximately 125,000 people were injured and around 1.69 million were driven from their homes. Some of these found their way to refugee camps where, as this picture shows, conditions were far from ideal.

Changing coastlines

Waves cause erosion. They also transport eroded material parallel to the coast, depositing it elsewhere and building beaches or sandbars that may grow into barrier islands. Waves may approach a beach from any angle, but they slow down as they enter shallow water. The first part of the wave to reach the shore slows first. Faster waves catch up with it, refracting all the waves so that they come ashore at an angle that is approximately, but seldom precisely, at right angles to the shoreline. Where they are not moving exactly at right angles to the shore, the waves produce longshore currents that run parallel to the shore. Water flowing away from the shore often produces rip currents.

Some cliffs rise sheer from deep water, which moves past them, eroding them slowly. However, most rise from sloping shores, where waves build into breakers that hurl water at the rocks and compress air in small rock cavities, causing rapid erosion. Rocks in horizontal strata erode to form level surfaces called platforms. Beaches mainly form from sand and pebbles—transported by waves. They erode in one place and grow in another, which sometimes results in a series of indentations called cusps.

→ **Cliff erosion** can be rapid where soft rock is exposed to violent winter storms. Not long ago this tree grew in soil on the cliff top. Waves have cut away the material near the bottom of the cliff and the cliff face has collapsed, bringing the tree down with it. Along some coasts cliff erosion has caused houses to fall.

↓ **Sea caves, arches and stacks** form where the waves erode softer rock more easily than stronger, more resistant material. Eventually this arch will fall, producing another stack. It is not only wave action that erodes exposed coastal rocks; the salt and other chemicals in seawater also cause chemical weathering.

← **The painted cliffs** in Maria Island National Park, Tasmania, Australia, owe their bright colors to iron oxide and other insoluble compounds that have formed through chemical reactions with sea water, then been deposited. The sea has eroded the upper strata and has produced a shore platform at the level of wave action. This platform absorbs wave energy and so protects the cliff.

↓ **Barrier islands** are forming offshore from Separation Point, in the Abel Tasman National Park, South Island, New Zealand. They are ridges of sand parallel to the coast that have been deposited by longshore drift—the transport of material by longshore currents. Sheltered lagoons lie between the islands and the shore.

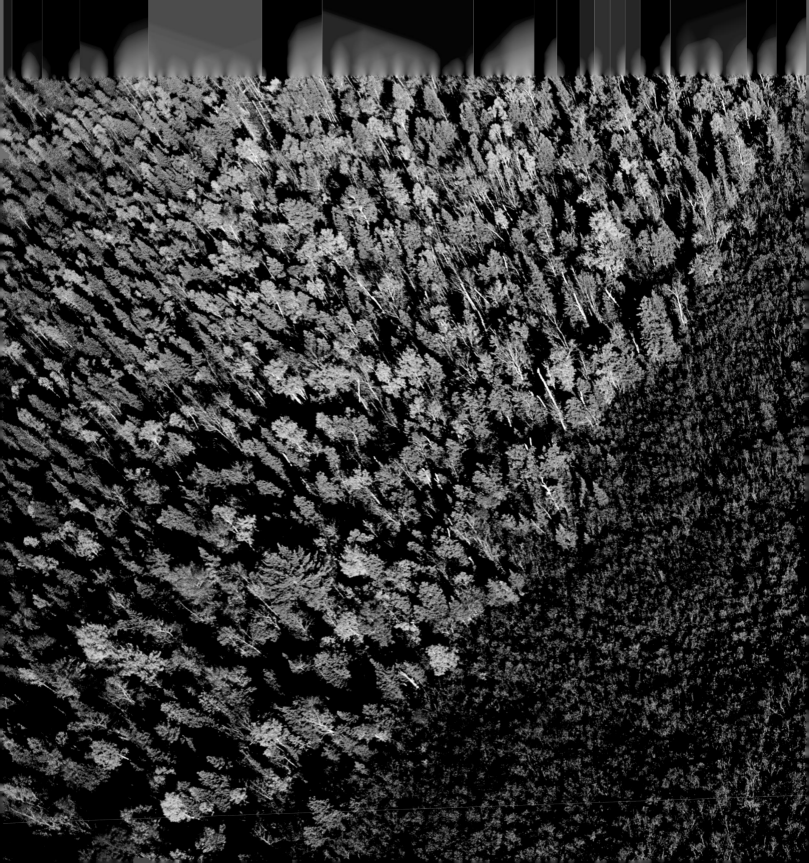

A unique combination of forces—most particularly the interaction of sunlight and water—has enabled life on Earth to develop and diversify. Plants and animals survive, and thrive, in environments as varied as deserts and polar regions, mountains and forests, rivers and tundra. Humans, too, utilize Earth's varied landscapes—sometimes destructively.

Kingdoms of life

Biologists classify organisms hierarchically. Individuals that are similar and can interbreed comprise a species and similar species form a genus. Genera are grouped into families, families into orders, orders into classes, classes into phyla and phyla into kingdoms. Although each higher level seems more abstract, in fact it represents a more fundamental grouping. There have been many attempts to group phyla into kingdoms, but in 1990 Carl Woese, now a professor at the University of Illinois, proposed a new classification based on three domains: Bacteria (or Eubacteria), Archaea and Eukaryota (or Eukarya). This is now widely used. The domain Bacteria comprises all bacteria, including cyanobacteria, in the kingdom also called Bacteria. Archaea comprises two kingdoms: Crenarchaeota—extreme heat- and cold-loving organisms; and Euryarchaeota—organisms that live in other extreme environments. The domain Eukaryota contains the kingdoms Protoctista, Fungi, Plantae and Animalia.

→ **Salinity levels** in the Great Salt Lake, Utah, are variable but the water is always saltier than seawater and sometimes seven times as salty. The lake supports brine shrimps but no fish, and the high salinity suits halophiles—salt-loving archaean microorganisms.

→› **Few organisms can survive** in the boiling graphite mud at Rotorua, New Zealand, but hyperthermophiles—heat-loving archaeans—thrive there. Some flourish at 113°C (235°F) and cannot reproduce below 90°C (194°F).

PHYLOGENETIC TREE OF LIFE
A tree of life is a diagram that illustrates the relationships among groups of organisms. This tree groups the organisms into three domains: Bacteria, Archaea and Eukaryota. All of these are descended from the last universal ancestor (LUA), shown by the blue line at the bottom. Biologists believe that the LUA lived about 3.5 billion years ago, possibly in deep ocean vents. The Archaea are placed between the other two domains, but are more closely related to Eukaryota than to Bacteria.

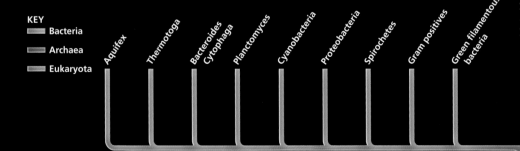

KEY
▬ Bacteria
▬ Archaea
▬ Eukaryota

Aquifex
Thermotoga
Bacteroides Cytophaga
Planctomyces
Cyanobacteria
Proteobacteria
Spirochetes
Gram positives
Green filamentous bacteria

LUA

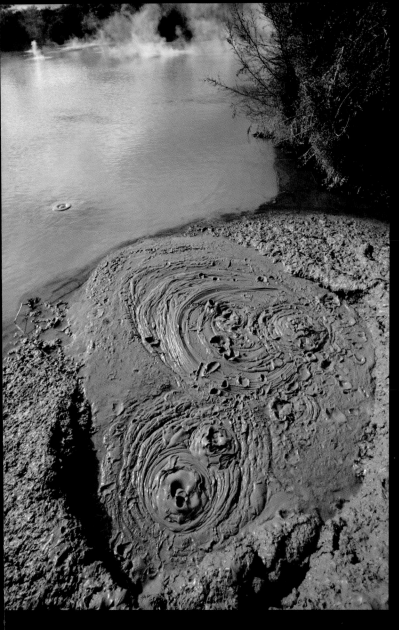

↓ **Some mammals,** such as this pair of beef cattle on a Welsh hilltop, and humans, have populations of methanogens in their guts. These archaeans release methane as a metabolic by-product. Oxygen kills them.

↓ **Staphylococci,** here greatly magnified, are bacteria that live mainly on or inside mammals. Many are harmful, causing boils, abscesses, food poisoning and diseases of the throat, respiratory system, heart and urinogenital tract.

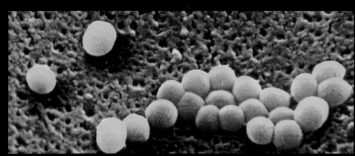

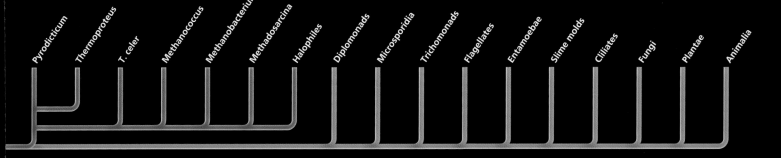

Pyrodicticum · Thermoproteus · T. celer · Methanococcus · Methanobacterium · Methadosarcina · Halophiles · Diplomonads · Microsporidia · Trichomonads · Flagellates · Entamoebae · Slime molds · Ciliates · Fungi · Plantae · Animalia

Kingdoms of eukaryotes

Eukaryotes are cells that are larger and much more complex than bacteria and archaeans. They are the cells that form the bodies of all members of the domain Eukaryota. Plants, fungi and animals are all made from eukaryotic cells, but, as well as the kingdoms Plantae, Fungi and Animalia, the Eukaryota contains the kingdom Protoctista, which comprises a wide range of aquatic organisms. Amoebae, diatoms, algae—including all seaweeds—protozoa and slime molds are all protoctists, and there are many more. Although protoctists are eukaryotic, they are not plants, fungi or animals.

Plants are the most familiar members of the Eukaryota. They have established themselves on land wherever there is moisture and nutriment, and they range in size from the tiny, delicate mosses to the coast redwood (*Sequoia sempervirens*), a tree that can grow up to 390 feet (120 m) tall.

→ **Mosses form a carpet** that consists of many species, with plants packed tightly together and supporting each other. Mosses cover rocks, soil, tree bark and fallen logs wherever there is an abundant supply of water. These plants reproduce by spores, have unstalked leaves that are only one cell thick except at the rib, and absorb moisture through their cell walls. There are approximately 15,000 species.

→ **Ferns are plants** that first appeared in the Devonian period. They reproduce by means of spores produced in sori on the underside of their leaves. These uncurling fronds belong to Japanese holly fern (*Cyrtomium falcatum*).

→→ **Fungi obtain nutrients** by absorbing organic compounds from their surroundings through a network—or "mycelium"—of fine hyphae. The visible parts are fruiting bodies, in this case of the amethyst (or violet) deceiver (*Laccaria amethystea*), a species that is edible, but not one that is grown commercially.

SLIME MOLD—
A PROTOCTIST

The image above is of a plasmodium, the feeding stage of one of the three types of slime mold. It is a single giant cell that contains thousands of nuclei. When a slime mold is threatened, it produces masses of spores, often on the tips of stalks, that disperse into new and possibly more favorable habitats. True molds are fungi, but slime molds belong to the kingdom Protoctista.

Biomes

articular types of plants grow in certain large areas of the world, where the soils and climate low them to flourish. Grasslands cover much of central North America, South America and urasia, although large areas have been plowed to grow arable crops, which are also grasses. rasslands thrive where the climate is too dry for forests. Forests of broad-leaved evergreen ees grow in the tropics and forests of broad-leaved deciduous and coniferous trees occur middle latitudes. Deserts support only plants that are adapted to the scarcity of moisture. nimals feed on plants, so each type of vegetation supports communities of animals that are hited to the food supply and climate.

These large groupings of plants and animals are called biomes. Biomes correspond pproximately to climatic regions and several of their names reflect this. Climatic regions e determined mainly by latitude and proximity to the ocean, but also by elevation.

EGETATION ZONES
he biome is the largest natural geographic community, its composition determined ainly by the climate. The world's terrestrial biomes correspond to climatic regions, but ountains and highlands constitute a biome that exists in all latitudes. Some biomes can e broken down into smaller units. The map illustrates all the major biomes.

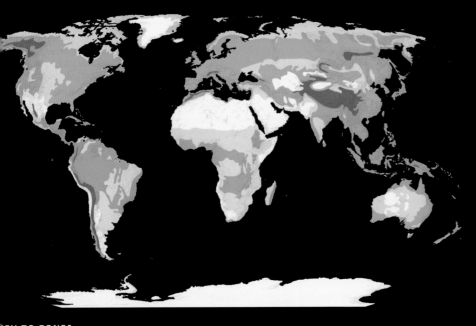

EY TO ZONES

Tropical forest	Tundra
Desert	Polar regions
Grassland	Mountains and highlands
Temperate forest	

← **The setting Sun** shines on a broad-leaved temperate forest on Mount Katahdin, in Baxter State Park, Maine. This type of forest occurs in middle latitudes.

← **This herd of antelope** is grazing on the African savanna, which is tropical grassland adapted to a climate with hot summers and pronounced wet and dry seasons.

⟵ **A sand sea,** or erg, in the Sahara appears lifeless, but many species are adapted to those parts of desert regions where the ground is more stable.

← **The steppe,** here in Kazakhstan, is a region of temperate grassland that extends from eastern Europe across central Asia. The steppe contains grass and many wild flowers.

⟵ **There are several types** of tropical forest. This is rain forest. It is growing in a perpetually wet climate in the Cape Tribulation National Park, in Australia.

← **Mountain climates** resemble those of higher latitudes, but the plants are related to those that grow at the foot of the mountains. This is Mount McKinley, Alaska.

Temperate forests

The temperate regions lie between the tropics and the Arctic and Antarctic circles, and this is the part of the world where temperate forests grow. The temperate climate is highly seasonal, with the seasons defined mainly by temperature. Winters are cold, with snow and frozen ground often restricting the water supply to plants. Summers are warm, but seldom hot. Rainfall is distributed fairly evenly through the year.

There are several types of temperate forest. A wide belt of conifer forest stretches across North America and Eurasia. This is called boreal forest (boreal means northern), but in Russia it is often known as the taiga. It does not occur in the southern hemisphere, because there is no land in the relevant latitude. Broad-leaved deciduous, or summer, forest grows where summers are longer. Mediterranean climates, found in both hemispheres between latitudes 30 degrees and 45 degrees, support forests of broad-leaved evergreen trees.

→ **Winter snow has settled** on the branches and twigs of these aspen trees (*Populus tremula*). Aspens grow from suckers, so these trees at Narke in southern Sweden probably share a root system. Aspens are broad-leaved trees that grow naturally throughout Europe.

TEMPERATE FOREST LOCATIONS
Broad-leaved deciduous forests occur naturally in North America from the US–Canada border to Florida and westward to Minnesota and Missouri; throughout Europe as far north as southern Scandinavia; in eastern Siberia and China from the Sea of Okhotsk south to the Vietnamese border; in Japan; and in southern Australia and New Zealand.

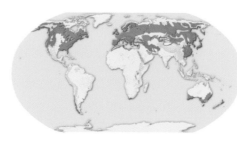

↓ **Mosses require constant moisture.** They blanket the exposed roots and the ground around this tree at the Bird River World Heritage Site, Tasmania, Australia. Temperate rain forests occur where the annual rainfall is typically between 60 and 120 inches (1500–3000 mm) or where fog is common.

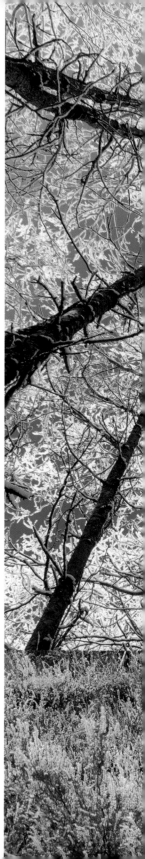

↑ **This elk stag** (*Cervus canadensis*) was photographed in Yellowstone National Park, Montana. The elk, or wapiti, lives on grasslands and at the edge of forests in western North America and parts of Mongolia and China. It is closely related to the smaller red deer (*C. elaphus*) that inhabits the edges of Eurasian temperate forests and the open moors of Scotland.

← **Heathers require sunlight** and acid soil. These ones are flowering in clearings between the trees in the Landes Forest, France. Planted in the nineteenth century, the Landes Forest covers 3900 square miles (10,000 km²) and is one of Europe's largest forests.

Conifer forests

Conifer forests form a broad belt. They grow across North America and Eurasia and are bounded by mixed conifer and broad-leaved forests to the south and the treeless tundra to the north. The forest is known as boreal forest in North America and taiga in Russia. This broad swathe around the northern hemisphere contains one-third of all the world's forests. Coniferous trees thrive where summers are brief and winters long and severe.

Although most of the trees are conifers, there are many species and the composition of the forest varies. In Europe and western Russia it is dominated by spruce (*Picea*), fir (*Abies*) and pine (*Pinus*) species that cast a deep shade. Farther east and in the north larches (*Larix* species) allow more light to penetrate. Near the edges, and wherever trees have been felled, silver birch (*Betula pendula*) appears amid the conifers.

→ **This young woodchuck** (*Marmota monax*), a conifer forest dweller, is feeding voraciously. It spends seven months of the year in hibernation—the shortest hibernation period of any of the 14 species of marmot. The woodchuck is the only marmot species that grows to sexual maturity in a single year. Mother is nearby; young woodchucks stay with their mothers for their first year.

→→ **A finger of conifer forest** extends down the western coast of North America, where high rainfall and frequent fog allow temperate rain forest to flourish. Mosses and ferns carpet the floor here in the Redwood National Park, California, near the coast and amid the Sierra redwoods—some of the world's largest trees.

CONIFER FOREST LOCATIONS

The boreal (or northern) forests and taiga consist of coniferous trees, which thrive in climates that are too cold or dry for broad-leaved trees. Conifer forests form a belt across the northern hemisphere, with a finger extending southward along the Pacific coast of North America. Some species, especially spruces such as the Sitka spruce (*Picea sitchensis*) seen here, cast a deep shadow, making the forest a gloomy place.

↑ **Different subspecies of gray wolf** (*Canis lupus*) inhabit a variety of northern hemisphere habitats, but the most common (*C. l. lupus*) is the timber wolf of temperate forests. When members of a pack meet they greet one another and quickly affirm the social hierarchy. These wolves are near the US–Canada border.

← **These spruce trees** (*Picea* species) are in the Bavarian Alps. Their conical shape and flexible branches allow most coniferous trees to bend under the weight of winter snow and thus shed excess snow. Broken branches would leave wounds open to infection.

Tropical forests

Tropical rain forest grows in the equatorial lowlands where the climate is permanently wet and the difference in temperature between day and night is greater than that between summer and winter. It is dominated by broad-leaved evergreen trees at least 100 feet (30 m) tall and thick lianas.

Where the climate is seasonal, with rainy and dry seasons, the tropical seasonal forest contains deciduous trees as well as evergreens. Montane forests grow on tropical mountains. Low-level forests comprise tall trees, but at higher elevations the trees are smaller, and on the highest mountains small, stunted trees form subalpine forest. Belts of permanent mist at between 6500 and 10,000 feet (2000–3000 m) produce cloud forest, where the trees are covered with mosses and lichens.

TROPICAL FOREST LOCATIONS
Tropical forests occur in Central and South America, the Caribbean, West and Central Africa, Madagascar, South and Southeast Asia and northern Australia. Most lie between the tropics of Cancer and Capricorn. Some, however, grow beyond the tropics—along the Brazilian coast, in eastern Australia and, as monsoon forests, in northwestern India and Bangladesh.

↓ **Ochagavias** are three species of plants that are native to Chile and Juan Fernandez Island ("Robinson Crusoe Island"). This is a flower of *Ochagavia carnea*, a plant cultivated outside the tropics as a garden ornamental.

↓ **Buttress roots** help support the tree. They resemble extensions of the tree trunk and are partly trunk and partly root. This tree, with planklike buttress roots, is in the Daintree National Park, Queensland, Australia.

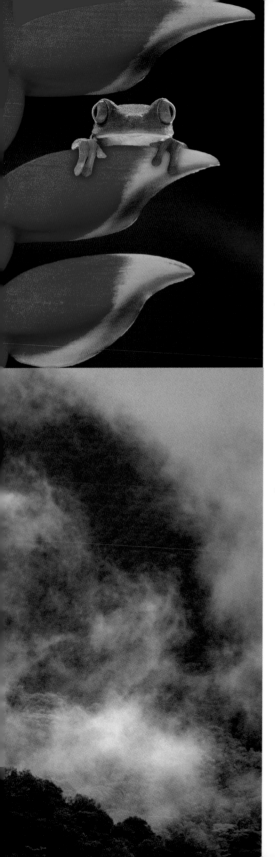

← **A red-eyed tree frog** (*Agalychnis callidryas*), with its characteristic bulging red eyes, peers over a heliconia flower, with which its colors almost blend. These nocturnal Central and South American frogs are between two and three inches (5–7.5 cm) long. Their upper legs are blue and their feet orange or red.

→ **Bromeliads and other epiphytes** grow on the trunk of a tree in the Caribbean National Forest, Puerto Rico. An epiphyte is a plant that uses another plant only for support. It is not a parasite. Bromeliads are a family of about 2400 species of plants, many of them epiphytes.

← **Clouds hover above the forest canopy** in the Braulio Carrillo National Park, Costa Rica. The forest rises to 9500 feet (2906 m), an elevation where perpetual mist favors mosses that cover the trees and lichens that festoon branches. This is cloud forest.

Deforestation

Global demand for high-quality timbers and local desire for agricultural land have led to the clearance of large areas of tropical forest. Many tropical species of plants and animals occupy restricted ranges. When the forest disappears so do they. Forest clearance also affects the regional climate. The maps to the right show the likely effect of removing all the forest from the Amazon basin. Temperatures would increase from between 0.9°F and 1.8°F (0.5–1°C) (pale yellow) up to between 5.4°F and 6.3°F (3–3.5°C) (red). Rainfall would decrease from between 0.04 and 0.08 inch (1–2 mm) per day (yellow) to between 0.1 and 0.2 inch (3–4 mm) per day (red).

Fortunately, governments are now taking steps to reduce deforestation and the rate of clearance has slowed. Between the years 2000 and 2005, South America lost 16,600 square miles (4.3 million ha) a year, Africa 15,400 square miles (4 million ha), tropical Asia 6600 square miles (1.7 million ha) and Central America 1100 square miles (285,000 ha).

TEMPERATURE

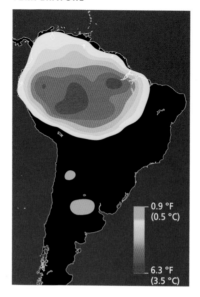

0.9 °F (0.5 °C)

6.3 °F (3.5 °C)

RAINFALL PER DAY

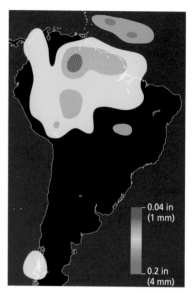

0.04 in (1 mm)

0.2 in (4 mm)

→→ **Rio de Janeiro, Brazil,** borders part of the Atlantic Forest, a biodiversity hotspot with 20,000 species of plants, 40 percent of which are found nowhere else, and more than 950 species of birds, many of them unique. Rio and Saõ Paulo can expand only by encroaching still further into the forest.

→ **Deforestation at Syabru, Nepal,** has left a large area of bare earth exposed to the weather. The soil is now likely to erode. Forest clearance from hillsides has caused severe erosion in Nepal, and the soil is choking rivers and killing fish.

↑ **The progressive clearance of tropical forest** is seen clearly in these false-color images taken in 1975, 1992 and 2000 by Landsats 2, 4 and 7. They show part of the Santa Cruz de la Sierra region of Bolivia. Vegetation appears red and the solid red areas are tropical forest, which is being cleared to make room for the resettlement of people who are being moved from the high Andean plains (Altiplano). Fields, in which people grow crops—mainly soybeans for export—in order to earn a living, surround each settlement. Such tropical deforestation releases significant amounts of carbon dioxide into the atmosphere and contributes to global warming. Fortunately the deforestation rate is now decreasing.

← **Logging affects not only trees** that are removed; it also damages trees that have no commercial value. Once an area has been logged, there is a risk that it will be converted to farmland. There are, however, logging techniques that can maintain, and not destroy, forests. These logs, which are stacked and awaiting transportation to a sawmill, are from a sustainable conifer plantation in the north of Scotland.

Grasslands

Grasses can grow where the climate is too dry for trees. Because of this, the world's grasslands are located in the interior of continents. Even there the amount of annual precipitation determines the character of the grassland. In North America, for example, tall grass prairie grows in the east, where rainfall is relatively high, and short grass prairie in the drier west. In between is a belt of mixed prairie. Prairie (which is the French word for meadow) is the North American temperate grassland. Its Eurasian equivalent is the steppe, which extends from eastern Europe to Mongolia. The pampa and veld are the grasslands of temperate South America and South Africa respectively. Llanos, the tropical grasslands of South America, are found wherever the climate is too dry for forest. Africa has the largest area of tropical grassland. Called the savannah, it extends across the continent to the south of the Sahara, as well as to the south of the tropical forest, and through East Africa.

→ **Silver pampas grass** (*Cortaderia selloana*) once covered much of the eastern pampa, shading out other grasses. Pampas grass forms large tussocks and grows up to 12 feet (3.7 m) tall, with plumes up to 2 feet (60 cm) long. Most of the pampa now grows European grasses to feed livestock.

FOOD WEB
Food preferences define the relationships among all the plant and animal species within every ecosystem. Those relationships form a web that links species to the food they eat. Real food webs are extremely complex. This diagram shows a greatly simplified web.

Carnivore

Insect

Bird

Herbivore

Scavenger

Decomposers   Plants   Decomposers

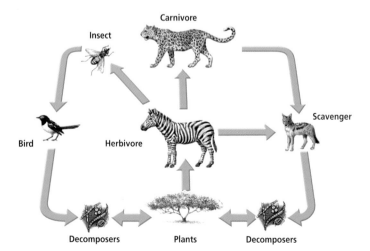

← **A cheetah takes advantage** of the cover afforded by the tall savannah grasses in the Masai Mara National Reserve, Kenya. The cheetah (*Acinonyx jubatus*) stalks its prey, for hours if necessary, until it is close enough to give chase. Then it can run at up to 60 miles per hour (95 km/h).

↓ **These prairie dogs** (*Cynomys* species), sitting at the entrance to one of their tunnels, are members of a "township" of up to 5000 animals. Small groups, called coteries, live in underground chambers linked by tunnels to those of neighboring coteries. The township may cover 150 acres (60 hectares).

← **A herd of bison** (*Bison bison*) grazes beside a stream that winds across the prairie. Bison are the native cattle of the North American plains and roamed the prairie in vast herds until hunting brought them to the brink of extinction. They are now protected and no longer endangered.

GRASSLAND LOCATIONS

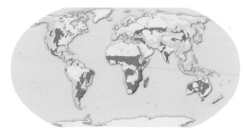

A flooded grassland

←← **The Florida Everglades** are unique. In winter the area is dry subtropical grassland, but in summer it floods and becomes a "river of grass," in places 50 miles (80 km) wide and nowhere more than 3 feet (90 cm) deep. The water flows southward from Lake Okeechobee at 100 feet (30 m) a day.

← **Schemes to drain** what some considered a useless swamp, and the building of roads, canals and levees, threatened to destroy the Everglades. It is now a national park and is being restored. Its water, grasses, herbs and trees provide habitat for many species, some of them endangered.

↓ **A purple gallinule** (*Porphyrula martinica*) is one of 300 species of birds in the Everglades. There are also 1000 species of seed plants, including 120 trees and 25 orchids, and 36 endangered animal species. The Everglades is an International Biosphere Reserve, World Heritage Site and Wetland of International Importance.

Tundra

Close to the Arctic Circle, at 66.5 degrees North, lies a region of biting winds, long, dark winters and short summers with long days. About 10 feet (3 m) below the surface the ground remains frozen throughout the year. This is permafrost. It forms a layer up to 2000 feet (600 m) thick in parts of Alaska and more than 3300 feet (1000 m) thick in those parts of Siberia where the ground has still not thawed from the last ice age. Plant roots cannot penetrate the permafrost and in summer, when for a brief time the upper layer—called the active layer—thaws, the ground becomes waterlogged.

Apart from dwarf birch (*Betula nana*) and willow (*Salix* species), which are about 3 feet (90 cm) tall, no trees grow here. There are sedges (*Carex* species), rushes (*Juncus* species) and wood rushes (*Luzula* species), as well as a few grasses, flowering herbs, mosses and lichens. This vegetation is tundra. Widespread in the northern hemisphere, it occurs in only a few places in the southern hemisphere.

→ **Alpine tundra** grows around Summit Lake, just below the summit of Mount Evans, Colorado, 14,246 feet (4345 m) above sea level. Alpine tundra develops above the tree line on high mountains outside the polar regions. Although the ground is not permanently frozen, no trees can tolerate the harsh climate.

← **This Norway lemming** (*Lemmus lemmus*), seen peering from its burrow, is active all year. In winter lemmings dig tunnels and build nests for breeding beneath the snow and continue feeding on tundra plants. In spring, when the snow melts, they emerge above ground. Every few years, population pressure sends lemmings on mass migrations during which many die.

↓ **The Jakobshavn Isbrae glacier,** near Ilulissat, Greenland, flows at up to 100 feet (30 m) per day, releasing about 38.5 billion tons (35 billion t) of icebergs a year. This valley glacier flows through a tundra landscape of rushes, sedges, lichens and bare rock.

TUNDRA LOCATIONS

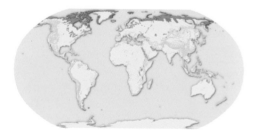

STAR MOSS AND FEATHER MOSS
For most of the year tundra plants must survive extreme drought, because all water is frozen and unavailable to them. Star moss (*Tortula ruralis*) shrivels and looks completely dead, but revives within seconds of coming into contact with water. It grows here beside the golden-green feather, or plume, moss (*Ptilium crista-castrensis*) among the tundra plants in the Katmai National Park, Alaska.

High Arctic tundra

For most of the year the lands of the high Arctic, beyond the Arctic Circle, are deeply frozen. Ice and snow cover large areas and where it is too dry for snow, icy winds scour the bare rock and loose stones. Plants that survive the extreme cold and aridity do so by producing colorful flowers to attract pollinating insects and by producing seed very quickly. As the days shorten, mountain sorrel (*Oxyria digyna*) produces new flower buds that remain tightly closed through the winter and open as soon as the days begin to lengthen. Other plants reproduce from small bulbs.

↓ **The Trans-Alaska pipeline** carries oil across the tundra from the oilfields on the North Slope to Prince William Sound in the south. Supports hold the pipeline above the ground to avoid melting the permafrost and to allow migrating caribou to pass beneath it. It causes no disturbance to the environment.

→ **The Arctic fox** (*Alopex lagopus*), found throughout the Arctic, is the most heavily insulated of all mammals. It has underfur beneath its outer coat and fur on its feet.

↘ **Patterned permafrost** results from the repeated freezing and thawing of the surface layer on level or gently sloping ground. This churns the soil and pushes surface stones into geometric shapes—circles, nets or polygons. The ones here are called low-centered polygons.

↓ **Arctic bearberry** (*Arctostaphylos uva-ursi*), blueberry (*Vaccinium uliginosum*) and crowberry (*Empetrum nigrum*) are attractive, low-growing shrubs that are locally common in the Alaskan tundra, carpeting the ground in some places. These are among the few woody plants that thrive in this environment.

Desert

If, over an extended period, more water evaporates from an exposed water surface than falls on it as rain or snow, the area will dry out and become desert. The warmer the climate, the faster the evaporation, but a desert will form anywhere that regularly receives less than 10 inches (250 mm) of rain a year. Deserts such as the Gobi, in China, form deep inside continents, far from the ocean. Coastal deserts, such as the Namib, in Namibia, and the Atacama, in Chile, form where the prevailing wind crosses the continent to reach them. All deserts are dry, but not all are hot. Despite its thick ice, Antarctica is one of the world's driest deserts.

→ **Monument Valley,** in Utah, is a wide, arid plain renowned for its many flat-topped hills, called buttes. Buttes form when rock strata that are almost horizontal erode, leaving behind towers of the more resistant sandstone rocks. Similar, but much bigger landforms in Monument Valley are called mesas.

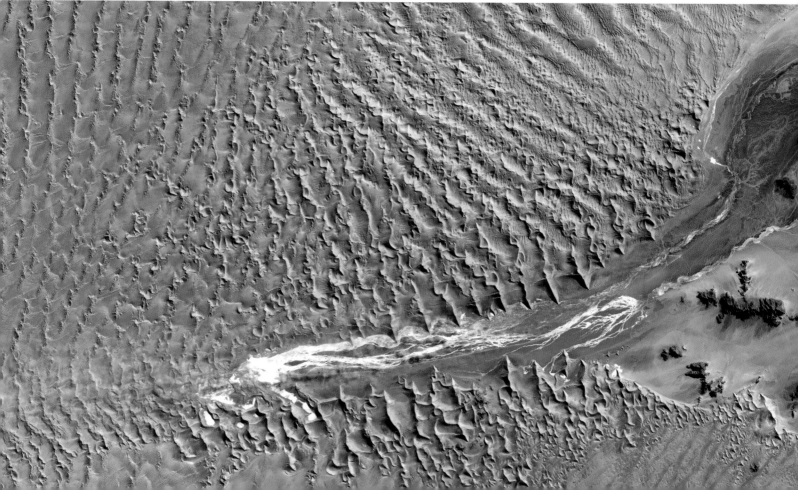

← **The Namib Desert,** seen here in a satellite image, is swept by winds that have blown its sand into dunes so large they are visible from space. Some are 980 feet (300 m) high. Fog is common in the Namib, but it brings little moisture and the desert receives only about 2 inches (50 mm) of rain a year.

↑ **South African ostriches** (*Struthio camelus australis*) run across salt flats in the Namib Desert. The ostrich, the world's largest flightless bird, stands about 8 feet (2.5 m) tall. It can walk immense distances without tiring and can run at up to 30 miles per hour (50 km/h). Ostriches have keen eyesight, which helps them to find food in the harsh desert environment.

DESERT LOCATIONS

Desert life

Sand dunes occur in most deserts and they sometimes cover vast areas, forming "sand seas," known as "ergs" in the Sahara. The Great Eastern Erg, in Algeria, covers approximately 74,000 square miles (192,000 km²). Sand seas fill depressions in the land surface where windblown sand accumulates. Dunes grow because the wind blows dry sand grains into piles. The wind repeatedly lifts and drops the grains, moving them in short hops up the side of the pile. This movement produces a fairly gentle slope on the side that faces into the wind. When they reach the top, the grains roll down the sheltered side, where the slope is much steeper.

↓ **Desert plants** must flower and produce seed rapidly—during the brief periods when moisture is available. They must also protect themselves from hungry herbivores, often with sharp spines. These are flowers of the brittlebush (*Encelia farinosa*), a small shrub, and spines of saguaro cactus (*Carnegiea gigantea*), growing in the Saguaro National Park, Arizona.

↘ **Pan de Azucar National Park,** in the Atacama Desert, extends over 170 square miles (438 km²) along the Chilean coast. Summers are hot, but fog often rolls in from the sea. As well as the cacti seen here, the park supports many seabirds, including pelicans and cormorants. The Humboldt penguin (*Spheniscus humboldti*) breeds there.

SAND DUNE FORMATION

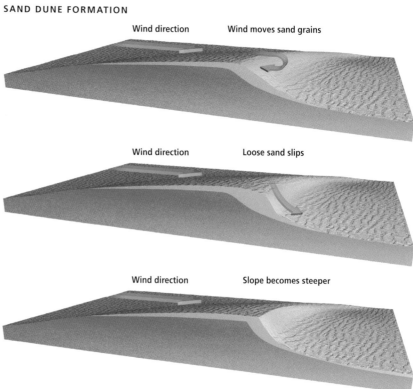

Wind direction — Wind moves sand grains

Wind direction — Loose sand slips

Wind direction — Slope becomes steeper

← **Red-tailed hawks** (*Buteo jamaicensis*) have built their nest inside a saguaro cactus plant and are raising three young. Nesting sites are at a premium in the treeless desert, and the fierce spines of the saguaro afford some protection against predators. Red-tailed hawks feed on small animals such as desert mice.

↞ **An adult and young meerkat** (*Suricata suricatta*) warm themselves in the sunshine in the Kalahari Desert, in Botswana. Meerkats live in groups of up to 30 individuals. There will always be an adult to watch over a six-week-old youngster such as this one. Adults teach the young how to catch and handle prey, which includes scorpions.

Mountains and highlands

There are mountain ranges in every continent and in all latitudes. They provide a variety of habitats that change as greater elevations result in increasingly severe climates. These climatic changes parallel those that occur with increasing distance from the equator. Mountain plants and animals, however, are more closely related to those that live in the lowlands, at the foot of the mountains, than to those found in similarly harsh climates at higher latitudes. At the highest elevations conditions are too severe for trees to survive, and a belt of small, stunted and increasingly widely scattered trees gives way to the treeless zone above the tree line. Higher still there is the snow line, beyond which temperatures remain below freezing all year. The average height of the snow line ranges from sea level in the Antarctic to about 10,000 feet (3000 m) in middle latitudes, and 15,500 feet (4730 m) in the tropics.

MOUNTAIN AND HIGHLAND LOCATIONS

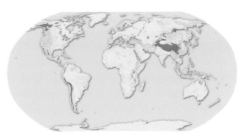

← **The peaks of the Andes,** some which rise to more than 20,000 feet (6100 m) above sea level, are permanently covered in snow, except where the incessant wind blows the snow away or the rocks are too steep to hold it. The Andes is the world's longest mountain chain, extending 4000 miles (6400 km) from the southernmost tip of South America to the coast of the Caribbean. The range is, on average, 150 miles (240 km) wide, with a high plain, the Altiplano, between the western and eastern Andes.

←← **The Andean condor** (*Vultur gryphus*) is the largest flying bird, with a wingspan of 10 feet (3.3 m). This juvenile female is flying over southern Peru. Andean condors build their nests between 10,000 and 15,000 feet (3000–4500 m) above sea level and feed mainly on carrion. They sometimes take sick sheep or llamas, and they will descend to sea level to feed on dead whales and fish, and on shellfish.

← **An alpine meadow** on Figueroa Mountain in Los Padres National Forest, California, is ablaze with the flowers of sky lupine (*Lupinus nanus*). The clearing of trees to provide summer grazing for livestock has created alpine meadows in the European alps, but alpine meadows occur naturally above the tree line in all mountain ranges, where there are no tall plants to shade the grasses and flowering herbs. Because the growing season is short, all herbs flower at the same time.

Mountain life

Mountains provide different habitat zones. In the humid tropics rain forest grows at sea level, but on the mountainside above, the composition of the forest begins to change. With increasing height this transitional forest gives way to montane (mountain), then alpine, forest and, above the tree line, to grassland. The type of vegetation is similar in South America, Africa and eastern New Guinea, but it is composed of different plants.

→ **Bighorn sheep** (*Ovis canadensis*), also called mountain sheep, are found in mountains from southwestern Canada to northern Mexico. This group is walking across an alpine meadow in Glacier National Park, Montana. These agile and sure-footed animals avoid predators by climbing onto high, narrow ledges, beyond the reach of potential attackers.

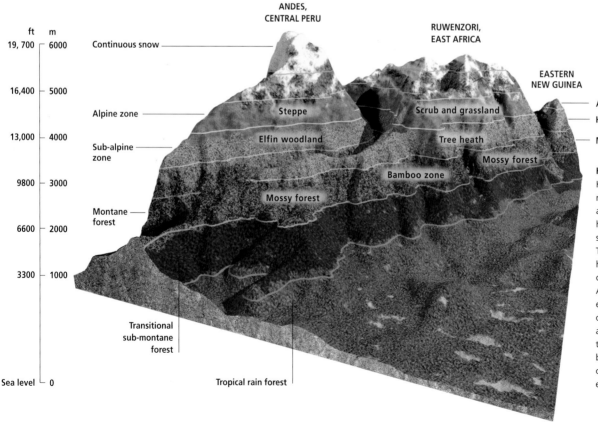

ANDES, CENTRAL PERU

RUWENZORI, EAST AFRICA

EASTERN NEW GUINEA

ft	m	
19,700	6000	Continuous snow
16,400	5000	
13,000	4000	Alpine zone / Sub-alpine zone
9800	3000	
6600	2000	Montane forest
3300	1000	
Sea level	0	

Steppe

Elfin woodland

Mossy forest

Scrub and grassland

Tree heath

Bamboo zone

Mossy forest

Alpine grassland and savanna

High montane forest

Mossy forest

Transitional sub-montane forest

Tropical rain forest

HABITAT ZONES

Habitat zones in different mountain environments form as many as five approximately horizontal bands between sea level and the snow line. This diagram illustrates these habitat zones in three parts of the world: tropical South America, East Africa and eastern New Guinea. In each case the zone boundaries are at the same elevation and the vegetation type is similar, but the species composition of the zones is different in each region.

↑ **Gelada baboons** (*Theropithecus gelada*) are found only in the highlands of Ethiopia. They are the only primates—the order that includes all monkeys and apes, as well as humans—that are true grazers. They eat nothing but grass. Their long hair insulates them against the intensely cold mountain winters.

← **Ghandrung village** in Nepal nestles in a valley overshadowed by Annapurna South, one of the Himalayan peaks. The village is 6365 feet (1940 m) above sea level. The villagers live by farming and tending sheep. Some of their young men serve as Gurkha soldiers in the Indian and British armies.

Volcanic landscapes

An erupting volcano releases lava, ash and pyroclastic flows—clouds of burning gas and ash that advance at terrifying speed and destroy everything in their path. But afterwards, as the surface cools, the volcanic material weathers and matures into rich soil that supports plants of every kind and that also produces abundant farm crops. Eruptions are rare events and between them people settle on the lower slopes of volcanoes and farm their fertile soils. Many volcanoes eventually die, and extinct volcanoes provide the structure for some of the most beautiful and productive landscapes. A chain of former volcanoes, the Chaîne des Puys, dominates the landscape in the Auvergne, one of the most popular tourist regions of central France. The largest of these volcanoes, the Puy de Dôme, last erupted in about 5760 BC.

↓ **Red ginger** plants (*Alpinia purpurata*) flowered on the slopes of Arenal Volcano, Costa Rica, before a recent eruption destroyed them. Arenal is a stratovolcano—a steep conical volcano built by successive pyroclastic flows—5479 feet (1670 m) high. Once believed dormant, it erupted in 1968, 1987, 1992 and again in 2007.

VOLCANIC LOCATIONS

↓ **Maelifell Mountain,** Iceland, is an extinct volcano, 3763 feet (1147 m) high, that offers spectacular views over the surrounding countryside. It overlooks the 193-square mile (500-km²) Myrdalsjökull ice cap, beneath which lies Katla, one of Iceland's most active volcanoes. Its eruptions melt the ice, sending floods, called jökulhlaups, bursting through the glacier.

← **A cultivated volcano** near Lake Itsay in the central highlands of Madagascar is laid out with fields of crops. There are several extinct volcanoes in this part of Madagascar and the fertile soil on their slopes makes excellent farmland. Cultivating such steep slopes, however, requires care. Soil must be plowed into furrows that are at right angles to the slope; otherwise tropical rains will erode it into deep gullies, such as those visible here.

← **The rim of the central caldera,** or crater, of Mount Saint Helens National Volcanic Monument, in Washington State— seen here from directly above—is 8375 feet (2554 m) above sea level. Mount Saint Helens had been inactive for centuries, but on May 18, 1980 it erupted after being destabilized by an earthquake. The north face of the mountain collapsed and nearly 230 square miles (595 km²) of forest were destroyed.

Volcanic islands

Volcanoes are not confined to continents. They also erupt on the ocean floor and form mountains that sometimes emerge above the surface as islands. Surtsey, to the south of Iceland, emerged in 1963 following a violent eruption that occurred when seawater flooded into a magma chamber. Surtsey now rises 570 feet (174 m) above sea level, covers 1 square mile (2.8 km²), and has been colonized by plants and birds.

→ **Hawaii's Big Island** is the largest of the Hawaiian islands. Each of the Hawaiian islands has formed volcanically as the Pacific Plate has moved across a hot spot—where material from Earth's mantle rises to the base of the crust. The islands are at one end of the Hawaiian–Emperor chain of submarine volcanoes, which extend to Kamchatka, Siberia.

↓ **Cerro Azul** is an active volcano, 5541 feet (1690 m) high, on the Galápagos Island of Isabela. Its caldera, shown here, measures 2.5 miles x 2 miles (4 km x 3 km) across and is 2000 feet (610 m) deep. It formed when the volcano's magma chamber collapsed, and today the caldera is filled by a lake.

↘ **Molten lava,** covered by a thin crust of solidified rock, is slowly spreading across this landscape in the Hawaii Volcanoes National Park. The park includes Mauna Loa, which, at 13,677 feet (4171 m) high is the world's biggest volcano, and Kilauea, the world's most active volcano and the source of this lava.

↑ **Saint Michel d'Aiguilhe Church,** an important pilgrimage site, is built on top of the Rocher Saint Michel, overlooking the town of Le Puy, in the Auvergne region of central France. The Rocher Saint Michel is a volcanic chimney—a channel through which magma once rose, but that later solidified. "Puy" means an isolated hill in the local dialect. There are many puys, all of them extinct volcanoes, in the Auvergne.

Polar regions

In the lands beyond the Arctic and Antarctic circles, at 66.5 degrees North and South, there is a period in midwinter when the Sun never rises above the horizon, although some of its light is refracted by the atmosphere to produce a dim twilight. For part of the summer the Sun never sets, though even then it remains low in the sky, moving around the horizon. In central Greenland the average summer temperature is 13°F (−10°C), and at the South Pole the average is −17.5°F (−27.5°C).

Apart from Greenland—*Kalaallit Nunaat* in Greenlandic—most of the Arctic is covered by water. The continent of Antarctica has an area of 4.8 million square miles (12.4 million km²).

POLAR LOCATIONS

→ **Penguins** swim in search of fish beneath an Antarctic ice shelf. They may look ungainly on land, but they are superb submarine hunters. Emperor penguins (*Aptenodytes forsteri*) can pursue their prey to depths of more than 650 feet (200 m) and remain underwater for two and a half minutes.

→→ **Sheer cliffs,** between 500 and 800 feet (150–243 m) high, surround Akpatok Island, in Ungava Bay, Québec, Canada. It is only accessible only by air. The many ice floes around the island attract walruses and whales also frequent here, in this traditional Inuit hunting ground. The island is an important breeding sanctuary for cliff-nesting seabirds.

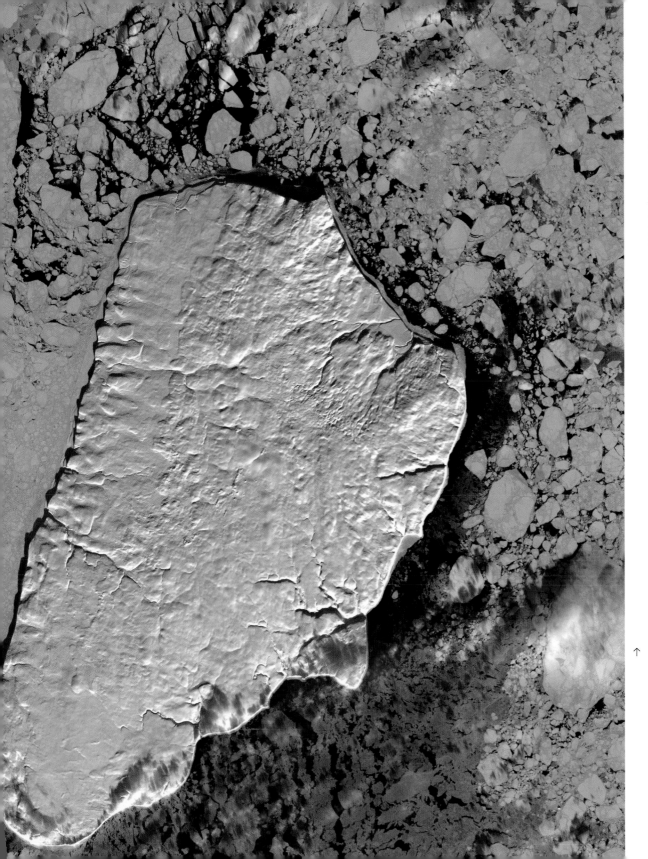

↑ **Tufted saxifrage**
(*Saxifraga cespitosa*)
grows on ledges and
in gravel throughout
the Arctic. The plants
here are growing in
Svalbard, a Norwegian
archipelago about
midway between
Norway and the
North Pole.

Polar life

Many birds avoid the cold polar winter by migrating, and some travel immense distances. The greater shearwater (*Puffinus gravis*) breeds from January to March on Tristan da Cunha in the South Atlantic, then spends the northern summer in Newfoundland, Greenland, Iceland or the Faroe Islands. When winter approaches, it returns to Tristan da Cunha. Wilson's storm petrel (*Oceanites oceanicus*) breeds in Antarctica, then flies to the northern hemisphere.

← **The longest bird migration** is that of the Arctic tern (*Sterna paradisaea*). It breeds north of the Arctic Circle then flies approximately 9300 miles (15,000 km) across the Atlantic to Antarctica. It migrates north again as the Antarctic winter approaches.

↓ **The polar bear** (*Ursus maritimus*) evolved from brown bears about 100,000 years ago. It is the largest of all bears and most of the time lives on the ice near continental and island coasts. It feeds mainly on ringed seals (*Phoca hispida*). Cubs are born in snow dens in winter. They emerge in spring and stay with their mothers for 30 months.

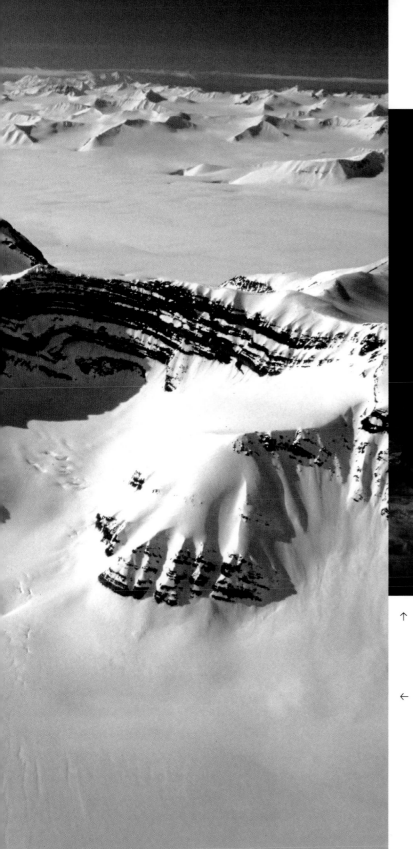

↑ **Inuit igloos,** where families in Nunavut, northern Canada, spend the
winter, take about two hours to build. Having found a level site, the builder
cuts rectangular blocks of snow with a long-bladed knife. He lays a circle of
blocks, trimming them so they slope inward, then adds more circles on top.
The final block is made from transparent sealskin or ice.

← **Spitsbergen** is the largest island of the Svalbard archipelago, to the north
of Norway. Glaciers permanently cover more than half of its 14,550 square
miles (37,685 km²), as this view of the cold, bleak interior shows. Sharp
mountain peaks—*spitsbergen* in Norwegian—project through the ice.
About 2700 people live in Svalbard.

A corallite is the external calcium carbonate covering that is secreted by polyps—cylindrical-shaped animals between 0.04 and 0.12 inch (1–3 mm) wide. A juvenile polyp resembles a jellyfish and drifts in the ocean. When it is ready to mature it anchors itself to a solid surface and at the other end it grows tentacles with which it gathers food items that float past. The polyp lives inside its hard skeleton, known as corallite, in close association with particular algae and dinoflagellates—single-celled protozoa—called zooxanthellae, with which it exchanges nutrients. Madreporaria, or stony corals, live in vast colonies where the corallites merge and grow into coral reefs.

Reefs occur in all tropical and subtropical oceans. They grow best in clear, shallow water at a temperature between 73°F and 77°F (23–25°C). On Earth, the total reef area is about 68 million square miles (175 million km²). Coral reefs are highly vulnerable to pollution, especially from sediment that clouds the water and interferes with photosynthesis by the corals' algae. They are also threatened by global warming.

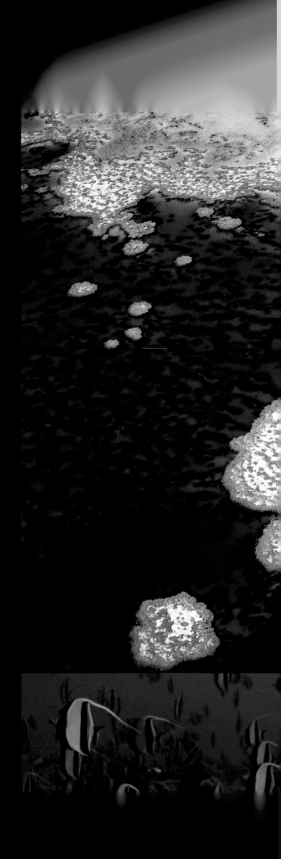

← **This is one of more than 400 coral species** found in the Red Sea. Because this sea is deep and its shores slope steeply, reefs grow only on the continental shelf, which is between 9 and 18 miles (15–30 km) wide in the north and 75 miles (120 km) wide in the south.

→ **The Great Barrier Reef,** which stretches for 1616 miles (2600 km) off the coast of Queensland, Australia, is visible from space. Set in the Coral Sea, it consists of about 3000 individual reefs and 900 islands. It supports a wide range of organisms, but is vulnerable to a number of environmental threats including coral bleaching.

REEF LOCATIONS

→ **Colorful fish** move in shoals above the reef, searching for food and evading predators such as groupers, eels and sharks. More than 4000 species of fish live around coral reefs. They feed on algae that grow on the coral and small animals that drift in the water, and shelter in crevices in the reef. This is a shoal of longfin bannerfish (*Heniochus acuminatus*).

↑ **A sponge,** seen here growing on a reef with a treelike gorgonian coral (Gorgonacea) behind it, lacks definite tissues or organs, but consists of cells of different types that line canals and pores. The whole structure is supported by a fibrous skeleton, sometimes strengthened by small spines called spicules, and enclosed in a skin. It feeds by filtering particles from the water. Sponges reproduce sexually, producing free-swimming larvae. If a small piece breaks off a sponge it will grow into a new sponge.

Reef life

Coral reefs grow in clear water that supports little life, but
the reefs themselves provide shelter and sustenance for a
bewildering variety of species. The actual reef is formed
from the fused corallites of polyps, and its irregular surface
is covered in algae that produce sugars by photosynthesis.
Fish and invertebrate animals graze the algae. Anemones
use stinging tentacles to trap small animals as they pass.
Predatory fish, including groupers and sharks, hunt smaller
prey. Cleaner fish feed on parasites they find on these predators'
bodies and on food fragments from between their teeth.

→ **Blue starfish** (*Linckia laevigata*) occur on coral reefs and in seagrass in
shallow waters of the Indian and Pacific oceans. They are up to 16 inches
(40 cm) across and feed on invertebrate animals and dead organisms.
This one is lying on a *Porities* species coral, a slow-growing stony coral
(Madreporaria) found over large areas of the Great Barrier Reef.

↓ **Gorgonian coral,** seen here with its tentacles extended to catch
plankton, is anchored to the underlying rock and has branches
supported by a skeleton—either of limestone or of an organic, horny
material called gorgonin. The order Gorgonacea also includes sea fans.

↓ **Brain coral** (*Diplora* species), growing here in the Netherlands
Antilles, is spherical and is named for its resemblance to a human
brain. It lives for up to 200 years. At night it folds its tentacles
over the surface grooves in order to protect them.

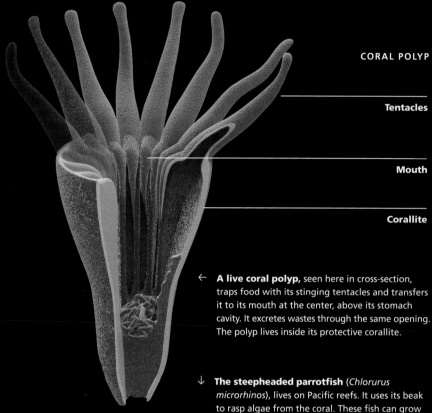

CORAL POLYP

Tentacles

Mouth

Corallite

← **A live coral polyp,** seen here in cross-section, traps food with its stinging tentacles and transfers it to its mouth at the center, above its stomach cavity. It excretes wastes through the same opening. The polyp lives inside its protective corallite.

↓ **This bleached coral** (*Acropora* species), growing off the Maldive Islands in the Indian Ocean, has lost the symbiotic dinoflagellates (zooxanthellae) that give it its color. Bleaching is caused by stress. If different zooxanthellae species colonize the coral, it may recover.

↓ **The steepheaded parrotfish** (*Chlorurus microrhinos*), lives on Pacific reefs. It uses its beak to rasp algae from the coral. These fish can grow up to 227 inches (70 cm) long.

Rivers

Rivers supply people with fresh water for domestic use and irrigation as well as with fish and other foods. They are also important transport routes. Riverbanks provide habitats for plants and animals, and the clearing of bankside vegetation can adversely affect wildlife. Rainwater either runs over the surface into a river or drains downward through the soil until it accumulates above an impermeable layer and flows as groundwater. Groundwater eventually reaches lakes or rivers. Many climates have a rainy season and a dry season, and melting snow also flows into rivers. As a result, the amount of water rivers carry often varies seasonally. The annual Nile flood brought water and silt to the farms that sustained ancient Egyptian civilization.

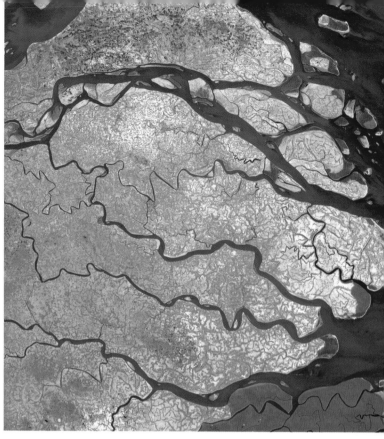

↓ **An underground river** flows through a cave. The cave walls are covered in algae, which thrive in the moist conditions. Carbon dioxide dissolves in river water, making it slightly acidic and therefore able to erode limestone. Underground rivers are common in limestone regions, where the water has eroded the rock and thus formed caves.

← The Ganges Delta, south of Kolkata, is where India's mightiest river flows into the Bay of Bengal. It consists of many channels that cross low-lying ground. Mangrove swamp and marshland, called the Sunderbans, cover 3900 square miles (10,000 km²) of the delta. This is home to the Royal Bengal tiger (*Panthera tigris tigris*).

← The Ganges is considered a sacred river in India and here at Varanasi (also called Benares), in Uttar Pradesh, pilgrims crowd on the steps, called ghats, from where they ritually purify themselves by bathing in the river. About 90 ghats line 4 miles (6 km) of the riverside at Varanasi.

A RIVER FLOODPLAIN

Halalei Valley, on Kauai, Hawaii, is a typically fertile river floodplain. The Halalei River, which crosses it, provides abundant water for irrigation and the level ground is enriched by plant nutrients mixed with the silt deposited by past floods. The plain is excellent farmland. The area is known for growing taro (*Colocasia antiquorum*), a starchy root crop that grows best in wet ground. Many river valleys have fertile soil and are popular locations for farms and homes, though they can be prone to flooding.

MAJOR RIVERS LOCATIONS

River flow

Most rivers begin as small mountain streams that carry clear water with few nutrients in it. Farther downstream small rivers merge and material washed in from the land on either side contributes nutrients that support an increasing variety of plants and animals. As it approaches the sea, the river may slow down as it crosses more level ground. The moving water follows the course that offers the least resistance. Dams regulate river flow by holding water back and releasing it at a controlled rate.

→ **A mountain stream** is too fast and turbulent to freeze over completely in winter, but ice may form on the rocks on either side, where friction slows the flow and allows time for the water to freeze. Rivers always freeze from the edges inward. Slow-moving rivers may freeze over completely.

↓ **The Yukon River,** in central Alaska, flows along many channels that divide and rejoin to form a complex braided pattern. Sediment deposited by the river has accumulated in particular places to form temporary bars and permanent islands. The river divides to flow round these obstructions, deposits more sediment, and divides again.

The world's largest waterlilies (*Victoria amazonica*) have leaves up to 10 feet (3 m) across that can support the weight of an adult human. They have stalks between 23 and 26 feet (7–8 m) long. The ones in this image are in the Pantanal, Brazil. It is the world's largest wetland area and covers about 58,000 square miles (150,000 km²).

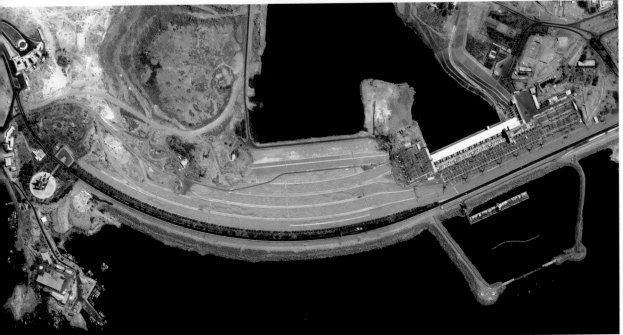

The Aswan High Dam on the Nile River in Egypt, shown here in a satellite image, was completed in 1971. The large dam wall is 2.36 miles (3.8 km) long, 364 feet (111 m) high, and 3280 feet (1000 m) thick at the base. The hydroelectric plant inside the wall supplies almost half of Egypt's electricity.

Lakes

Given a plentiful supply of water, a lake can form wherever there is a depression in poorly drained land or an outlet channel at a higher elevation than the bottom of such a depression. Glacial action has produced many lakes. Widened sections of rivers are called lakes, as are bodies of water along coasts that are linked directly to the sea.

Lake water may be fresh or salty and lakes can occur at any altitude. For example, Lake Titicaca, on the border between Peru and Bolivia, is 12,507 feet (3812 m) above sea level, and the Dead Sea, between Israel and Jordan, is 1302 feet (397 m) below the level of the Mediterranean Sea. Baikal, in Siberia, is the lake with the greatest volume of water: 5663 cubic miles (23,600 km³). Lake Superior, in North America, has the largest surface area: 31,820 square miles (82,414 km²).

↗ **Tufa formations** at Mono Lake, California, were exposed when water that flowed into the lake was diverted to supply Los Angeles, and the evaporation rate came to exceed the inflow. The lake is more than twice as salty as the ocean. Tufa is calcium carbonate that is precipitated under the extremely alkaline conditions. The lake is now protected and its level is rising.

→ **The Pantanal** is a vast, flat area of swamp and marsh. This section is in the 520-square-mile (1350-km²) Pantanal Matogrossense National Park, Brazil. During the rainy season, water covers four-fifths of the Pantanal, which contains the world's richest variety of aquatic plants. It also supports more than 650 species of birds, 400 species of fish, 100 species of mammals and about 80 species of reptiles. Pesticide pollution, recreational fishing, illegal hunting and deforestation all pose threats for the Pantanal.

MAJOR LAKE LOCATIONS

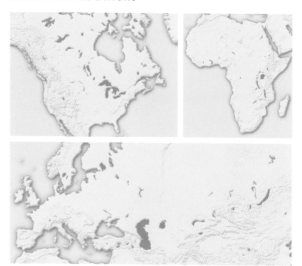

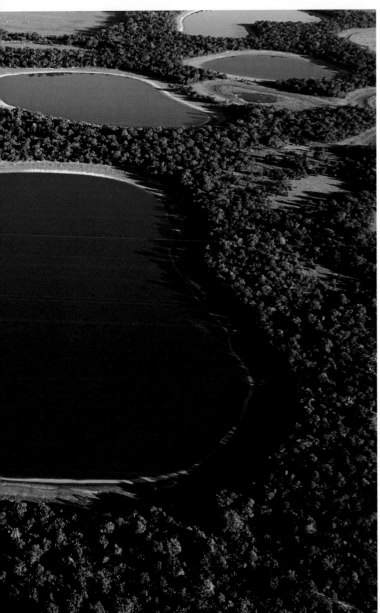

→ **The Aral Sea,** bounded by Kazakhstan and Uzbekistan, was once the fourth-largest lake on Earth. When, beginning in the 1950s, two rivers that flowed into it were diverted to provide irrigation for local cotton growing, the lake began to shrink. By 1973, it was separating into two. Evaporation increased salinity and greatly reduced the fish catch.

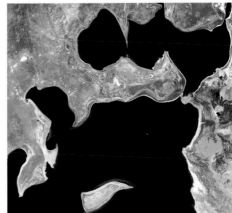

→ **By 1989** the sea had divided into two, to form the Large and Small Aral seas. Salt blown from the dry lakebed had poisoned surrounding farmland, most of the fish population had died, and fishing boats were marooned miles from the water on which they once floated.

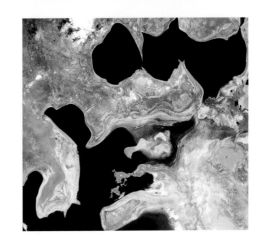

→ **By 2000** the lake was shrinking still further, but by this time measures to reverse the damage had been put in place. Scientists and engineers from many countries are now collaborating in attempts to restore the sea, which may eventually return to its former state.

Lake life

Lake waters vary in chemical composition. All of them support living organisms, although in extreme acid or alkaline conditions the numbers of plants and animals are much reduced. Many small lakes slowly disappear as lake-edge plants trap sediment, making the water shallower. The plants root in the sediment and expand farther from the shore until they cover it completely. The lake becomes marsh, and the marsh dries out.

Brine shrimps (*Artemia* species) are tiny crustaceans that thrive in salt lakes. Alkaline lakes also support certain species of algae and extremophile archaeans known as alkaliphiles. Acidophiles are extremophiles found in very acid water. Apart from these, acid lakes support few organisms and the lack of algae means that their water is usually clear.

→ **Walden Pond,** in Concord, Massachusetts, is inside a 333-acre (135-ha) state reservation. The pond, a kettlehole with a surface area of 61 acres (25 ha) and a depth of 102 feet (31 m), was formed between 10,000 and 12,000 years ago by retreating glaciers. Many species of fish and waterbirds live and breed here.

↓ **Cattails** (*Typha* species), also called reed-mace and bulrush, grow all over the world in the mud around lake shores. In some places their leaves are used to make matting and chair seats. Cattails grow from rhizomes—horizontal underground stems—which are rich in starch.

↗ **Lake Natron,** in Tanzania, is a saline lake—natron means sodium—less than 10 feet (3 m) deep. Salt-loving *Spirulina* cyanobacteria give the open water its red or pink, and the lake edges their orange, colors. The lake is the only breeding area for 2.5 million lesser flamingos (*Phoeniconaias minor*).

→ **Hippopotamuses** (*Hippopotamus amphibius*) are clumsy on land but, buoyed by the water, they move gracefully through shallow African lakes. These herbivores are seen here feeding on water lettuce (Pistia stratiotes) in South Luangwa National Park, Zambia. Although generally placid, these territorial animals have an uncertain temper and will attack if disturbed.

⇢ **Zebra mussels** (*Dreissena polymorpha*) are native to the Caspian and Black seas and Russian freshwater lakes. They appeared in the Netherlands in 1827 and have become highly invasive in Europe and in North America, where they were first seen in 1986.

Wetlands

On low-lying ground beside rivers and river estuaries, in deltas and along some coastlines, there are areas of land that are waterlogged or covered by shallow water, either permanently or for part of the year. These are wetlands, and they include marshes, bogs, fens, peatlands and swamps, as well as shallow lakes and ponds.

Wetlands are often attractive sites for development. Some can be drained for conversion to farmland or forest, others developed for tourism. Their survival is severely threatened everywhere.

WETLAND LOCATIONS

↓ **A snowy egret** (*Egretta thula*) perches on a mangrove root. Hats decorated with this wetland dweller's feathers were once fashionable and it was hunted almost to extinction. It is now protected.

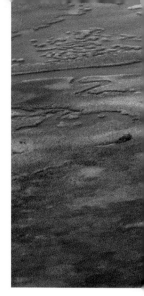

↑ **This salt marsh** on the coast of eastern Virginia is inundated each time the tide flows in along the many interlinked channels. At low tide it is exposed to the air. Salt marshes are home to specialized plants and animals that can tolerate the changes in salinity and temperature.

↑ **Mangrove crabs** bury leaves, preventing them from being washed away, and they produce larvae that are an important food for fish. Birds feed on the adult crabs. Mangrove crabs of different species are found in mangrove forests throughout the tropics. This one is in the Umlalazi Nature Reserve, in South Africa.

← **Mangrove forests** grow along the coast at Cape Tribulation, Queensland, Australia. Mangrove trees produce stilt roots that trap mud. As the accumulation of mud raises the seabed, the trees are able to root farther from shore and the forest advances into the sea. Mangrove fruit is highly nutritious.

Wetland life

Wetlands, which occur in all parts of the world, support a wide variety of plants and animals. In particular, they provide food and safe resting places for migrating water birds. In 1971 delegates to a conference at Ramsar, Iran, agreed on a convention to protect designated wetlands of international significance, especially those important to water birds. By 2007, 154 governments had signed the Ramsar Convention, and 1650 sites, covering 370 million acres (149.6 million ha), had been listed and protected.

→ **Camargue horses** live wild in the wetlands of the Rhône delta, in southern France. Small, but rugged and very strong, they belong to an ancient breed and are carefully managed. The Camargue wetlands, 360 square miles (930 km²) in area, are also famous for their greater flamingos (*Phoenicopterus roseus*).

↓ **Flowers of bog pimpernel** (*Anagallis tenella*), seen here growing in South Wales, are only 0.5 inch (14 mm) across. Bog pimpernel is a creeping, perennial plant that grows in wet mud, bogs and fens throughout western Europe. It flowers from June to August and belongs to the primrose family (Primulaceae).

→ **These American alligators** (*Alligator mississippiensis*) lie in the shallow water of a Florida swamp, their bodies green because they are covered in duckweed. American alligators are found only in wetlands of the southeastern United States. Most of these reptiles grow to about 14 feet (4.3 m) long, but large adults can reach 19 feet (5.8 m).

← **Alaskan marshland,** also known as muskeg, supports cotton sedge (*Eriophorum* species) and scattered, stunted trees, but is dominated by bog moss (*Sphagnum* species). The dead cells of bog moss can hold many times their own weight of water. Other plants grow on top of the moss, and their flowers add some color.

About 11 percent of the world's total land area is devoted to growing arable crops—annual field crops such as cereals—and another 26 percent is permanent grassland and rangeland, on which sheep and cattle are raised. When every type of agricultural use is counted, 38 percent of the world's land area is being exploited to feed the human population. Clearing the natural vegetation and plowing the land to grow crops or raise livestock is by far the biggest change humans make to the natural environment.

↗ **Mixed farming,** seen here in Nottinghamshire, England, produces cereals and vegetables and raises dairy cattle and sheep. The small fields are bounded by dense, stock-proof hedges and scattered trees provide shelter. This landscape supports much wildlife, especially in and alongside the hedges.

↘ **Tulip fields** in the Netherlands are large and the crops are managed very intensively. They lack trees and hedges and are an inhospitable environment for most wild plants and animals.

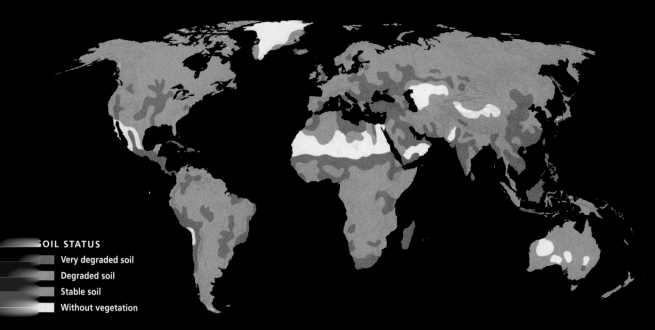

SOIL STATUS

- Very degraded soil
- Degraded soil
- Stable soil
- Without vegetation

↗ **Wheat fields** in the Palouse hills, Washington State, extend to the horizon. This land was once Palouse prairie. Wheat is a grass, so the environmental change is less dramatic than it looks.

→ **Slash-and-burn** farming, seen here in Kikori Basin, Papua New Guinea, can support only a sparse human population. Intensifying this type of farming to feed more people destroys large areas of forest.

← **This child, tending water buffalo** in Lombok, Indonesia, is caring for the family's most valuable possession. Buffalo provide milk, as well as manure to fertilize cropland. They also serve as draft animals.

agriculture

Farmers today produce more from each acre of land than was ever possible in former times. Famine has been banished from most countries and although many people still go hungry, there is hope that in the foreseeable future they, too, be adequately fed. This increase in food production has been achieved by the use of new crop varieties, fertilizers and pesticides that reduce crop losses. The adverse environmental consequences of more intensive agricultural practices are being addressed, with some success.

Sprinkler irrigation for a potato crop at Bakersfield, California, ensures a good harvest, but places a heavy demand on the water supply. In hot weather, when irrigation is needed most, much of the water evaporates. Applying water at ground level or from buried pipes is more efficient, but is costly.

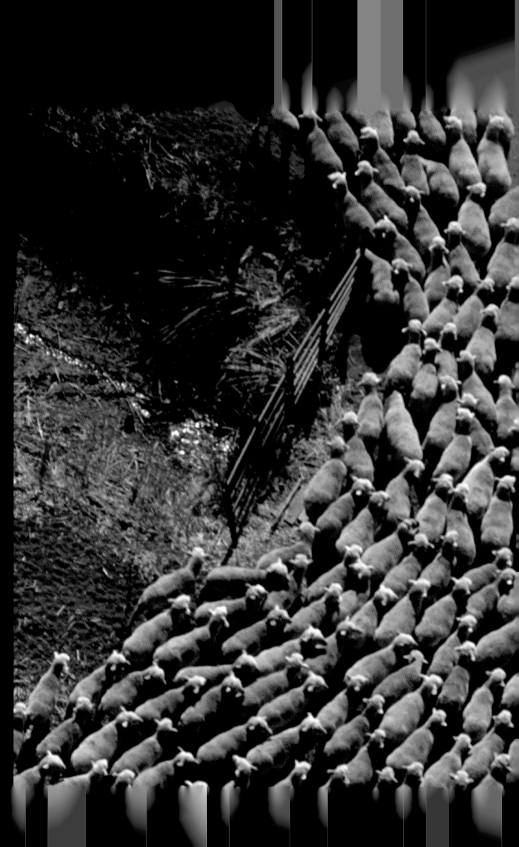

← **This New Zealand flock of sheep,** passing through a gate, probably comprises 1400 individuals. There are 43 million sheep in New Zealand—12 for every person. The predominant breed, originally from England, is Romney. It produces meat, as well as wool that is used for carpets, upholstery, blankets and for knitting. The sheep graze in paddocks on carefully managed pastures.

→ **Rice paddy fields,** seen here on a terrace in Bali, Indonesia, are probably the most intensively managed farmlands in the world—and the most productive. Seedlings are grown in nurseries and planted individually in fields flooded to about ankle depth. A few weeks before harvest the fields are drained to allow the grain to ripen.

Urban areas

By early in the twenty-first century more than half the world's population was living in towns and cities. The fast rate of urbanization has generated serious environmental issues. In many places there are problems with the provision of basic services such as housing, water and sanitation, as well as with waste disposal and the maintenance of essential infrastructure. The increasing mechanization of modern agriculture has reduced the availability of rural employment and forced more people into cities. One positive result of this has been a reduced threat to the well-being of many wildlife species.

POPULATION GROWTH

World population has risen dramatically since about 1800, and the rate of growth increased during the first half of the twentieth century. The rate of increase peaked in the 1960s, at about 2 percent per year. It has been declining since then. The rate of annual increase in early 2007 was about 1.14 percent and falling. Total world population is projected to reach about 9.1 billion by 2050.

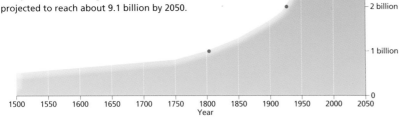

Graph axes: Total world population (0 to 9 billion), Year (1500 to 2050)

↑ **The gray squirrel** (*Sciurus carolinensis*), like this one in New York City, is one of many wild animals that thrive in cities. Gardens and parks often provide good habitat for wildlife.

→ **London** has a population of about seven million. As this aerial view shows, there are many public parks, private gardens and cemeteries that provide wildlife habitat, and the Thames supports fish and other aquatic organisms. The eight principal parks, apart from many smaller parks, cover 8.5 square miles (22 km²).

↘ **Shanty towns,** like this one in Mumbai, India, have appeared in cities throughout the developing world. The population of Mumbai increased from 8.2 million in 1981 to 16.4 million in 2001 and the city is unable to house everyone. Most of the slum population lives below the poverty line.

↓ **Garbage** provides food for scavenging birds and rodents at landfill sites, such as this one on Staten Island, New York. Many cities are running out of sites for commercial and domestic waste disposal.

Urban life

Cities, even if they are often congested and dirty, are designed for people. Many wildlife species, however, that have long existed in close association with people follow human populations into urban environments. The house mouse (*Mus musculus*), originally from the Eurasian steppe, is now found throughout the world. So too are the feral pigeons that descended from the rock dove (*Columba livia*). These opportunists find shelter in buildings and feed on scraps left by humans. They in turn attract predators.

→ **A peregrine falcon** (*Falco peregrinus*) dives from the George Washington Bridge, New York City, in an attempt to protect her chicks from a team that is banding them. Peregrines live on cliffs and hunt birds as large as pigeons. City buildings resemble cliffs and there are abundant pigeons for the taking.

↓ **A traffic jam** forms as vehicles try to drive through an improvised livestock market in Pakistan. These vehicles release exhaust fumes, which in bright sunlight can react with the air to form photochemical smog. The smog reduces visibility and can harm people with respiratory complaints. City pollution affects much of South Asia.

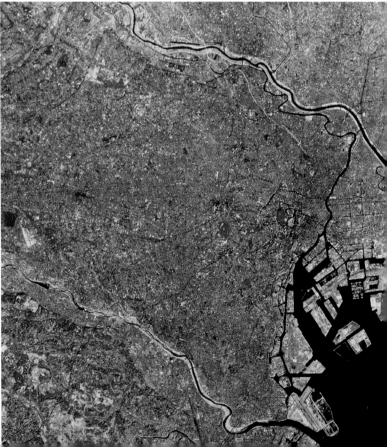

→ **New York City** at night is ablaze with color. Illumination from buildings and traffic fills the streets with light. Modern cities consume large amounts of energy in sustaining the needs of their populations— although one night's street lighting in New York uses only as much energy as is released in an average tornado.

← **This false-color image,** taken from an orbiting satellite, shows the metropolitan area of Tokyo, Japan. Buildings appear as blue and vegetation as red. The picture shows that even in a city as large as Tokyo, with eight million inhabitants, there are significant green areas where plants and wild animals can thrive.

Industrial processes

Manufacturing processes convert raw materials into products. Metals and petroleum are among the most important industrially exploited raw materials and their processing takes place in stages. Metals must be extracted from the ground and separated from the chemical compounds in which they occur naturally before they can be shaped and assembled into finished products. Petroleum must be refined into "fractions"—oils with differing properties. All industrial processes use energy, mainly in the form of heat or electrical power. Some, such as steelmaking, take place at high temperatures, and energy is needed to power all industrial machines. The mining and preparation of fuel, its delivery to users and conversion to heat and electricity comprise another suite of industries. Industries produce wastes and by-products for which no use can be found. If these are released into the outside environment they cause pollution.

→ **Robots** now perform many of the repetitive operations in factories. These robots are welding the parts of cars in an automobile production line. Robots tolerate a wide temperature range and do not need rest breaks. Their use increases production efficiency.

GLOBAL ENERGY DEMAND

As the graph shows, the world's demand for energy has been rising very steeply since about the middle of the nineteenth century. Energy demand is stabilizing in the most economically developed countries, but still rising rapidly in countries that are industrializing. There are fears that petroleum supply may soon be unable to match demand. Although coal and gas remain abundant and nuclear energy is available to supply electricity, the world needs new sources of energy.

World energy use in mtoe (metric tons of oil equivalent)

15 billion
14 billion
13 billion
12 billion
11 billion
10 billion
9 billion
8 billion
7 billion
6 billion
5 billion
4 billion
3 billion
2 billion
1 billion
0

1500 1550 1600 1650 1700 1750 1800 1850 1900 1950 2000 2020
Year

↑ **A pulp mill** emits steam and hot gases from its chimneys, and uses water that it returns to the river. The pulp industry was formerly a major source of pollution. Today its emissions are strictly regulated.

← **Textiles** are made from natural fibers such as wool and cotton, but also from synthetic fibers that derive mainly from petroleum products. Spinning, dyeing, weaving, printing and tailoring transform fibers into clothes like the 2004 Versace dress in this shop window.

Industrial developments

The goods and services people need have traditionally been provided by small local workshops. These are now giving way to factories. An ever-growing number of national economies is emerging from a former reliance on agriculture, mining and small-scale production of goods for domestic use, to an emphasis on the manufacture of industrial goods for export. The burgeoning Chinese economy is now the world's fourth largest, after those of the United States, Japan and Germany. Brazil's economy is ranked number 10 and India's is ranked number twelve.

↓ **Household waste disposal** is a major problem in cities. The solution involves a reduction in the amount of waste that is generated during the manufacture, distribution, packaging, retailing and domestic use of materials and the recycling of items that are no longer needed. These cans are being sorted for recycling.

← **Dyeing cloth** involves moving lengths of material through a succession of vats that contain chemical solutions. Here, in a town in Morocco, the operation is conducted outdoors, and the many vats take up considerable space. This traditional dyeing method is still employed in many developing countries.

→ **These ships in Kowloon Bay,** Hong Kong, are waiting near the Hutchinson Container Terminal, either to unload incoming cargoes or load ones for export. Owned by Hutchinson Whampoa Limited, this is Hong Kong's largest container terminal and one of the biggest in the world. Most of China's overseas trade passes through here.

← **These saris, drying** on racks in the sunshine outside a factory in Pali, Rajasthan, after being dyed and printed, have been made using traditional, labor-intensive processes. These are now being replaced in many parts of India by more mechanized methods of manufacture that involve many fewer workers.

Biodiversity

"Biodiversity" is a contraction of "biological diversity." It refers to the number of species, the number of intact ecosystems or the amount of genetic variation in a given area. These factors are interdependent: the more ecosystems there are, the greater the number and the wider the genetic variation of the species that will inhabit them.

Expansion of agriculture involves clearing forests, damming rivers—and flooding valleys—and draining wetlands. The result is the destruction or disruption of ecosystems and a loss of biodiversity. At the United Nations Conference on Environment and Development, held in Rio de Janeiro in 1992, world leaders agreed a Convention on Biological Diversity, also known as the Biodiversity Convention.

GLOBAL BIODIVERSITY
This map records the extent of biodiversity in different regions. It takes account only of vertebrate animals and seed plants. Its measures are based on the total number of species in a region and on the species that are found nowhere else.

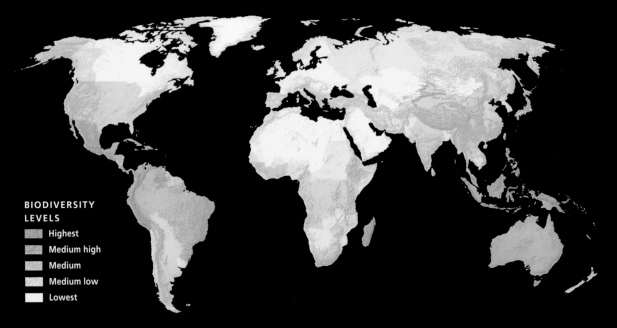

BIODIVERSITY LEVELS
- Highest
- Medium high
- Medium
- Medium low
- Lowest

← **Nujiang Valley** in Yunnan Province, China, is part of the Three Parallel Rivers World Heritage Site, designated by UNESCO because of its rich biodiversity. The Chinese government had planned to build 13 dams along the Nu River, but has postponed the project indefinitely. The heritage site is now protected.

↙ **Amazon rain forest** covers approximately 2 million square miles (5.5 million km²). The forest contains an estimated 150,000 species of plants, including 75,000 trees, as well as 2.5 million species of insects and thousands of species of vertebrates. Since 1970 deforestation has removed almost 20 percent of the forested area.

↙ **Thousands of blue wildebeest** (*Connochaetes taurinus*) move across the grassland of the Masai Mara National Reserve, Kenya. It was established in 1961 to protect animals from hunters. The Serengeti Plains cross its southern end. More than a million wildebeest and hundreds of thousands of zebra migrate through the reserve annually.

↓ **Although coral reefs** are vulnerable, they support thousands of fish and invertebrate animal species. The diversity of coral reef ecosystems rivals that of tropical rain forests. This shoal of emperor angelfish (*Pomacanthus imperator*) is swimming above gorgonian corals that form part of a coral reef in the Red Sea.

Conservation

The nineteenth century was a time of rapid industrialization throughout Europe and North America. It was also an age of reform. While many reformers concentrated on the harmful social effects of rapid industrial change, others devoted their attention to the degradation of the natural environment. Their concerns led to the founding of the first conservation groups and societies. Today much larger and more powerful conservation organizations continue the work of these pioneers in their campaign for the protection of wild plants and animals. They are endorsed by many governments and intergovernmental organizations, including the United Nations, and enjoy widespread popular support. Their work is ongoing. No species or habitat area is ever entirely free from threat.

PROTECTED AREAS

- Less than 1%
- 1 to 5%
- 5 to 10%
- 10 to 20%
- More than 20%
- Insufficient data

CONSERVATION AREAS
In most countries land is set aside to provide habitat for wildlife. The map shows the proportion of the total land area in different regions that has been designated as national parks, wildlife sanctuaries, nature reserves or other places for wildlife conservation.

↖ **The tusk** of an African elephant (*Loxodonta africana*), held here by a conservation worker, is of ivory, which has a high market value. Elephant hunting increased rapidly during the 1970s, and seriously threatened the survival of both African and Asian elephants. The international trade in ivory is now banned.

↖ **Coral reefs** throughout the Pacific and Indian oceans are under attack from increasing numbers of crown-of-thorns starfish (*Acanthaster planci*), which eat coral polyps. This diver is clearing starfish from a reef near Palau. He works carefully, because the starfish can deliver a painful sting.

↑ **Three young giant pandas** (*Ailuropoda melanoleuca*) enjoy a play-fight at the China Conservation and Research Center for the Giant Panda, in the Wolong Nature Reserve, China. Giant pandas are endangered because of loss of habitat and a low birth rate.

← **The cheetah** (*Acinonyx jubatus*) differs from other cats in having non-retractable claws. A narrow genetic base allows diseases to spread rapidly through populations, where cubs have a high mortality rate. This cheetah is playing on the roof of a car in the Masai Mara National Reserve, Kenya.

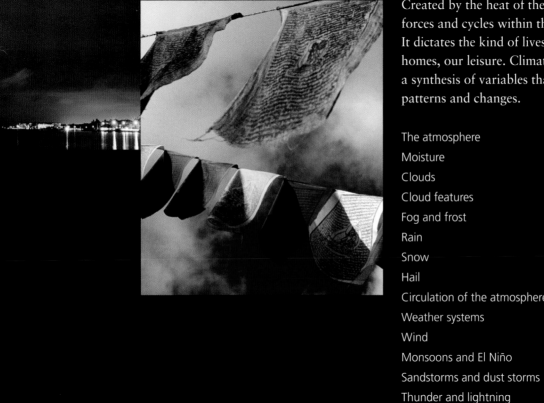

Created by the heat of the Sun, weather is a system of forces and cycles within the atmosphere that envelops Earth. It dictates the kind of lives we lead, the way we build our homes, our leisure. Climate is a long-term look at weather, a synthesis of variables that allows us to understand global patterns and changes.

The atmosphere

Earth's atmosphere extends from the surface to the edge of interplanetary space, where it merges with the Sun's atmosphere. At that height, in the exosphere, the air is so thin that gas molecules and atoms rarely collide. Increasing height within the atmosphere brings a decrease in temperature; as sunshine warms Earth's surface, air is heated from below, by contact with the warm land and sea. The temperature does not decrease evenly, however, and there are regions where it stays constant or even rises at higher altitudes. These differences produce boundaries that rising air cannot easily cross; as a result they divide the atmosphere into layers.

In the two lowest layers—the troposphere and stratosphere—air is composed of 78.08 percent nitrogen, 20.95 percent oxygen, 0.93 percent argon, and there are traces of other gases. This region is sometimes called the homosphere. Above it, in the heterosphere, the composition changes with height. Nitrogen is predominant at lower levels, together with molecular (O_2) and atomic (O) oxygen. Above that, atomic oxygen is mixed with molecular (N_2) and atomic (N) nitrogen.

↗ **The view from** the International Space Station shows how thin the atmosphere is. Weather phenomena occur only in the troposphere, which extends from the surface to a height of between 5 and 10 miles (8–16 km).

→ **A Dynamics F-16** flies above the clouds. Jet aircraft use fuel more efficiently at high altitude because the thinner air causes less drag. That is why aircraft on long journeys fly as high as possible. Most of them cruise at around 30,000 feet (9150 m), at the top of the troposphere.

↠ **Forest trees** form canopies as their leaves compete for the sunlight they need for photosynthesis. The key atmospheric ingredient for photosynthesis is carbon dioxide, a trace gas that accounts for only about 0.04 percent of the air. All life depends on carbon dioxide; without it there could be no plants and, therefore, no animals.

↠↠ **An anvil**—the technical name is incus—marks the top of a big cumulonimbus storm cloud. It also marks the tropopause. Moist air rises vigorously through the cloud, but the tropopause is a boundary that rising air cannot cross, because air above is at the same density.

THE LAYERS OF EARTH'S ATMOSPHERE

← **Our atmosphere** is divided into several distinct regions, each with different properties such as temperature, density and pressure. We live in the troposphere, a region which extends from Earth's surface to a height of between 5 and 10 miles (8–16 km).

Exosphere
Above 310 miles (>500 km)

Thermosphere
50–310 miles (80–500 km)

Mesosphere
30–50 miles (50–80 km)

Stratosphere
10–30 miles (16–50 km)

Troposphere
0–10 miles (0–16 km)

Moisture

Water is one of the very few substances that can exist as a gas, a liquid and a solid at the temperatures normally experienced at Earth's surface. Water exists in the air as vapor—an invisible gas. Clouds form from minute liquid droplets or from ice crystals. As the temperature rises, water molecules locked together in ice absorb energy. This allows them to vibrate more vigorously. When they have absorbed sufficient energy, small groups of molecules break free and flow past each other as liquid. The ice has now melted. If the temperature continues to rise, molecules may absorb enough energy to break free from their groups and escape into the air. The liquid has now evaporated. Water evaporates from the surface of oceans and lakes. It enters the air as vapor, where it cools, condenses into droplets and ice crystals and eventually returns to the surface as precipitation—rain, snow, hail, fog, mist, dew and frost—and back to the sea. It is the response of water to changing temperature that produces weather.

↓ **Water evaporates** from the oceans. Some returns directly to the sea as precipitation, but some is carried over land and falls there. Water evaporates from the land and is transpired back into the air by plants. The water that falls on land flows back to the ocean via rivers, streams and underground channels, thus completing the cycle.

THE WATER CYCLE

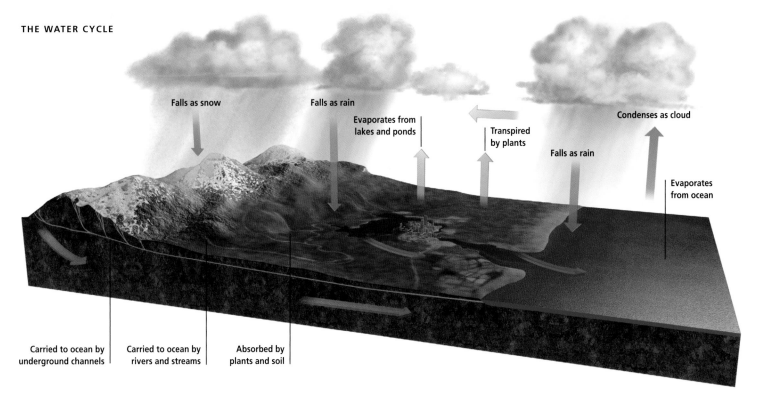

Falls as snow

Falls as rain

Evaporates from lakes and ponds

Transpired by plants

Condenses as cloud

Falls as rain

Evaporates from ocean

Carried to ocean by underground channels

Carried to ocean by rivers and streams

Absorbed by plants and soil

← **Sea smoke,** seen here at sunrise over Halifax harbor, Nova Scotia, Canada, is a type of fog. Cold, dry air that has crossed ice and snow moves over the sea, where warmer air contains water vapor. The moist air rises into the cold air, where its moisture condenses, producing the "smoke."

← **Clouds are building** and some threaten rain; one has an anvil. Moist air is rising rapidly. As it cools with increasing height, its moisture condenses to form cloud. Condensation releases heat, warming the air and making it rise farther, with more condensation. This air is said to be unstable.

← **Condensation on a windowpane** happens when cold glass chills a layer of warm, moist air just a few molecules thick, and its water vapor condenses onto the glass. As air movements replace that layer with another, more condensation occurs.

← **Clouds building** over this field may bring a summer shower later in the day. The clouds are cumulus—heaped cloud—and may indicate the approach of an active cold front, where cold air pushes beneath warmer air, forcing it to rise. This brings showers with fine periods.

Clouds

People who are interested in weather need an unambiguous means of classifying the many different cloud types. The search for such a classification system was pioneered by the ancient Greeks, who used descriptions such as "streaks" and "like fleeces of wool." It was not until 1803, however, that Luke Howard (1772–1864), an English pharmacist and amateur meteorologist, devised the system of cloud classification that, with some later modifications, is the one we still use today. Howard proposed that all clouds can be described in terms of four basic types: cumulus (heaped), stratus (layered), cirrus (wispy) and nimbus (producing precipitation).

In 1896, Howard's system was adopted for the first edition of the *International Cloud Atlas*. Now published by the World Meteorological Organization, the *Atlas* still uses these universally accepted descriptions.

→ **Thunderhead over Red Canyon,** Utah, is a rapidly growing cumulonimbus cloud. Fueled by heat released by condensation, warm, moist air is rising in currents that are moving at up to 100 miles per hour (160 km/h), and cold air is sinking in downcurrents. Cumulonimbus clouds can produce hail and violent thunderstorms.

↘ **The stratus clouds** on the horizon were photographed at dawn from Niue Island, in the Pacific. At ground level stratus is fog; when it rises above the ground it forms a uniform, featureless, gray layer that can be thin enough for the Sun or Moon to show faintly through it. The cloud layer in the foreground is stratocumulus.

↓ **Stratocumulus** cloud forms isolated sheets of gray and white cloud, with dark areas shaped like rolls or rounded masses, and clear sky between the patches. Stratocumulus forms when rising moist air encounters warmer air overhead. It can rise no higher and flattens itself out against the ceiling of warmer air.

CLOUD CLASSIFICATION

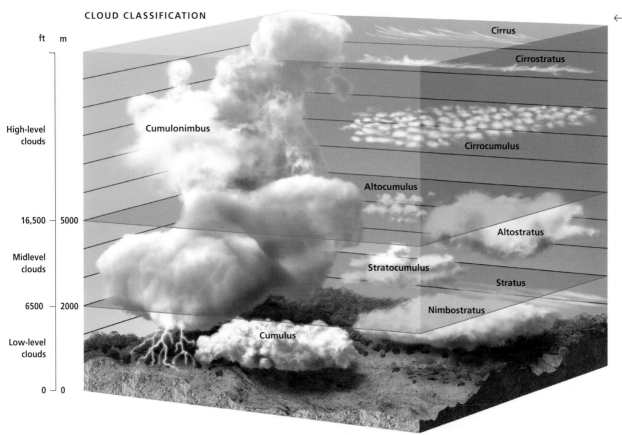

ft m

High-level
clouds

16,500 — 5000

Midlevel
clouds

6500 — 2000

Low-level
clouds

0 — 0

Cirrus

Cirrostratus

Cumulonimbus

Cirrocumulus

Altocumulus

Altostratus

Stratocumulus

Stratus

Nimbostratus

Cumulus

← **Clouds are classified** in two ways. The first is based on the usual height of the cloud base and describes clouds as low, middle or high. The second, based on appearance, places clouds in one of 10 genera: stratus, stratocumulus, cumulus, cumulonimbus (low); altostratus, altocumulus, nimbostratus, (middle); cirrus, cirrocumulus, cirrostratus (high). The genera are divided into 14 species, such as calvus (bare) and lenticularis (lens-shaped); and nine varieties, including intortus (twisted) and undulatus (wavelike). Accessory clouds, such as pileus (capped) and velum (veiled), can be attached to main clouds. Supplementary features can include incus (anvil-shaped) and virga (fallstreaks).

Cloud features

The 10 cloud genera and 14 species are not sufficient to fully describe every cloud type. The *International Cloud Atlas* contains 196 pages of cloud photographs and even the abridged version has 72 photographs. So many photographs are needed because of all the accessory clouds that may be attached to a main cloud and the supplementary features that modify a cloud's appearance. These additional features produce some of the most beautiful and extraordinary cloud shapes.

Small clouds that rise vertically from the top of their parent cloud, most often altocumulus, sometimes resemble the turrets of a medieval castle. This cloud species is called castellanus, Latin for "castle." Many of the clouds that form sheets can occasionally appear as waves, like the waves on the sea, in the cloud variety undulatus. Seen from below, cumulonimbus storm clouds are dark, sometimes almost black, because of the number of cloud droplets and ice crystals that reflect the light. Sometimes the darkest part of the cloud can curve upward. This supplementary feature is called arcus. The top of a cumulonimbus often extends into the anvil shape of the supplementary feature incus.

↓ **Iridescent cloud** is most often seen when the Sun or Moon is in the same part of the sky as a barrier of cloud that hides it from view. The colors, most often red or green, but sometimes blue or yellow, are caused by the diffraction of light by water droplets or ice crystals that are all approximately the same size.

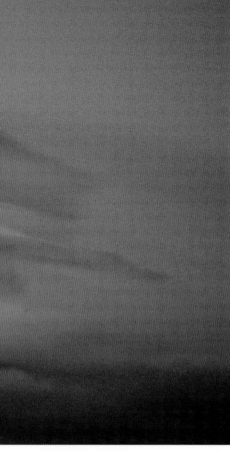

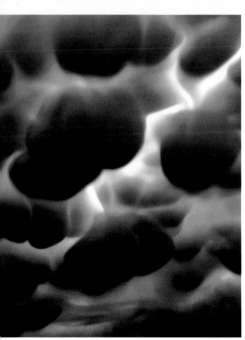

→ **Virga,** or fallstreaks, which form a thin veil beneath a cloud, are rain that fails to reach Earth's surface. The cloud base is at the height where moisture in rising air begins to condense. Air below the cloud is drier and raindrops begin to evaporate the moment they enter it. Very small drops evaporate before reaching the ground.

← **Lenticular cloud** forms extraordinary shapes that sometimes resemble flying saucers. As it passes over the top of a mountain, air rises, then sinks a little. This sets up a standing wave in the moving air. If the air is almost saturated, a lens-shaped (lenticular) cloud forms at the top of each wave.

← **Mammatus** is a supplementary cloud feature that forms on the underside of a large anvil (incus). Ice crystals at the top of the anvil sublime (turn directly to vapor) in the dry air above the cloud. Sublimation absorbs latent heat, chilling the air locally and making it denser. Small pockets of dense air sink through the cloud to the bottom of the anvil.

Fog and frost

Fog, formed from water droplets smaller than 0.004 inch (0.1 mm) across, is cloud that touches the surface and reduces visibility to less than 3300 feet (1 km). If the visibility is greater than this, the culprit is called mist or haze. Fog forms when atmospheric water vapor condenses at the surface. Advection fog develops when wind carries warm, moist air slowly across a cold surface. It often occurs in early morning in summer, when the land has cooled faster than the nearby sea and the air crosses both. Radiation fog develops on clear nights when the ground radiates away the heat it absorbed during the day. The ground becomes very cold and water vapor condenses in moist air adjacent to it. If the air temperature is below freezing, fog will freeze directly onto surfaces. This is freezing fog.

When coal was widely used as a domestic and industrial fuel, soot and smoke mixed with fog to form smog. This produced the "pea-soupers" for which London and other industrial cities were once notorious.

→ **Advection fog** is a familiar feature of San Francisco Bay. The cold California Current flows parallel to the coast. Moist air that approaches land is chilled as it crosses the current; its water vapor condenses, and the resulting fog rolls into the bay.

↓ **Hoar frost** creates a beautiful winter scene. During the night the plants radiated away warmth they absorbed by day and their surfaces fell below freezing. Water vapor in contact with the surfaces was deposited directly onto them as ice crystals.

↑ **Rime frost** coats a geranium leaf, which cooled to freezing temperature or below, then came into contact with fog or drizzle consisting of supercooled droplets—liquid droplets a little below freezing temperature. The droplets froze immediately on contact.

← **Radiation fog** lies over a hayfield, hiding distant buildings. The night was clear and the ground radiated away the heat it absorbed during the day. As the surface temperature fell, the air next to the ground chilled to below its dew point temperature. Water vapor condensed and by morning a thin layer of fog covered the ground.

→ **Icicles** are conical columns of ice. In order to grow, they require melting snow to send constant streams of liquid water trickling slowly downward, and an updraft of air. The rising air carries heat away from the liquid water, which freezes, releasing latent heat that warms the air and sustains the updraft.

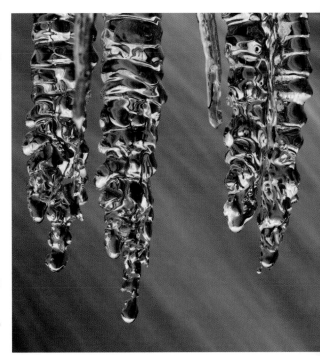

Rain

The amount of water vapor air can hold depends on the temperature. Cold air can hold less than warm air, and if the temperature of moist air falls to below a critical value, called the dew point, some of its water vapor will condense—provided there are surfaces for it to condense onto. Suitable surfaces are provided by minute particles called cloud condensation nuclei. These consist of dust, salt crystals and, best of all, droplets of sulfuric acid. Sulfuric acid forms from sulfate molecules by reactions that involve cosmic radiation. Cosmic rays play a crucial role in the formation of low-level clouds. High-level clouds consist of ice crystals, formed when water vapor freezes directly onto freezing nuclei. Cloud droplets grow into raindrops either by colliding and coalescing as they fall, or by freezing into crystals that join together as snowflakes and then melt as they fall into warmer air. Droplets fall as rain when they grow too heavy for the updrafts in the cloud to support them. They begin to evaporate the moment they enter the drier air below the cloud.

↓ **A typical raindrop** is between 0.08 and 0.2 inch (2–5 mm) across and falls at between 14 and 20 miles per hour (23–33 km/h). Air resistance flattens large raindrops into an oblate shape. Drizzle consists of drops smaller than 0.02 inch (0.5 mm) across. They fall at about 0.4 miles per hour (0.64 km/h).

RAINDROP SIZE

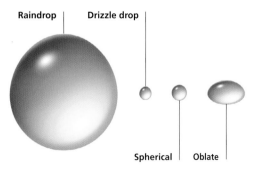

Raindrop | Drizzle drop

Spherical | Oblate

Steady rain falling from nimbostratus cloud over the plains of New South Wales, Australia, moistens the soil but will not end a prolonged drought. The ground is so dry that the rain is not sufficient to recharge water below ground.

Three boys walk through a heavy shower of summer rain in the Paro Valley, Bhutan. Most of the rain in Bhutan, between India and Tibet, falls from June to September, and winters are fairly dry.

A rainbow shows that the rainstorm has passed. Bright sunlight shining from behind the observer is refracted as it enters water droplets, then reflected from the rear of the droplets and refracted a second time as it leaves. This breaks white light into its constituent colors, with red on the outside.

Cloud patterns over southern Brazil include warm clouds of water droplets below 3 miles (5 km), cold clouds of ice crystals above 6 miles (10 km), and mixed clouds that contain both. The wispy edges are the cold anvil tops of cumulonimbus clouds.

Snow

Cloud droplets can be cooled to below freezing temperature, but when supercooled droplets encounter solid particles of a suitable size and shape—called freezing nuclei—they freeze instantly. Water vapor also changes directly into ice in the presence of sublimation nuclei. Within an ice crystal, each water molecule is bonded to four others, but the shape of the molecule allows it to be oriented in six different ways. Consequently, although ice crystals are always six-sided—hexagonal—they have a variety of shapes. Once an ice crystal has formed, more water vapor freezes onto it, building a snowflake that is based on the shape of the initial crystal. Fragments that break from a snowflake seed the growth of new snowflakes. They grow arms and spikes, and when small flakes collide they tend to stick together. Snowflakes melt in warm air and turn into rain unless the temperature beneath the cloud is below about 39°F (4°C). Snow will not settle unless the ground temperature is below freezing.

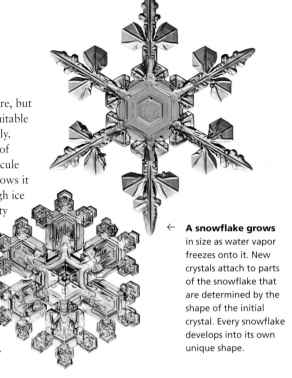

← **A snowflake grows** in size as water vapor freezes onto it. New crystals attach to parts of the snowflake that are determined by the shape of the initial crystal. Every snowflake develops into its own unique shape.

↑ **Gudauri is situated** in the Caucasus Mountains, Georgia, near the border with Russia. It is a popular ski resort. Because air temperature decreases with height, there is an elevation—which varies with latitude— above which precipitation always falls as snow. These high mountains retain their snowcaps throughout the year.

← **People in Times Square,** New York City, trudge to work on February 17, 2003, after a blizzard. A blizzard can produce snowfalls 10 inches (250 mm) deep, driven by a wind of more than 35 miles per hour (56 km/h), with a temperature below 20°F (–7°C).

LAKE-EFFECT SNOW

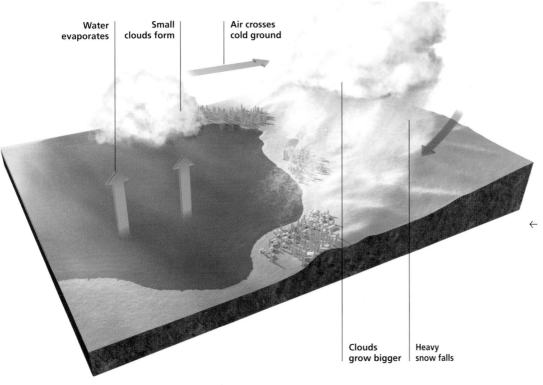

Water evaporates

Small clouds form

Air crosses cold ground

Clouds grow bigger

Heavy snow falls

← **Northeastern United States,** including New York City, experiences heavy snow—caused by the effect of the Great Lakes—early in most winters. Cold, dry air moves eastward across the continent, then crosses the unfrozen water of the lakes. Water evaporates into the dry air. Carrying moisture from the lakes, the air continues eastward, but now across very cold ground where its moisture turns to snow. In most winters the lakes remain unfrozen; if they freeze the effect ceases.

Hail

A hailstone begins to form when a water droplet near the bottom of a big cumulonimbus cloud is swept upward in an updraft and freezes when it reaches air below freezing temperature. Supercooled water droplets collide with the ice pellet, spread across its surface and freeze as a thin layer of clear ice. The pellet also encounters much colder water droplets that freeze on contact, depositing a layer of ice crystals with air spaces between them. A layer of white, opaque ice then encloses a layer of clear ice. Vertical currents in the cloud carry the hailstone aloft once more, to acquire new layers of ice. When rime frost collects on ice pellets it produces graupel, or soft hail, which consists of hailstones that splatter when they strike a hard surface.

→ **Giant hailstones** can cause serious damage. Stones this size may be falling at 100 miles per hour (160 km/h) when they hit the ground. The size of a hailstone depends on the number of times it travels to and from the top of the cloud, gaining layers of ice on each trip.

↓ **Hail forms only in cumulonimbus clouds,** and the bigger the clouds the bigger the hailstones they produce. Updrafts carry water droplets above the freezing level and downdrafts carry ice pellets to the base of a cloud. The layers of clear and rime ice that the hailstone acquires on successive trips to and from the cloud top give it a layered structure.

HAILSTORM

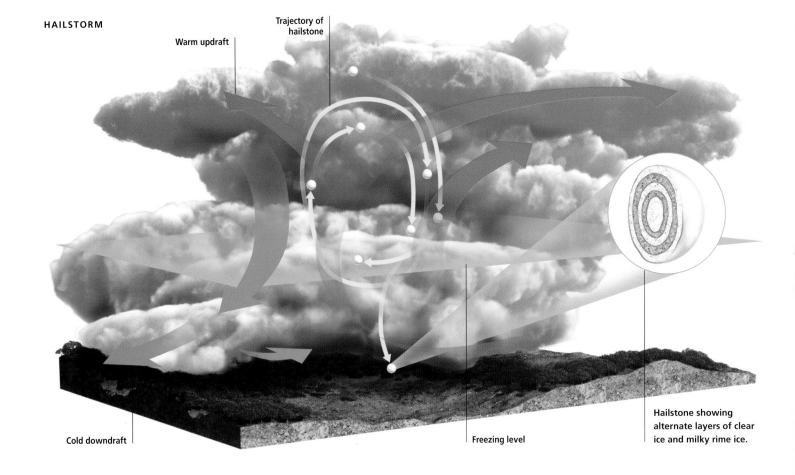

Warm updraft

Trajectory of hailstone

Cold downdraft

Freezing level

Hailstone showing alternate layers of clear ice and milky rime ice.

↑ **Severe hailstorms** create hazardous driving conditions. Giant hailstones can smash windshields, dent car bodywork and seriously damage other property. The United States is divided into 13 hail regions, classified according to the frequency and intensity of the hailstorms they experience and the months when most storms occur.

← **Hail can cause serious damage** to crops. People once used to fire cannons upward into storm clouds in attempts to disrupt hailstone formation. In a modern equivalent, explosions of acetylene and air are detonated to send shockwaves into clouds. There is no evidence that these measures have any effect.

Circulation of the atmosphere

Warm air rises and cold air subsides, and the Sun shines more strongly over the equator than over the poles. These facts combine to produce a constant movement of air throughout the troposphere—a general circulation of the atmosphere—that has the overall effect of transporting heat away from the equator.

The discovery of this convective system began as scholars tried to explain the constancy of the northeast and southeast trade winds that blow on either side of the equator. In 1735 George Hadley (1685–1768) proposed that warm air rises over the equator, cools, sinks over the poles and flows back toward the equator as a surface wind that is deflected by Earth's rotation. It is more complicated than that, but his mechanism does operate in the tropics, producing the Hadley cells. A second set of cells, the polar cells, combine with the Hadley cells to drive a third set, the Ferrel cells, which were described by William Ferrel (1817–91) in 1856.

INTERTROPICAL CONVERGENCE ZONE

The diagram shows the average July and January positions of the intertropical convergence zone, where the northeast and southeast trade winds converge.

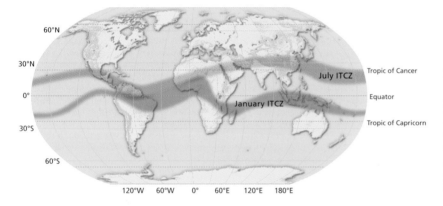

↗ **The jet streams** are fast, high-level winds that blow from the west in both hemispheres and are often marked by a line of cloud. They are caused by the sharp difference in temperature and air density across the top of the boundaries between tropical, subtropical and polar air. In summer an easterly jet blows over India and Africa.

↗ **Equatorial rain** is heavy and frequent. Oceans cover most of the equatorial region, so equatorial air is moist. Warm, moist air rises by convection into the Hadley cells, cooling as it rises, and its water vapor condenses to create towering clouds that produce the rain. Having lost its moisture, air moving away from the equator is dry.

→ **The Sahara** is part of a belt of deserts that surround the world in the subtropics of both hemispheres. Dry air that lost its moisture as it rose subsides on the poleward side of the Hadley cells. As it sinks, this dry air heats up by compression.

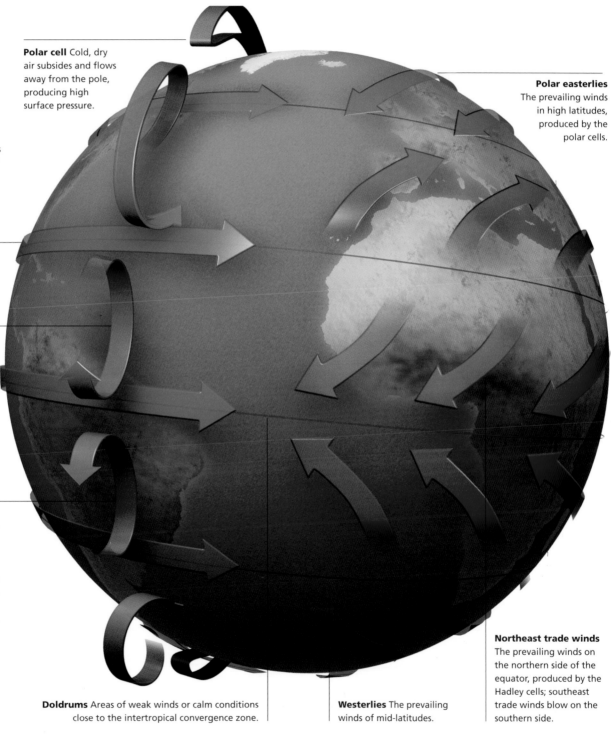

THREE-CELL MODEL
Atmospheric circulation is described in this model as three vertical cells in each hemisphere. It is a simplification of the true circulation, where heat is also transported horizontally, but it provides a useful approximation of the way air movements transport heat.

Polar cell Cold, dry air subsides and flows away from the pole, producing high surface pressure.

Polar easterlies The prevailing winds in high latitudes, produced by the polar cells.

Jet stream A fast, high-level wind that blows from west to east in both hemispheres.

Hadley cell Warm, moist air rises over the equator, loses its moisture as it rises and moves away from the equator at high altitude. The name honors George Hadley, who described the cell in 1735.

Ferrel cell Some air from the Hadley cell rises, flows away from the equator, subsides on the edge of the polar cell and moves away from the pole at the surface. The name honors William Ferrel, who described the cell in 1856.

Doldrums Areas of weak winds or calm conditions close to the intertropical convergence zone.

Westerlies The prevailing winds of mid-latitudes.

Northeast trade winds The prevailing winds on the northern side of the equator, produced by the Hadley cells; southeast trade winds blow on the southern side.

Weather systems

When air remains for a time over a large area, such as a continent or ocean, its properties of temperature, humidity and density at the same altitude become broadly similar everywhere. The air then constitutes an air mass with distinctive characteristics. Air masses are classed first as continental or maritime, and then as arctic, polar, tropical or equatorial; this allows such categories as maritime arctic and continental polar.

Air of different densities does not mix easily. Where air masses meet there is a boundary, or front, between them. Waves can develop along fronts, with areas of low pressure, called frontal depressions, at the crest. Fronts separate relatively warm and cold air. Warm air follows behind a warm front and cold air behind a cold front. Cold fronts generally move faster than warm fronts, with cold air moving beneath the warm air and raising it from the surface. When all the warm air is clear of the surface the fronts merge, or occlude, to form an occlusion.

→ **Anticyclones** are areas of high surface pressure. Air inside them subsides and circulates clockwise in the northern hemisphere and counterclockwise in the southern. Anticyclones bring light winds and fine weather. The evaporation of surface moisture can produce small cumulus clouds—fair weather cumulus.

→→ **Cyclones** are areas of low surface pressure in which air rises and turns cyclonically—counterclockwise in the northern hemisphere and clockwise in the southern—about the low-pressure center. Winds may be strong. The air is relatively warm and if it is moist, layers of stratus, stratocumulus, nimbostratus, altostratus and cirrostratus cloud will form, bringing dull, overcast skies, often with persistent precipitation.

↓ **A cold front** that extends across the Gulf of Mexico is marked by cloud formations in this photograph taken by a weather satellite. As cold air pushes beneath warmer air, the warm air is forced to rise up the cold front. Cumulus and cumulonimbus clouds form. These clouds are producing a severe thunderstorm.

↑ **Drought** is a prolonged period with less rain than usual for a place and time of year. In Britain more than 15 consecutive days without rain can bring a drought. In this scene near Brancaster, Norfolk, moisture has evaporated, causing the clay soil to crack.

← **Winter in Stockholm,** Sweden, is severe. In January and February, the average daytime temperature does not rise above freezing and there is much snow and ice. Stockholm has a high-latitude continental climate.

Wind

Relatively cool and dense air produces high surface pressure. Warmer and less dense air results in low pressure. The difference in pressure between adjacent areas of high and low pressure constitutes a pressure gradient that exerts a pressure-gradient force (PGF), which pushes air toward the center of low pressure at a speed proportional to the gradient. Wind is that air movement.

Earth, however, also moves beneath the moving air, and this deflects the air—to the right in the northern hemisphere and to the left in the southern hemisphere. This called the Coriolis effect (abbreviated to CorF, because it was once incorrectly thought to be a physical force). The magnitude of the CorF varies according to the latitude and speed of air movement. The PGF and CorF balance each other when the air follows a circular path around the centers of high and low pressure. The general circulation of the atmosphere produces prevailing winds, the most constant being the easterly trade winds of the tropics.

↗ **A gentle breeze** stirs prayer flags in Kathmandu, Nepal. Wind force is described by the Beaufort wind scale, devised in 1805 by Admiral Sir Francis Beaufort (1774–1857). This force 3 wind blows at between 8 and 12 miles per hour (13–19 km/h).

→ **A sea storm** produces stronger winds than a storm over land because there are no buildings or other obstructions to slow the wind. This force 8 gale is blowing at between 39 and 46 miles per hour (63–74 km/h).

↓ **This wind,** in Hong Kong, may look like a gale, but it is classed as a strong breeze—force 6 on the Beaufort scale and blowing at between 25 and 31 miles per hour (40–50 km/h). A gale, force 7, makes walking difficult.

LAND AND SEA BREEZES

During the day, the land along the coast warms up much faster than the nearby sea. When warm air rises over land and moves seaward at a higher level, cool air blows from the sea to replace it. This is a sea breeze, which usually develops by mid-afternoon. At night the land cools more quickly than the sea, so cool air moves from land to sea, as a land breeze.

AFTERNOON

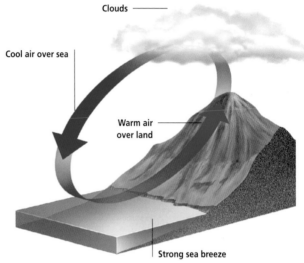

Clouds

Cool air over sea

Warm air over land

Strong sea breeze

NIGHT

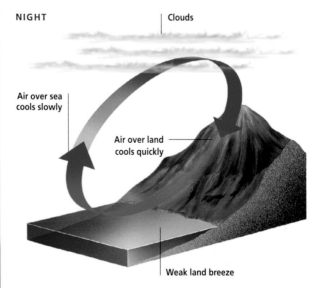

Clouds

Air over sea cools slowly

Air over land cools quickly

Weak land breeze

Monsoons and El Niño

"Monsoon" comes originally from mausim, Arabic for "season." Monsoons affect tropical Asia Africa, Australia, Mexico and southwestern United States. There are two monsoon seasons; both are associated with the direction of the prevailing winds. During winter monsoons, prevailing winds blow from the center of a large continent, bringing dry air. Mumbai, in India, receives on average only 4 inches (102 mm) of rain from October until May. This is the dry, winter monsoon. Then the wind direction reverses and moist air flows in from across the ocean. Between June and September, 67 inches (1702 mm) of rain fall on Mumbai. This is the wet, summer monsoon.

El Niño is a change in wind and rainfall patterns that happens every few years. It begins in the tropical South Pacific but affects a much larger area. It is linked to changes in pressure distribution, called a southern oscillation, which weakens or reverses the trade winds and the ocean currents that drive warm water westward.

SUMMER MONSOON

WINTER MONSOON

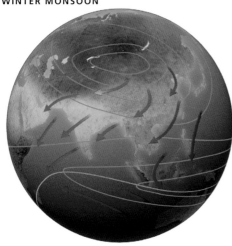

→ **Summer monsoon weather in India** brings heavy rain. Farmers depend on it, but it makes life difficult for city-dwellers. This is the financial center of Mumbai in July 2006, where office workers are wading knee-deep as they struggle to work. They must walk because floods swamped the rail lines after 14 inches (356 mm) of rain fell on a single day. Further rain was forecast.

← **Summer monsoon is wet.** As the temperature rises over central Asia the anticyclone weakens and the land becomes warmer than the sea. The wind direction reverses, bringing moist air across the Indian Ocean. The air rises when it crosses the coast, becoming unstable. Cumulonimbus clouds develop, then suddenly the monsoon bursts. It begins in the south and spreads northward.

↙ **Winter monsoon over southern Asia** is characterized by northeasterly winds that blow out of a center of high pressure over central Asia. During its passage over the Himalayas, the air loses what little moisture it carried and warms by compression as it sinks on the southern side of the mountains. As the season nears its end the humidity and temperature rise sharply.

↠ **Drought in Australia** is one result of El Niño, which drains the pool of warm water around Indonesia, drastically reducing the rate of evaporation and rainfall. El Niño also brings heavy rain to southwestern United States. It is linked to a weakening in pressure over Tahiti and a strengthening over Darwin, Australia—a change known as a southern oscillation.

↓ **Western trade winds** usually drive a current that carries warm water away from South America and toward Indonesia, where it accumulates in a warm pool. During an El Niño the pattern reverses.

NORMAL CONDITIONS

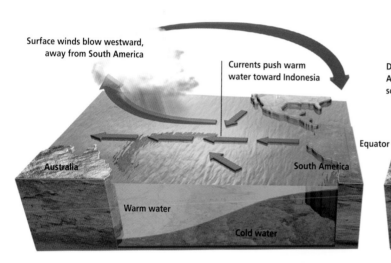

Surface winds blow westward, away from South America

Currents push warm water toward Indonesia

Australia

South America

Warm water

Cold water

EL NIÑO CONDITIONS

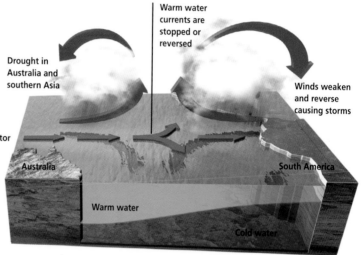

Warm water currents are stopped or reversed

Drought in Australia and southern Asia

Winds weaken and reverse causing storms

Australia

South America

Warm water

Cold water

Equator

Sandstorms and dust storms

Incessant desert winds steadily blow dust and sand—the only difference is in the size of their particles—away from some areas and deposit them in others. A wind of 12 miles per hour (19 km/h) will lift dry sand grains into the air. Where two air masses meet, one pushes beneath the other, generating winds and raising the warmer air. Dust and sand are lifted aloft along the front, often to a height of 5000 feet (1500 m). The front continues to advance, appearing to those in its path as an approaching wall of sand. Depending on the size of the particles, this is a dust storm or sandstorm. It reduces visibility, damages engines and penetrates buildings and clothing.

By the afternoon some desert surfaces are much hotter than others. Warm air rises over the hot surface and cooler air is drawn in from different directions to replace it, producing a wind that will raise dust and sand. As opposing wind currents mingle, they spiral upward, swaying erratically. Small, weak spirals are dust devils. Big ones, rising to 100 feet (30 m) or higher, are desert whirlwinds.

↓ **A Saharan dust storm** advances along a front several hundred miles long across parts of Algeria and Libya. It generates strong, squally winds that raise dust particles and sand grains to a great height. A large storm may cover 5000 square miles (13,000 km²) and carry more than 7 million tons (7.14 million t) of dust.

→ **A dust devil** is a common sight. Local surface heating makes air rise, drawing in cooler air from the sides. As the incoming winds meet, the air begins to turn. It spirals wildly upward, carrying dust, leaves, scraps of paper and other loose debris with it. The incoming air cools the surface, and the devil dies down after a few minutes.

↘ **A dust storm** moves through the slums of Yamuna Pushta, New Delhi, India, during the dry winter monsoon. Such storms are common. They can last for several hours and reduce visibility to a few yards. The dust can penetrate the eyes, ears, noses, mouths and clothing of people caught out in the open. As seen here, they are forced to do whatever they can to protect their faces.

TRAVELING STORMS

Dust storms and sandstorms are associated with deserts, but they can travel much farther. Every spring, sand from the deserts of central Asia produces severe storms in northern China. These reduce Beijing traffic almost to a standstill and pile up dunes in villages. They also bury crops and grass. In 2001 a cloud of dust drifted across the Pacific from China to the United States.

↓ **A sandstorm in Egypt** partly obscures a pyramid with dust and sand from the Sahara. These storms usually arrive in April, with winds, called sirocco in Europe and khamsin in Egypt, of up to 87 miles per hour (140 km/h) that can raise the temperature by 36°F (20°C) in two hours. The storms may last several days. They can make people and animals sick and damage crops. Sometimes they even damage buildings.

Thunder and lightning

Conditions inside a giant cumulonimbus cloud are violent. Warm air rises in currents that move at up to 100 miles per hour (160 km/h). When it reaches the top of the cloud the air subsides in downcurrents. These leave the cloud base as downdrafts, producing wind gusts often of gale force. The downcurrents carry snowflakes and raindrops, each surrounded by an envelope of cold air. Eventually this chills adjacent upcurrents, they lose energy and the cloud dissipates.

During its active phase, the cloud accumulates positive electric charge in its upper layers and negative charge near its base. Small ice crystals and water droplets carry positive charge and the larger snowflakes and droplets carry negative charge—gravity separates the charges. The low-level negative charge induces a positive charge on the ground surface. Natural radiation, including cosmic radiation, releases free electrons that accelerate in the strong electrical field and become an avalanche that turns into a lightning flash.

→ **Lightning at night** over Florida's Gulf Coast flashes from cloud to cloud and cloud to ground. A lightning flash is about 8 inches (20 cm) in diameter and it heats the air by up to 54,000°F (30,000°C) in less than 1 second. Thunder is the sound of the air exploding.

↓ **This approaching storm** will die within an hour or two as downdrafts in the cloud suppress the updrafts that sustain it with moisture and heat. Squall line storms last longer, because gusts from the cloud base push beneath warm air and trigger the formation of another cloud.

↑ **Cloud-to-air** lightning occurs when a branch from a lightning stroke inside a cloud emerges into clear air from the side of the cloud. A lightning stroke follows the line of least electrical resistance and will be attracted to a region of negative charge.

↗ **Cloud-to-cloud** lightning flashes between adjacent clouds when the region of positive charge near the top of one cloud is closer to the region of negative charge in an adjacent cloud than it is to the negative charge at its own base.

→ **Cloud-to-ground** lightning occurs in stages. A leading stroke passes in phases from a cloud toward the positive charge at the highest point on the ground. It is met by a return stroke from the ground. The sequence repeats three or four times to make a 0.2-second flash.

Tornadoes

A tornado is a funnel of wind that spirals upward into a storm cloud and produces the strongest winds known. Most begin inside cumulonimbus clouds where the updrafts and downdrafts have separated to form a single convection cell, called a supercell, in which the downdrafts do not suppress the updrafts. A change in wind speed or direction high in the cloud sets the rising air turning. The rotation extends downward until all the upcurrents are turning. It is then a mesocyclone. It continues to extend downward, finally emerging from the base of the cloud as a funnel, or tuba. If it reaches the ground it becomes a tornado.

The rotating air feeds the updrafts in the cloud and as air rises, more air is drawn into the vortex. Air approaching the tornado turns in an ever-narrowing spiral. As the radius of rotation decreases, the rotational speed increases. The wider the tornado vortex, the stronger are the winds around its center. Tornadoes are visible because water vapor condenses in the air that is drawn into the area of low air pressure inside the vortex.

↗ **The funnel has touched down** and become a tornado. Even in very dry air, most tornadoes can be seen. They are formed, not from cloud drawn down from above, but from the condensation of water vapor in air that flows into the tornado as a result of the low pressure inside the vortex. The cloud at the base consists of dust and debris that is swept into the spiral. Tornadoes move erratically over the ground. Not many last longer than about 20 minutes, and few spend more than 5 minutes in contact with the ground or travel more than 25 miles (40 km).

THE FUJITA SCALE		
Scale no.	Speeds (mph [km/h])	Damage type
F0	40–73 (64–117)	Light
F1	74–112 (118–180)	Moderate
F2	113–157 (181–251)	Considerable
F3	158–206 (252–330)	Severe
F4	207–260 (331–417)	Devastating
F5	more than 260 (>417)	Incredible

↑ **Tornado damage** is often severe, as it is here in Moore, Oklahoma, but it is confined to the area traversed by the vortex and, in the case of major tornadoes, the small but violent suction vortices around it. Oklahoma is in "Tornado Alley," a region of the US Great Plains where tornadoes are more frequent and more severe than they are elsewhere.

← **This boat was upended** by a tornado in Bermuda. Tornadoes can occur anywhere in the world, but they are rare in the tropics and those that do occur there are weak. Bermuda is just outside the tropics. On January 12, 1986, one tornado struck the north coast of Bermuda Island and less than 2 hours later another struck the south coast.

←← **A waterspout,** seen here off the beach at Skala, on the Greek island of Kefalonia, is an aquatic tornado. It appears white because it contains no dust or debris and the funnel consists only of condensed water vapor. A spray ring around the base consists of seawater whipped up by the wind. Waterspouts usually form over warm, shallow water, which is why they often occur close to shore. Alternatively they may begin as tornadoes on land and then cross over water. If a waterspout comes ashore it becomes a tornado.

Tropical cyclones

Tropical cyclones are known as hurricanes in the North Atlantic and Caribbean, typhoons in the Pacific and Indian oceans and the China seas, and cyclones in the Bay of Bengal. They are areas of low air pressure, surrounded by bands of cloud, and they have a calm, fairly cloud-free, central "eye," where warm air is subsiding. Tropical cyclones sustain winds of at least 75 miles per hour (120 km/h); the fiercest have winds that exceed 150 miles per hour (240 km/h). They produce torrential rain. The combination of low pressure and high onshore winds creates storm surges that often cause coastal flooding. These are tropical phenomena. Their storm clouds are fueled by convection of very moist air supplied by a high rate of evaporation. They can develop only where the sea-surface temperature is at least 82°F (28°C), but in regions less than 5 degrees from the equator the Coriolis effect is too weak to set them rotating. In summer and fall they develop in latitudes of between 5 and 20 degrees.

↓ **Typhoon Utor** developed over the South China Sea and struck the Philippines on December 9, 2006, bringing heavy rain and sustained winds of 109 miles per hour (175 km/h). Satellite images reveal the structure of a fully developed tropical cyclone. The spiral banks of cloud are clearly visible, as is the central eye, although here it is not completely cloud-free. An international network monitors these disturbances.

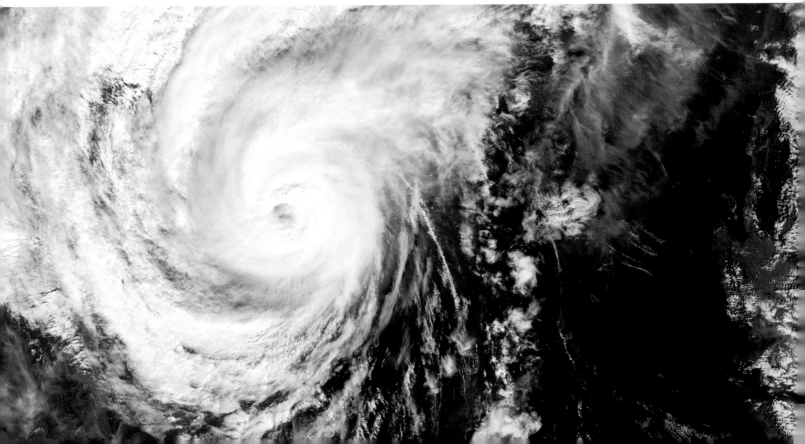

← **On August 29, 2005,** Hurricane Katrina devastated the city of Waveland, Mississippi. It brought winds of 135 miles per hour (217 km/h) and torrential rain. The storm surge, which coincided with high tide, raised the sea level by 32 feet (10 m). An estimated 50 people lost their lives and in the most severely affected area 80 percent of buildings were destroyed.

→ **These shrimp boats** were blown ashore and wrecked along the Gulf Coast by Hurricane Katrina, the most destructive hurricane to hit the US in almost 80 years. Katrina's winds and floods killed more than 1800 people and caused more than 80 billion US dollars in damage in Louisiana, Mississippi and Alabama.

THE COURSE OF A TROPICAL CYCLONE

A tropical cyclone is about 400 miles (640 km) in diameter. The first sign of its approach is high cloud.

Bands of cumulus and cumulonimbus cloud, growing in size and producing rain nearer the center, are separated by clear skies.

In the eyewall that surrounds the eye, air spiraling upward produces storm clouds that tower to more than 50,000 feet (1.5 km).

Sinking air makes the eye calm and dry, but the eye is surrounded by the fiercest winds and heaviest rain.

Low air pressure and strong winds drive water ashore as a storm surge that can cause flooding some distance inland.

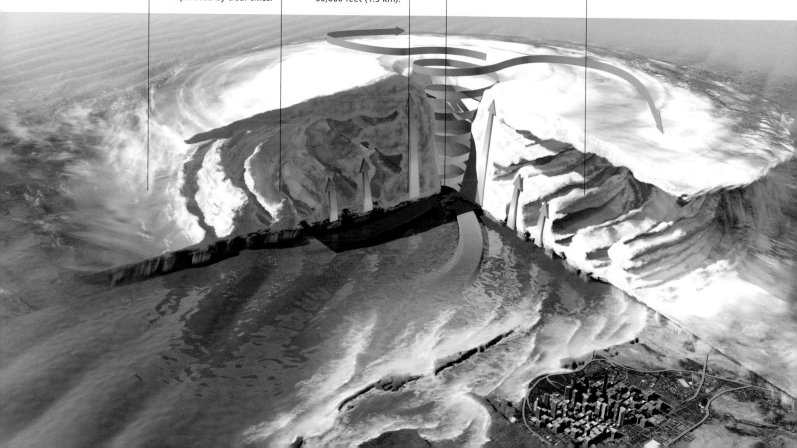

Climate classification

Classification provides a kind of shorthand, where a simple designation describes a wide variety of characteristics. Modern climate classifications are either genetic or generic. Genetic classifications relate climates to their physical causes, describing them in terms of those features of the general atmospheric circulation that produce them in particular places. Generic classifications are based on the effects different climates have on plant growth. There are more generic than genetic classifications. Charles Warren Thornthwaite (1899–1963) and Wladimir Peter Köppen (1846–1940) devised the two most widely used generic systems. The Köppen classification is the more popular. It uses letters to designate six major climate categories and subdivisions: tropical rainy (A); dry (B); warm temperate rainy (C); cold boreal forest (D); tundra (E); and perpetual frost (F). Additional letters qualify these categories. For example, a Csa climate has mild winters and hot, dry summers.

→ **Tropical rain forest** grows in an A climate. Temperature in the coldest month is above 64.4°F (18°C), and in the hottest month it is about 71.6°F (22°C). It is wet all year.

↘ **Uluru,** in central Australia, is in a B climate, which is typical of a hot desert. As potential evaporation exceeds precipitation, there is a permanent water deficiency in this region.

↘ **Snow-covered conifers** grow in a D climate. Winter temperatures are below 26.6°F (–3°C), and summer temperatures are above 50°F (10°C). Summers are short in these regions; the climate is wet right throughout the year.

CLIMATE ZONES

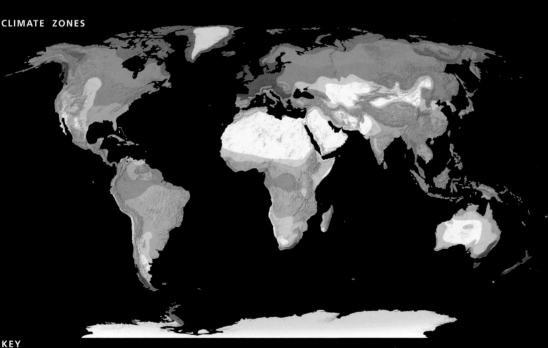

KEY

■ **Wet tropical:** Hot and wet year round; short or no dry season

■ **Seasonal tropical:** Hot and wet, but with distinct dry season

■ **Arid:** Little or no rainfall year round; hot days and cold nights

■ **Semiarid:** Low rainfall; less temperature variation than arid

■ **Mediterranean:** Hot, dry summers and cool, wet winters

■ **Subtropical:** Warm and moist; hot summers and possibly dry winters

■ **Continental:** Cool and moist; warm summers and severe winters

■ **Temperate:** Four distinct seasons; warm summers and cold winters

■ **Cold temperate:** Cool summers and severe, snowy winters

■ **Subpolar:** Very cold year round; no true summer; tundra vegetation

■ **Polar:** Extremely cold and dry year round; ice sheet

■ **Highland:** Colder than low-level locations at same latitude

Climates in the past

Climatic changes have been occurring for thousands of years. They are linked to changes in solar activity and to the intensity of cosmic radiation that penetrates the atmosphere. The Middle Ages in Europe were a time of great prosperity. In this period, known climatically as the Medieval Warm Period, the world was warmer than it is today. It was followed by a worldwide Little Ice Age, when temperatures fell. The Middle Ages followed the cold Dark Ages, which were preceded by the much warmer Roman period. Today the climate is again warming.

Ice ages, and the warmer interglacials that separate them, are climate changes on a grander scale. They are driven by changes in Earth's solar orbit, axial tilt and rotation. Right now we are living in an interglacial. Ice ages and interglacials are not constant; they are punctuated by shorter warmer and cooler episodes. Much farther back in time there were "Snowball Earth" periods, when sea ice extended to the equator.

→ **Bristlecone pine trees,** seen here in California, live for thousands of years. Scientists measure their annual growth rings, comparing samples from living and dead trees, to track climate changes over more than 8000 years.

LONG-TERM CLIMATE CHANGE
The left graph (below) shows how the average temperature has changed since Earth formed, 4.6 billion years ago. The horizontal line indicates the present-day average temperature. The changes were partly linked to continental drift, illustrated by the series of globes. The long Carboniferous–Permian ice age coincides with the formation of the supercontinent Pangea and is also linked to astronomical events.

The right graph (opposite page) traces changing temperatures through the Pleistogene period of the Cenozoic era. This time of repeated expansions and retreats of polar ice sheets began 1.8 million years ago (mya) and continues today.

Continental drift over time

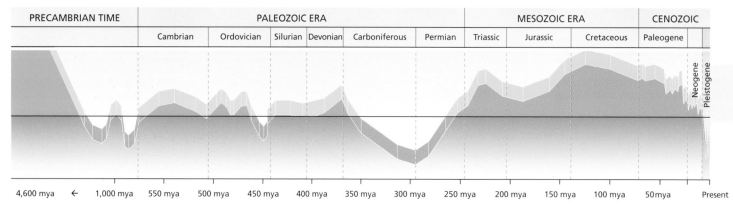

PRECAMBRIAN TIME	PALEOZOIC ERA						MESOZOIC ERA			CENOZOIC	
	Cambrian	Ordovician	Silurian	Devonian	Carboniferous	Permian	Triassic	Jurassic	Cretaceous	Paleogene	Neogene / Pleistogene

4,600 mya ← 1,000 mya 550 mya 500 mya 450 mya 400 mya 350 mya 300 mya 250 mya 200 mya 150 mya 100 mya 50 mya Present

Extent of glaciation   Last ice age ——————————————————— Today

| Pleistogene | |
| Pleistocene | Holocene |

Present average temperature

Holocene maximum   Medieval climatic optimum

←1.8 mya 800,000 ya 600,000 ya 400,000 ya 200,000 ya 11,000 ya 8,000 ya 6,000 ya 4,000 ya 2,000 ya 1,000 ya Present

 The shrinking ice fields on Mount Kilimanjaro, in Tanzania, have attracted worldwide attention. Since the end of the nineteenth century the total ice area has decreased from about 5 square miles (12.5 km²) to 1 square mile (2.5 km²).

 Norse settlement ruins at Qagssiarssuk, Greenland, were founded between AD 985 and 1000, when the sea ice was farther north than it is now. By 1200 the ice was returning and there is no archaeological trace of human occupation after about 1430.

↑ **This traffic jam,** along the main avenue of Saõ Paulo, Brazil, on May 15, 2006, extended for 107 miles (173 km). Idling car engines pollute the air and the carbon dioxide they emit may contribute to rising temperatures.

Global warming

The Sun emits radiation most intensely at short wavelengths. Sunshine warms Earth's surface, which, as its temperature rises, also emits radiation, but at much longer, infrared wavelengths. Air is transparent to short-wave radiation but water vapor, and certain other gases, absorb infrared radiation. Consequently, the atmosphere retains some outgoing radiation. This is the "greenhouse effect" and without it the world would be much colder.

Over the past century, average global temperature has increased by about 1.3°F (0.7°C) and the atmospheric concentration of carbon dioxide, a gas that absorbs long-wave radiation, has increased from about 0.028 percent to 0.037 percent. This percentage is rising each year as a result of burning fossil fuels. Many scientists believe increasing greenhouse gases are causing the temperature rise; others that it is part of Earth's natural cycle.

↓ **The Keeling curve** shows how the atmospheric concentration of carbon dioxide, measured at Mauna Loa, Hawaii, has increased since 1960. In summer, as photosynthesis increases, more carbon dioxide is absorbed and its concentration decreases. In winter photosynthesis slows so the concentration increases. Fossil fuel combustion is the most likely cause of the overall rise. Cooling towers emit water vapor, which condenses in the atmosphere, thus adding to the greenhouse effect.

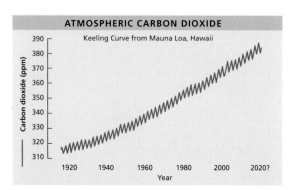

ATMOSPHERIC CARBON DIOXIDE

Keeling Curve from Mauna Loa, Hawaii

Carbon dioxide (ppm) vs. Year

← **Outlet glaciers** flow beneath polar ice sheets, draining ice from them, but the rate of glacier flow is not constant. The Greenland and West Antarctic ice sheets are losing mass, which could be causing a sea level rise of about 1.4 inches (3.5 cm) per century at the present rate. Overall, the average sea level is rising by between 7 and 12 inches (17–31 cm) per century.

→ **Summer drought** in 2001 emptied this reservoir near Montpellier, France, and in 2003 a widespread drought and heat wave caused more than 22,000 deaths across Europe. As the average temperature rises, summer heat waves and depleted reservoirs are likely to become more frequent.

→ **Floods in Venice,** like this one in 2005, make movement difficult. Autumn floods are common in a city that has been fighting the water since it was founded. Elsewhere, people who live on the floodplains of major rivers such as the Danube are recognizing their vulnerability to flooding after prolonged rain, especially when this adds to spring meltwater from the mountains. Leaving areas undeveloped to absorb excess water prevents rivers from bursting their banks, and thus protects people on the floodplain.

Extreme weather

Scientists who study the conditions astronauts might face on Mars look for guidance to the dry valleys of Antarctica. Covering 2200 square miles (5700 km²), these places are bitterly cold and far too dry for any snow or ice. Should any snow fall, the incessant 100-mile-per-hour (160 km/h) winds quickly sweep it away. Other places experience extremes of snow. Over a period of 19 hours on April 5 and 6, 1969, 68 inches (173 cm) of snow fell at Bessans, France, and a single snowstorm that lasted from December 13–19, 1955, dumped 189 inches (480 cm) of snow on Mount Shasta Ski Bowl, California.

Earth is our home, but not everywhere is congenial to humans. On September 13, 1922, the temperature at El Azizia, Libya, reached 136°F (57.8°C), breaking a record of 134°F (56.7°C) set by Greenland Ranch in Death Valley, California, on July 10, 1913. There are also extremes of wet and dry. Rainfall at Lloro, Colombia, was measured over a period of 29 years. In one year it reached a record of 523.6 inches (13,299 mm). In contrast, Wadi Halfa, Sudan, received an average of less than 0.1 inch (2.5 mm) of rain per year over 39 years.

↓ **Vostok Station,** Antarctica, is the coldest place on Earth. On July 21, 1983, scientists at this Russian research center measured the temperature as –128.6°F (–89.2°C). Cold poles are places that record the lowest temperatures and Vostok is the southern hemisphere's cold pole. Average winter temperature is –89.6°F (–67.6°C); summer is –25.7°F (–32.1°C). It is not especially windy, with usual maximum winds of between 29 and 40 miles per hour (47–65 km/h).

Vostok

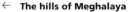

← **The Atacama Desert** in Chile is the world's driest. Over a 29-year period, Arica in northern Chile averaged less than 0.03 inch (0.75 mm) of rain per year. Iquique received an average 0.06 inch (1.5 mm) of rain per year over 21 years, including four years when no rain fell at all. Only one shower fell in the following year. Despite the aridity, the air is so humid that iron rusts quickly.

Atacama Desert

← **The hills of Meghalaya** (formerly Assam) in northeastern India have a wet climate. Air that approaches from the south is forced to rise and loses the moisture it gathered as it crossed the Bay of Bengal. Meghalaya also has a monsoon climate. Cherrapunji, one of the wettest places on Earth, has an average annual rainfall of 450 inches (11,430 mm). Between August 1860 and July 1861, almost 905 inches (22,987 mm) of rain fell there. Nearby Mawsynram averages an annual 467 inches (11,873 mm) and Mount Wai'ale'ale, Hawaii, averages 460 inches (11.684 mm).

Cherrapunji

← **Siberia** is notoriously cold, and Verkhoyansk, a Siberian gold-mining town of about 1400 inhabitants surrounded by the taiga (coniferous forest) is the Eurasian cold pole. On February 7, 1892, the temperature fell to −93.6°F (−69.8°C), although the average winter temperature is −58.5°F (−50.3°C). The other northern hemisphere cold pole is in Canada at Snag, Yukon. In February 1947 the temperature here, the coldest place in North America, fell to −81°F (−63°C).

Verkhoyansk

Optical phenomena

Cloud droplets, raindrops and ice crystals reflect sunlight. The way they reflect it depends on their size and, with ice crystals, their shape and orientation. The speed of light is constant within a medium that has the same density throughout, but it changes when light crosses from a region of one density to a different density. When this happens the light is refracted—it bends—at the boundary between the regions. This explains the apparent bend in a straw resting in a glass of water. The reflection and refraction of sunlight produce a variety of optical effects. There is a green flash, occasionally seen for up to 10 seconds, caused by refraction when the Sun is just below the horizon; the golden heiligenschein—or halo—around the shadow of an observer's head when dewdrops act as lenses; the heavenly cross when a horizontal bar crosses a sun pillar.

→ **Crepuscular rays** radiate upward from the Sun, hidden behind a cumulus cloud. Sunlight illuminates and is reflected by dust or smoke particles in the air above the cloud. "Crepuscular," meaning "of the twilight," rays are seen when the Sun is low.

↘ **A sun pillar,** seen here over West Antarctica extending upward and downward from the Sun, is caused by the reflection of sunlight from the undersides of ice crystals that are falling slowly. Sun dogs (parhelia or mock suns) are on either side.

↓ **Moon dogs** are caused by the refraction of light by ice crystals that fall slowly. Here they are associated with a halo whose radius subtends an angle of 22 degrees to the observer. The ice crystals are in the cirrostratus cloud that covers the Moon.

→ **A sun dog** is a patch of light on one side of the Sun—in this example the left—and slightly below it. The iridescence in the clouds results from the diffraction of sunlight by ice crystals that are all approximately the same size.

↓ **A fata morgana,** named after the fairy half-sister of King Arthur, is a mirage that produces an image, seen on the horizon across a body of water, of a distant landscape or of buildings—castles in the air. It is caused by the refraction of light that passes through a thin layer of cold, dense air that lies over the cold sea surface.

Factfile

EARTH THROUGH TIME

The present continents were once joined together in the supercontinent Pangea, surrounded by Panthalassa, a world ocean. "Pangea" means "all the land" and "Panthalassa" means "all the sea." About 250 million years ago, at the very end of the Permian period, an arm of the sea began extending into Pangea. This became the shallow Tethys Sea, named after Tethys, in Greek mythology the wife and sister of Okeanos, god of the ocean. About 200 million years ago, at the beginning of the Jurassic period, Pangea began to break apart and the rift had grown wider by the middle of the Jurassic. The Tethys Sea lay between what were becoming separate northern and southern sections of the supercontinent. The first globe shows the world map as it might have appeared then, with the Tethys Sea lying between what would later become Africa and Arabia in the west and southern Asia in the east. As the two sections moved farther apart, they formed two smaller supercontinents. The northern one, called Laurasia, contained what are now North America, Greenland, Europe and Asia. The southern supercontinent, called Gondwana, contained South America, Africa, Madagascar, India, Sri Lanka, Australia, New Zealand and Antarctica. The Tethys Sea was the western section of a larger area called the Tethys Ocean. Indonesia and the Indian Ocean now occupy the area that was once the Tethys Ocean and the Black, Caspian and Aral seas are what remains of the Tethys Sea. The South Atlantic began to open during the Cretaceous period, about 100 million years ago, and the North Atlantic began to separate North America from Europe during the Eocene epoch, about 50 million years ago. The present geography of the world was clearly evident by 30 million years ago. Since then the Atlantic Ocean has continued to widen.

30 million years ago

Present

GEOLOGICAL TIME

Phanerozoic

Era	Period/System	Epoch/Series	Began mya
Cenozoic	Pleistogene	Holocene	0.11
		Pleistocene	1.81
	Neogene	Pliocene	5.3
		Miocene	23.03
	Palaeogene	Oligocene	33.9
		Eocene	55.8
		Palaeocene	65.5
Mesozoic	Cretaceous	Late	99.6
		Early	145.5
	Jurassic	Late	161.2
		Middle	175.6
		Early	199.6
	Triassic	Late	228
		Middle	245
		Early	251
Palaeozoic	Permian	Late	260.4
		Middle	270.6
		Early	299
	Carboniferous	Pennsylvanian	318.1
		Mississipian	359.2
	Devonian	Late	385.3
		Middle	397.5
		Early	416
	Silurian	Late	422.9
		Early	443.7
	Ordovician	Late	460.9
		Middle	471.8

Phanerozoic

	Period/System	Epoch/Series	Began mya
		Early	488.3
	Cambrian	Late	501
		Middle	513
		Early	542

Proterozoic

Era	Period/System	Epoch/Series	Began mya
Neoproterozoic	Ediacaran		600
	Cryogenian		850
	Tonian		1000
Mesoproterozoic	Stenian		1200
	Ectasian		1400
	Calymmian		1600
Palaeoproterozoic	Statherian		1800
	Orosirian		2050
	Rhyacian		2300
	Siderian		2500

Archaean

Era	Period/System	Epoch/Series	Began mya
Neoarchaean			2800
Mesoarchaean			3200
Palaeoarchaean			3600
Eoarchaean			3800

Hadean

Era	Period/System	Epoch/Series	Began mya
Swazian			3900
Basin Groups			4000
Cryptic			4567.17

MINERAL PROPERTIES

Specific gravity	is the ratio of the weight of a substance to the weight of an equal volume of water. It is determined by comparing the weight of a sample of the mineral in air and in water.
Reflective index	is the relationship between the angle of incidence and angle of refraction of light entering and leaving a mineral sample. It is determined using a refractometer, which measures the angle of light reflected from a polished mineral surface.
Chemical formula	is part of the definition of a mineral, every mineral having a characteristic composition, which is determined by analyzing a sample. For example, the mineral cuprite (red copper ore) is a copper oxide, Cu_2O.
Hardness	is one of the most useful properties for identifying minerals, determined by scratching the sample with another mineral to discover which minerals will leave a scratch mark and reading the result from Mohs's hardness scale. A scratch from a fingernail gives a hardness of about 2.5 and a knife blade about 5.5.
Color	is a characteristic of most minerals, but minor impurities can sometimes produce a range of colors for the same mineral, so this is not a reliable identification. For example, apatite is usually green or gray-green, but can be white, brown, yellow, blue or red.
Crystal system	or crystal group is a set of seven possible types of crystals based on the angles at which the crystal faces intercept three or four imaginary lines. Crystals produce a characteristic external shape, called the habit.
Streak	is the color of a mineral when it is ground to a powder. This is often different from the color of the solid mineral. It is determined by rubbing the mineral against an unglazed porcelain plate, called a streak plate.
Luster	is a measure of a mineral's ability to reflect light and is often useful in identification. Lusters are described as adamantine, metallic, resinous, waxy, pearly, silky, greasy and vitreous, and the intensity of luster may be shiny, dull or splendent.
Sheen	is the effect on a mineral's appearance caused by the reflection of refraction of light from its internal structure or inclusions within it. Sheen effects include iridescence, asterism (starlike effect), adularescence (silvery blue color) and chatoyancy (cat's-eye effect).
Gemstone	minerals are naturally occurring minerals that have been cut, shaped, faceted and polished for decorative use. Many gemstones are hard and clear. They are classified as precious (diamond, emerald, sapphire) or semi-precious (topaz, garnet, amethyst).
Tectonic setting	is the way a mineral's host rock formed. This can be useful in identification. For example, kyanite occurs in regional metamorphic rocks that have been subjected to high pressure and low to moderate temperatures. Muscovite occurs in igneous alkali granites and as a secondary mineral in pegmatites, resulting from the decomposition of feldspars.

SOIL

Soil consists of mineral particles derived from the weathering of bedrock, mixed with the remains of once-living organisms in various states of decomposition. Living organisms mix the soil and rainwater draining downward dissolves some of its chemical ingredients and carries them in solution to lower layers. These processes lead to the layering of mature soils. The layers, called horizons, are exposed as a soil profile by cutting vertically downward from surface to bedrock. Organic debris forms the uppermost horizon. Lower horizons contain decomposed debris, nutrient substances translocated from above, and finally the parent material derived from the weathering of bedrock.

01	organic debris	A3	transitional layer
02	partly decomposed organic debris	B1	transitional layer
A1	mineral materials with fine particles of organic matter	B2	layers in which most nutrients accumulate
		B3	transitional layer
A2	mineral materials into which nutrients have moved from above	C	parent material
		R	bedrock

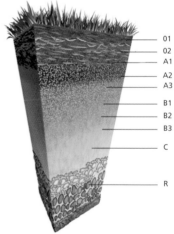

01
02
A1
A2
A3
B1
B2
B3
C
R

THE ROCK CYCLE

Rocks are classed as igneous, sedimentary or metamorphic. Igneous rocks form when magma cools, crystallizes and solidifies. Igneous rocks are then subject to weathering, which reduces them to particles that are transported by wind and water. Particles that accumulate as seabed sediments may then be compressed and heated, transforming them into sedimentary rocks. If either sedimentary or igneous rocks are subjected to high pressures, temperatures or changes in their content of volatile ingredients, their minerals may recrystallize into new forms. The process is called metamorphism and it produces metamorphic rocks. Oceanic crust is eventually subducted, carrying igneous, sedimentary and metamorphic rocks back into the mantle, completing the rock cycle.

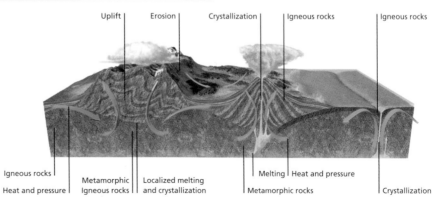

Uplift   Erosion   Crystallization   Igneous rocks   Igneous rocks

Igneous rocks
Heat and pressure   Metamorphic Igneous rocks   Localized melting and crystallization   Melting   Heat and pressure
Metamorphic rocks   Crystallization

The Physical World

MAP OF EARTH

Oceans and seas dominate the globe, covering 70.8 percent of its surface. The land between these large bodies of water is traditionally divided into seven main landmasses and continents: Europe, Asia, North America, South America, Africa, Australia and Antarctica. Europe and Asia form a single landmass, known as Eurasia, but are conventionally identified as two separate continents because of their distinct peoples and histories. Though technically a continent in itself, Australia is usually considered part of the large region of Oceania, which includes the other islands of the southwestern Pacific Ocean.

Circumference of Earth around the equator
24,902 miles (40,067 km)

Area of sea
139,782,000 square miles (362,033,000 km²)

Area of land above sea level
57,151,000 square miles (148,021,000 km²)

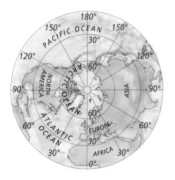

NORTHERN HEMISPHERE

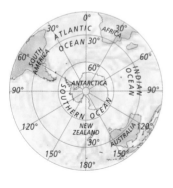

SOUTHERN HEMISPHERE

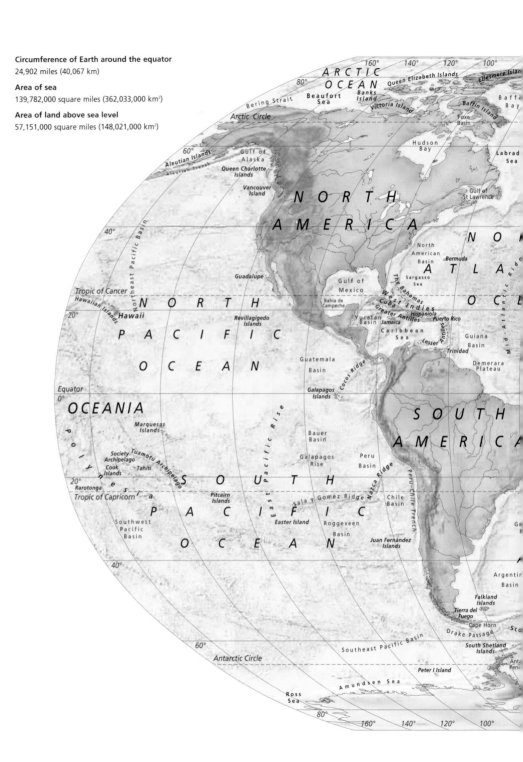

ARCTIC OCEAN

Greenland
Greenland Sea
Denmark Strait
Iceland
Faroe Islands
Norwegian Sea
British Isles
North Sea
Baltic Sea
Bay of Biscay
EUROPE
Corsica
Sardinia
Sicily
Crete
Cyprus
Mediterranean Sea
Black Sea
Caspian Sea
Aral Sea

Franz Josef Land
Svalbard
Barents Sea
Novaya Zemlya
Kara Sea
Laptev Sea
Severnaya Zemlya
East Siberian Sea
New Siberian Islands
Arctic Circle

ASIA

Turpan Depression

Bering Sea
Kamchatka Peninsula
Sea of Okhotsk
Sakhalin
Aleutian Islands
Emperor Seamount Chain
Hokkaidō
Kuril Islands
Sea of Japan
Honshū
Bo Hai
Yellow Sea
Kyūshū
Shikoku
East China Sea
Okinawa
Ryukyu Islands
South Honshū Ridge
Northwest Pacific Basin
NORTH
PACIFIC
OCEAN

Tropic of Cancer

Madeira
Canary Islands
AFRICA
Gulf of Guinea
São Tomé
Ascension
St Helena
Angola Basin

Red Sea
Gulf of Aden
Socotra
Arabian Sea
Persian Gulf
Gulf of Oman
Laccadive Islands
Maldives
Sri Lanka
Bay of Bengal
Andaman Islands
Andaman Sea
Nicobar Islands
Gulf of Thailand
Taiwan
Hainan
South China Sea
Luzon
Philippines
Mindanao
Celebes Sea
Palau Islands
Philippine Sea
Mariana Islands
Guam
Caroline Islands
Micronesia
Marshall Islands
Central Pacific Basin
Mariana Trench
Gulf of Tongking
Sunda Shelf

Tristan da Cunha
Somali Basin
Seychelles
Grande Comore
Mid-Indian Ridge
Chagos-Laccadive Plateau
Mid-Indian Basin
Cocos Basin
Borneo
Greater Sunda Islands
Sulawesi
Java Sea
Bali
Malay Archipelago
Lesser Sunda Islands
Banda Sea
New Guinea
Bismarck Sea
New Ireland
New Britain
Bougainville
Solomon Islands
Nauru
Melanesia
OCEANIA
Equator

Sumatra
Java
Timor
Cocos Islands
Christmas Island
West Australian Basin
Timor Sea
Arafura Sea
Torres Strait
Gulf of Carpentaria
Great Barrier Reef
Coral Sea
Guadalcanal
Espíritu Santo
Fiji
Vanua Levu
Viti Levu
Sava'i
Upolu

Mid-Atlantic Ridge
Madagascar
Mozambique Channel
Mauritius
Réunion
INDIAN
OCEAN
Ninetyeast Ridge
New Caledonia
Tongatapu Group
Tropic of Capricorn

SOUTH
ATLANTIC
OCEAN
Cape Basin
Cape of Good Hope
Cape Agulhas
Madagascar Basin
Natal Basin
AUSTRALIA
Perth Basin
Great Australian Bight
Lord Howe Island
Norfolk Island
Kermadec Islands
North Island
Tasman Sea

Agulhas Basin
Prince Edward Islands
Crozet Islands
Amsterdam Island
St Paul Island
Crozet Basin
Kerguelen Islands
Kerguelen Plateau
Heard Island
Southeast Indian Ridge
Southwest Indian Ridge
Tasmania
Bass Strait
Stewart Island
South Island
Chatham Islands
Bounty Islands
Auckland Islands
Campbell Island
Macquarie Island
New Zealand

Sandwich Trench
Weddell
SOUTHERN OCEAN
South Indian Basin
Australian-Antarctic Basin
Antarctic Circle

ANTARCTICA

Extreme Earth

KINDS OF VOLCANOES

Most of Earth's volcanic eruptions take place along the mid-oceanic ridges, but because they are almost entirely below the surface of the ocean, they go largely unnoticed. Earth's four main kinds of active volcanoes are shown below. All the large, classic, steep-angled cones around the world, such as Mt Fuji, are composite volcanoes and are associated with subduction zones. Shield volcanoes are more flattened and occur at hot spots.

Fissure or rift volcano

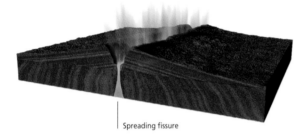

Spreading fissure

Shield volcano

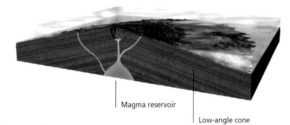

Magma reservoir

Low-angle cone

Cinder cone volcano

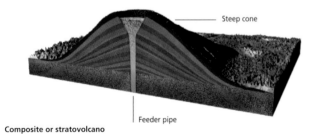

Steep cone

Feeder pipe

Composite or stratovolcano

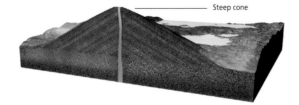

Steep cone

DEADLY VOLCANOES

Year	Volcano	Location	Fatalities	Major cause of deaths
1815	Tambora	Indonesia	92,000	ash, tsunami, disease, starvation
1883	Krakatau	Indonesia	36,400	tsunami, ash
1902	Mt. Pelee	Martinique	28,000	ashflows
1985	Nevado del Ruiz	Colombia	23,000	mudflows
79	Vesuvius	Italy	16,000	ash, ashflows
1792	Unzen	Japan	14,500	volcano collapse, tsunami
1586	Kelut	Indonesia	10,000	unknown
1783	Laki	Iceland	9350	disease, starvation
1919	Kelut	Indonesia	5000	mudflows
1631	Vesuvius	Italy	4000	mudflows; lava flows

TECTONIC PLATES

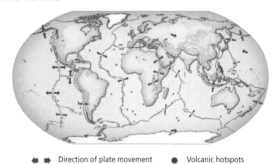

◀ ▶ Direction of plate movement   ● Volcanic hotspots

SPEED OF PLATE MOVEMENT

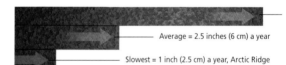

Fastest = over 6 inches (15 cm) a year, East Pacific Rise, near Easter Island

Average = 2.5 inches (6 cm) a year

Slowest = 1 inch (2.5 cm) a year, Arctic Ridge

DEVASTATING EARTHQUAKES

Year	Location	Fatalities
1201	Egypt–Syria	1,100,000
1556	Shanxi, China	830,000
1976	Tangshan, China	655,237
1139	Caucasus	300,000
1662	China	300,000
1737	Calcutta, India	300,000
115	Antioch, Turkey	260,000
1139	Aleppo, Syria	230,000
1876	Andaman Islands, India	215,000
856	Iran	200,000

AVALANCHES AND LANDSLIDES

While rocks appear strong, they are subject to the forces of gravity, erosion and weathering. An avalanche is a downward movement of snow, ice or debris that can be triggered by thawing snow. Landslides occur when gravity pulls huge amounts of soil or rock down a slope. Often they are triggered by heavy rainfall, but they can also result from human activity when, for example, forest clearing or mining undermines sloping ground.

AVALANCHE CLASSES

Class	Damage	Path width
1	Could knock someone over, but not bury them.	33 ft (10 m)
2	Could bury, injure or kill someone	330 ft (100 m)
3	Could bury and wreck a car, damage a truck, demolish a small building, break trees	3330 ft (1000 m)
4	Could wreck a railroad car or big truck, demolish several buildings, or up to 10 acres (4 ha) of forest	6560 ft (2000 m)
5	Largest known; could destroy a village or up to 100 acres (40 ha) of forest.	9800 ft (3000 m)

FORMATION OF AN AVALANCHE

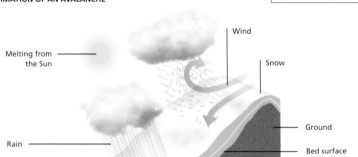

HAILSTORM INTENSITY SCALE

Intensity	Damage	Hailstone size
H0	None	0.2–0.4 in (5–10 mm)
H1	Makes holes in leaves and flower petals	0.2–0.8 in (5–20 mm)
H2	Strips leaves from plants, damages vegetables	0.2–1.2 in (5–30 mm)
H3	Breaks glass panes, scrapes paint, marks woodwork, dents trailers, tears tents	0.4–1.8 in (11–45 mm)
H4	Breaks windows, cracks windshields, scrapes off paint, kills chickens and small birds	0.6–2.4 in (16–60 mm)
H5	Breaks some roof tiles and slates, dents cars, strips bark from trees, cuts branches from trees, kills small animals	0.8–3 in (21–80 mm)
H6	Breaks many roof tiles and slates, cuts through roof shingles and thatch, makes some holes in corrugated iron, breaks wooden window frames	1.2–3.9 in (31–100 mm)
H7	Shatters many roofs, breaks metal window frames, seriously damages car bodies	1.8–4.9 in (46–125 mm)
H8	Cracks concrete roofs, destroys other roofs, marks pavements, splits tree trunks, can seriously injure people	2.4–more than 4.9 in (61–more than 125 mm)
H9	Marks concrete walls, makes holes in walls of wooden houses, fells trees, can kill people	3.2–more than 4.9 in (81–more than 125 mm)
H10	Destroys wooden houses, seriously damages brick houses, can kill people	4–more than 4.9 in (101–more than 125 mm)

FLOODS

Floods often involve property damage and loss of life and are therefore classified as disasters. In fact, floods account for about 40 percent of all deaths worldwide. Yet, in some parts of the world they are part of the natural annual weather cycle. For thousands of years, flooding along the Nile has sustained agriculture and, hence, civilization. Today, many seasonal tropical regions are dependent on flooding to nourish crops. Historically, while the flooding of the Huang He in China destroys lives and property, it is also necessary to bring down silt and fertilize the soil.

INUNDATIONS

Year	Location	Fatalities
1931	Huang He, China	1,000,000–3,700,000
1887	Huang He, China	900,000–2,000,000
1938	Huang He, China	500,000–900,000
1938	Banqiao Dam, China	231,000
1935	Yangtze, China	145,000
1935	North Vietnam	100,000
1911	Yangtze, China	100,000
1954	Yangtze, China	30,000
1954	Netherlands, Germany, Denmark	25,000
1954	Iran	10,000

Geographical Features

LARGEST ISLANDS

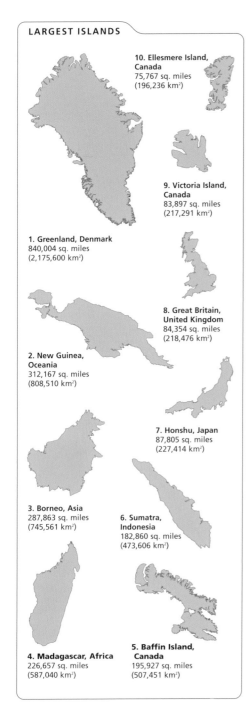

10. Ellesmere Island, Canada
75,767 sq. miles
(196,236 km²)

9. Victoria Island, Canada
83,897 sq. miles
(217,291 km²)

1. Greenland, Denmark
840,004 sq. miles
(2,175,600 km²)

8. Great Britain, United Kingdom
84,354 sq. miles
(218,476 km²)

2. New Guinea, Oceania
312,167 sq. miles
(808,510 km²)

7. Honshu, Japan
87,805 sq. miles
(227,414 km²)

3. Borneo, Asia
287,863 sq. miles
(745,561 km²)

6. Sumatra, Indonesia
182,860 sq. miles
(473,606 km²)

4. Madagascar, Africa
226,657 sq. miles
(587,040 km²)

5. Baffin Island, Canada
195,927 sq. miles
(507,451 km²)

LARGEST WATERFALLS

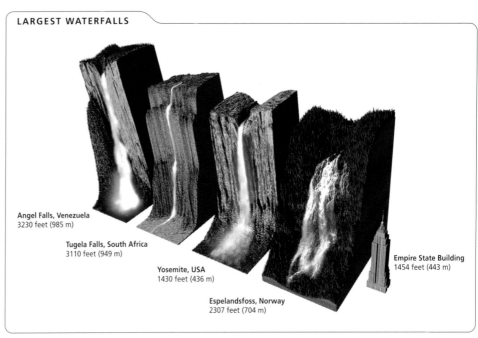

Angel Falls, Venezuela
3230 feet (985 m)

Tugela Falls, South Africa
3110 feet (949 m)

Yosemite, USA
1430 feet (436 m)

Espelandsfoss, Norway
2307 feet (704 m)

Empire State Building
1454 feet (443 m)

LARGEST LAKES

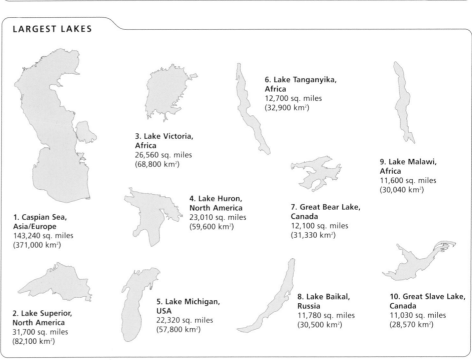

6. Lake Tanganyika, Africa
12,700 sq. miles
(32,900 km²)

3. Lake Victoria, Africa
26,560 sq. miles
(68,800 km²)

9. Lake Malawi, Africa
11,600 sq. miles
(30,040 km²)

4. Lake Huron, North America
23,010 sq. miles
(59,600 km²)

7. Great Bear Lake, Canada
12,100 sq. miles
(31,330 km²)

1. Caspian Sea, Asia/Europe
143,240 sq. miles
(371,000 km²)

5. Lake Michigan, USA
22,320 sq. miles
(57,800 km²)

8. Lake Baikal, Russia
11,780 sq. miles
(30,500 km²)

10. Great Slave Lake, Canada
11,030 sq. miles
(28,570 km²)

2. Lake Superior, North America
31,700 sq. miles
(82,100 km²)

LONGEST RIVERS

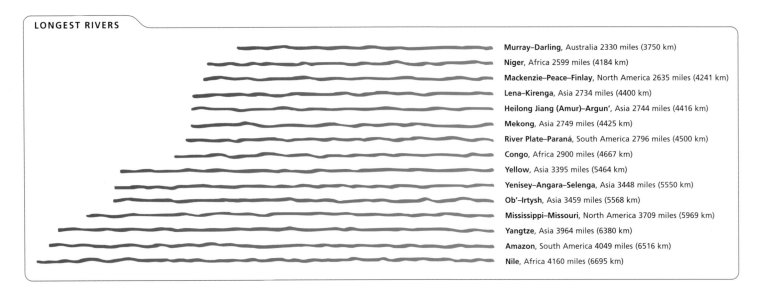

Murray–Darling, Australia 2330 miles (3750 km)

Niger, Africa 2599 miles (4184 km)

Mackenzie–Peace–Finlay, North America 2635 miles (4241 km)

Lena–Kirenga, Asia 2734 miles (4400 km)

Heilong Jiang (Amur)–Argun', Asia 2744 miles (4416 km)

Mekong, Asia 2749 miles (4425 km)

River Plate–Paraná, South America 2796 miles (4500 km)

Congo, Africa 2900 miles (4667 km)

Yellow, Asia 3395 miles (5464 km)

Yenisey–Angara–Selenga, Asia 3448 miles (5550 km)

Ob'–Irtysh, Asia 3459 miles (5568 km)

Mississippi–Missouri, North America 3709 miles (5969 km)

Yangtze, Asia 3964 miles (6380 km)

Amazon, South America 4049 miles (6516 km)

Nile, Africa 4160 miles (6695 km)

MAJOR MOUNTAINS

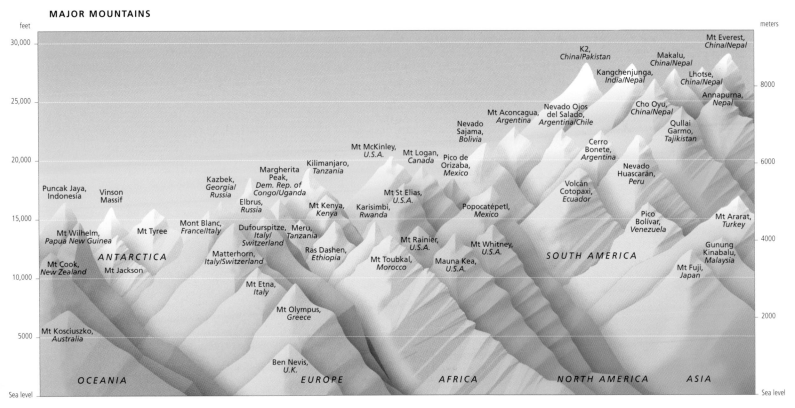

Earth's habitats

MAJOR BIOMES

A biome is a geographical community of animal and plant life, determined mainly by climatic regions. For example, there are grasslands in the center of each continent where the climate is too dry for forests; tundra vegetation grows north of the Arctic Circle where conditions are too harsh for forests. This vegetation supports communities of animals that are suited to the food supply and climate of the biome. Major biomes can be broken down into smaller categories based on other factors, such as human activity.

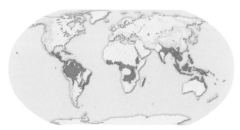

- Tropical forest
- Desert
- Grasslands
- Temperate forest
- Tundra
- Polar regions
- Mountains and highlands

TEMPERATE FOREST

Broad-leaved deciduous or summer forest occurs wherever rainfall is distributed evenly throughout the year and where winters are not too long and severe. They are found in eastern North America, western Europe including southern Scandinavia and extending as a narrow finger to central Siberia, in eastern China, Japan, parts of southern Australia and New Zealand.

CONIFEROUS FOREST

Coniferous forest, called boreal forest in North America and northern Europe, and taiga in Russia, thrives where long, cold winters and frozen soil restrict the growing season and supply of moisture. It covers much of the highlands of western North America, and a coastal strip along the Pacific. In Asia the forest extends in a central band to the Pacific coast and into the Arctic.

TROPICAL FOREST

Tropical forests occur between the Tropics of Cancer (23.5°N) and Capricorn (23.5°S), but extend a little way outside the tropics in Mexico, Brazil, and, as monsoon forest, in Bangladesh and Assam. They do not occupy all of the tropical region in Africa and occupy only a small area in Australia. There are several kinds of tropical forest. Lowland rain forest is the kind that occupies the largest area in all continents.

GRASSLANDS

Grasslands grow in continental interiors where the climate is too dry for forests. There are two types: temperate and tropical grasslands. Temperate grasslands are known as prairie in North America, pampa in South America, steppe in Eurasia and veld in South Africa. They also occur in New Zealand. Tropical grasslands, nowadays usually known everywhere as savanna, occur in South America and India, but are most extensive in Africa and Australia.

TUNDRA

Tundra vegetation, consisting of lichens, mosses, sedges, grasses, flowering herbs, shrubs and low-growing trees, grows where the climate is too harsh for full-sized trees. It occurs in northern Alaska, northern Canada, northern Scandinavia and across northern Russia. Except around Hudson Bay, it is confined mainly to north of the Arctic Circle (66.5°N). There are also small areas in the Falkland and South Shetland islands, north of the Antarctic Circle.

DESERT

Deserts occur in all the continents and are of several types. Subtropical deserts, such as the Sahara, form a belt across Africa and western Asia, Patagonia, southern Africa (Kalahari) and Australia, where subsiding air is dry and often hot. Rain shadow deserts are found in North America, west coast deserts in South America (Atacama) and Africa (Namib). Continental deserts occur in central Asia, a long distance from the ocean.

MOUNTAINS AND HIGHLANDS

Mountains and high ground occur in every continent. Air temperature decreases with height and vegetation reflects this change. With increasing elevation, the plant communities growing on a tropical mountain resemble those found in higher latitudes, but this applies only to the structure of the communities and not to the plant species, which are more closely related to those in the lowlands.

VOLCANIC LANDSCAPES

Volcanic eruptions destroy the surrounding vegetation by burning or by burying it beneath ash. Volcanoes also form hills and sometimes grow into high mountains. Between eruptions, the material ejected by a volcano provides the basis for highly fertile soils. Volcanic landscapes, found mainly along the "ring of fire" surrounding the Pacific Ocean and in East Africa, support rich plant communities.

POLAR REGIONS

Beyond the limit of the tundra, the temperature seldom or never rises above freezing. Lichens and mosses grow sparsely in the dry valleys of Antarctica, but conditions are generally unsuitable for plants. The polar regions are lands of bare rock, ice and snow, their only inhabitants the birds that visit and the mammals that wander into them. Life is abundant in the sea, however, where the temperature remains above freezing.

CORAL REEFS

Coral reefs occur in all tropical oceans where the water is clear, shallow and warm. Although the open sea contains few nutrients, photosynthesizing algae and dinoflagellates form the basis of rich communities of organisms living on and around the rock-like reefs constructed by coral polyps. Their requirement for shallow water means many coral reefs are on continental shelves, where they are vulnerable to pollution that clouds the water.

RIVERS

River systems transport fresh water to the sea. They provide habitat for aquatic algae and plants that grow in the water, bankside trees and other plants, and aquatic and riverbank animals. These habitats are quite different from those found some distance from a river. In their lower reaches rivers form floodplains that are enriched by flood deposits of silt. Where rivers meet the sea, estuaries produce mudflats, sand banks and salt marshes.

WETLANDS

Waterlogged land provides conditions suitable for a variety of plants and animals that are found nowhere else. Coastal wetlands, adjacent to river estuaries and deltas, support species tolerant of changes between saltwater and freshwater conditions. Inland there are swamps, marshes, bogs and low-lying ground beside rivers. A swamp is permanently wet (in American usage a forested wetland). A marsh is waterlogged mineral soil. A bog is wet, acidic peat.

FRESHWATER LAKES

Lakes are large bodies of fresh water, sometimes the size of a small sea, located in the interior of continents, far from the ocean. Lake size is usually reported as surface area, but volume may be more important ecologically. They support a wide range of plants and animals, often including species that are found nowhere else. As areas of habitat they are thus distinct from the rivers that feed water to them and from the oceans into which they eventually discharge. Lakes support fisheries, and provide recreational facilities and communications.

NORTH AMERICA

Low-lying depressions left by retreating ice sheets have formed lakes across the continent, including the Great Lakes.

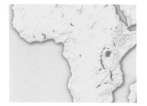

AFRICA

Lakes fill depressions associated with the East African Rift, including Lakes Victoria, Nyasa and Rudolf.

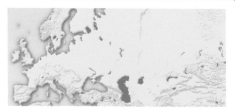

EURASIA

The world's biggest lake is the Caspian Sea. At one time the Aral Sea was among the largest but today it is a much smaller body of water. These, and the Black Sea, are the remains of the Tethys Sea.

Oceans

OCEAN CURRENTS

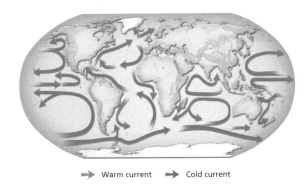

→ Warm current → Cold current

The circulation of the atmosphere transports warm air away from the equator at high altitude and replaces it with cool air flowing close to the surface. The low-level flow of air generates the prevailing winds, which blow across the ocean, pushing surface water and forming ocean currents. The system of currents transports warm water away from the equator, replacing it with cool water from higher latitudes.

Tropical trade winds, blowing from the east, produce equatorial currents that flow westward in both hemispheres. As they approach the continents the currents turn away from the equator, the Coriolis effect accentuates the deflection, and they enter the midlatitude westerly winds. These drive the currents in an eastward direction, but still turning due to the Coriolis effect, until they rejoin the equatorial currents. The resulting circular pattern in all oceans is called a gyre.

THE GREAT CONVEYOR

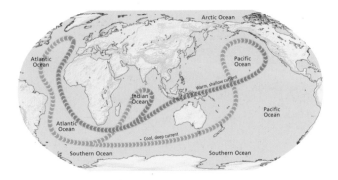

Close to the edge of the North Atlantic sea ice, the water is cold and salty because when water freezes only water molecules are involved and the salt moves into adjacent water. Low temperature and high salinity make the water denser than adjacent water. It sinks to the ocean floor and flows southward, driven mainly by tidal forces. In the Southern Ocean it joins the Circumpolar Current flowing eastward. Part of the current enters the Indian Ocean. The remainder passes south of New Zealand before turning northward into the Pacific, and rising to middle depths. It makes a clockwise loop in the North Pacific, flows through the Indonesian islands, around Africa, and returns to the North Atlantic. When it flows strongly this "Great Conveyor" brings more hurricanes, fewer El Niño events and climatic cooling. When it weakens the opposite occurs.

DISTRIBUTION OF WATER ON EARTH

The oceans hold 97.5 percent of all the water on Earth. Of the remainder, 79 percent is in the form of polar ice and glaciers and 20 percent is below ground, flowing as groundwater. This leaves 1 percent of the world's fresh water to fill the lakes, rivers and clouds.

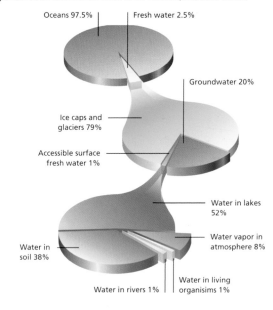

Oceans 97.5% Fresh water 2.5%

Groundwater 20%

Ice caps and glaciers 79%

Accessible surface fresh water 1%

Water in lakes 52%

Water vapor in atmosphere 8%

Water in soil 38%

Water in rivers 1% Water in living organisims 1%

WAVE FORMATION

Wind produces waves. Wave size depends on the strength of the wind and the distance it has blown without interruption, known as the fetch. As waves pass, moving in groups, the water moves in a circle, up and forward, down and back. Their height increases when waves enter shallow water.

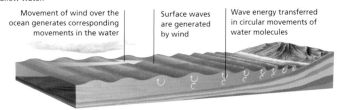

Movement of wind over the ocean generates corresponding movements in the water

Surface waves are generated by wind

Wave energy transferred in circular movements of water molecules

BIGGEST WAVES ON RECORD

As waves pass, the water moves vertically. Wavelength is the horizontal distance between wave crests and as waves grow bigger in the open ocean their wavelength usually increases. A wave that grows higher without an increase in wavelength becomes increasingly unstable, eventually falling forward as a breaker. Waves move in groups, with waves at the rear traveling faster and overtaking those in front. This allows waves to combine, producing giants.

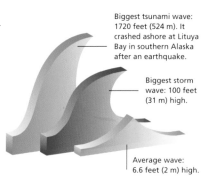

Biggest tsunami wave: 1720 feet (524 m). It crashed ashore at Lituya Bay in southern Alaska after an earthquake.

Biggest storm wave: 100 feet (31 m) high.

Average wave: 6.6 feet (2 m) high.

Weather

FAMOUS LOCAL WINDS

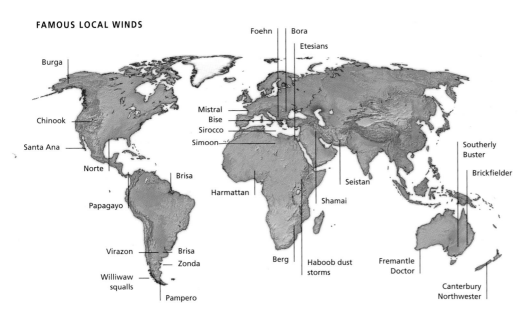

Foehn | Bora
Etesians
Burga
Mistral
Bise
Sirocco
Simoon
Chinook
Santa Ana
Norte
Brisa
Papagayo
Harmattan
Virazon
Brisa
Zonda
Williwaw
squalls
Pampero
Berg
Haboob dust
storms
Shamai
Seistan
Southerly
Buster
Brickfielder
Fremantle
Doctor
Canterbury
Northwester

EXTREME WEATHER FACTS

Wettest place Mawsynram, India 467 inches (11,874 mm) of rain in an average year.
Rainiest place Mount Waialeale Crater, Kauai, Hawaii 350 days of rain each year.
Driest place Arica in Chile's Atacama Desert annual average rainfall is one-third of an inch (8 mm).
Highest temperature Al Aziziyah, Libya, recorded a temperature of 136.4°F (58°C) on September 13, 1922.
Lowest temperature Vostok Base, Antarctica, recorded a temperature of –128.6°F (–89.2°C) on July 21, 1983.
Greatest temperature range Verhoyansk, Central Siberia Summer temperatures in this region can reach 98°F (37°C). Winter temperatures can go as low as –90°F (–68°C).
Highest non-tornado wind gust Mount Washington, USA, recorded a wind gust of 231 mph (371 km/h) on April 12, 1934.
Highest recorded tornado wind speed Oklahoma, USA, May 1999, 318 mph (512 km/h).
Heaviest recorded hailstones Gopalganj, Bangladesh, recorded hailstones that weighed up to 2 pounds 3 ounces (1 kg) on April 14, 1986, killing 92 people.
Hottest region Sahara Desert belt, Dallol, Ethiopia, averaged a daytime temperature of 94°F (34°C) between 1960 and 1966.

THE SAFFIR–SIMPSON SCALE

	Pressure (hectopascals)	Wind speed (mph [km/h])	Storm surge (ft [m])	Damage
1	more than 980	74–95 (118–152)	4–5 (1.2–1.6)	minimal
2	965–980	96–110 (153–176)	6–8 (1.7–2.5)	moderate
3	945–964	111–130 (177–208)	9–12 (2.6–3.7)	extensive
4	920–944	131–155 (209–248)	13–18 (3.8–5.4)	extreme
5	less than 920	more than 155 (248)	more than 18 (5.4)	catastrophic

Saffir–Simpson hurricane scale
Devised in 1955 by meteorologists at the US Weather Bureau to report tropical cyclone winds in excess of Beaufort force 12. The five-point scale also takes account of surface pressure and storm surge.

THE FUJITA SCALE

Scale	Speeds (mph [km/h])	Damage
F0	40–73 (64–117)	light
F1	74–112 (118–180)	moderate
F2	113–157 (181–251)	considerable
F3	158–206 (252–330)	terrible
F4	207–260 (331–417)	severe
F5	more than 260 (417)	devastating

Fujita tornado intensity scale
Devised in 1971 by Prof. T. Fujita and Allen Pearson to report tornadoes, based on the visible damage they cause. It is a six-point scale rating damage from light to devastating.

THE BEAUFORT SCALE

Wind speed (mph [km/h])	Description	Effects on land
0	below 1 (below 2)	calm	smoke rises vertically
1	2–3 (3–5)	light air	smoke drifts slowly
2	4–7 (6–11)	light breeze	leaves rustle; vanes begin to move
3	8–12 (12–19)	gentle breeze	leaves and twigs move
4	13–18 (20–29)	moderate breeze	small branches move; dust blown about
5	19–24 (30–38)	fresh breeze	small trees sway
6	25–31 (39–51)	strong breeze	large branches sway; utility wires whistle
7	32–38 (52–61)	near gale	trees sway; difficult to walk against wind
8	39–46 (62–74)	gale	twigs snap off trees
9	47–54 (75–86)	strong gale	branches break; minor structural damage
10	55–63 (87–101)	whole gale	trees uprooted; significant damage
11	64–74 (102–120)	storm	widespread damage
12	above 74 (120)	hurricane	widespread destruction

Beaufort scale
A 13-point scale devised in 1805 by Francis Beaufort, originally to advise mariners of the amount of sail they should carry under different wind conditions. Wind speeds were added later.

Glossary

Abyssal plain The flat area of an ocean basin between the continental slope and the mid-ocean ridge.

Aftershock A tremor that follows a large earthquake and originates at or near the hypocenter of the initial quake.

Antarctic circle The line of latitude at 66°33'S marking the northern limit of the Antarctic region.

Arctic circle The line of latitude at 66°33'N marking the southern limit of where the Sun does not set in June or rise at December solstices.

Ash Fine pieces of rock and lava ejected explosively during volcanic eruptions. Small particles may travel great distances.

Asteroid Belt A reservoir of asteroids orbiting the Sun in the ecliptic between the orbits of Mars and Jupiter.

Asthenosphere A layer in Earth's upper mantle that is semi-soft like modeling clay. It lies below the hard, rigid lithosphere.

Atmosphere A layer of gases attached to a planet or moon by the body's gravity.

Aurora Curtains and arcs of light in the sky over middle and high latitudes. They are caused by particles from the Sun hitting Earth's atmosphere and causing some of its gases to glow.

Bathypelagic zone The ocean between 656 and 13,120 feet (200–4000 m) deep.

Big Bang The eruption of a small, hot lump of matter about 14 billion years ago that marked the birth of the Universe, according to cosmological theory.

Biome The geographically largest biological community that comprises a characteristic type of vegetation, such as tropical forest, grassland or desert, together with the animals associated with it. Biomes approximately coincide with climatic zones.

Biosphere The part of the world that can support life.

Canyon A deep, steep-sided valley formed by river erosion.

Climate The pattern of weather that occurs in a region over an extended period of time.

Continents Earth's seven main landmasses: Africa, Antarctica, Asia, Australia, Europe, North America and South America.

Continental drift The movement of the continents relative to each other across Earth's surface, explained by plate tectonics.

Continental rise The gently sloping accumulation of sediments at the foot of the continental slope.

Continental shelf The gently sloping outer part of a continent beneath the ocean surface, extending from the shoreline to the edge of the continental slope, about 500 feet (150 m) deep.

Continental slope The surface, sloping at 1°15', from the outer edge of the continental shelf to the top of the continental rise.

Convection The transfer of heat by the movement of a gas or liquid. This is the principal mechanism by which heat is transported through the atmosphere.

Convection currents (mantle) Movement within the mantle caused by heat transfer from Earth's core. Hot rock rises and cooler rock sinks. This movement is most likely responsible for the motion of Earth's tectonic plates.

Convergent margin A boundary between two tectonic plates that are moving toward each other.

Core Earth's dense center. It consists of a solid inner core and a molten outer core, both of which are made of iron. No other terrestrial planet has this two-component core structure.

Corona The high-temperature, outermost atmosphere of the Sun, visible from Earth only during a total solar eclipse.

Crater A circular depression formed by a volcanic eruption (volcanic crater) or by the impact of a meteorite (impact crater).

Crust The outer layer of Earth. There are two types of crust: continental crust, which forms the major landmasses; and oceanic crust, which is thinner and forms the seafloor.

Crystal A solid mineral form with a characteristic internal molecular structure enclosed by faces that meet at definite and specific angles related to the structure of the substance.

Divergent margin A boundary between two tectonic plates that are moving apart.

Earthquake A sudden, violent release of energy in Earth's crust that generally occurs at the edges of tectonic plates.

Eclipse When one celestial body passes in front of another, dimming or obscuring its light.

Ecosystem A discrete unit comprising living organisms and their physical and chemical surroundings that interact to form a stable system. The concept can be applied at any scale, from a puddle to an ocean, or a forest to the entire planet.

El Niño A weakening or reversal of the southeasterly trade winds in the South Pacific, occurring at intervals of two to seven years, that brings rain to the ordinarily dry west coast of South America, dry weather to Indonesia, and alters weather patterns in some other parts of the world.

Epicenter The point on Earth's surface that is directly above the hypocenter, or starting point, of an earthquake.

Equator The imaginary line on a celestial body that lies halfway between its two poles.

Equinox One of the two days each year (March 20-21 and September 22-23) when the noonday Sun is directly overhead at the equator, and day and night are of equal length.

Erosion The gradual wearing away of rock or landscape by water, ice or wind.

Eukaryote An organism made up of one or more cells that have a complex structure containing defined nuclei and membrane-enclosed organelles. Fungi, plants and animals are eukaryotes.

Fault A fracture in Earth's crust along which displacement has occurred. Faults may be normal, reverse or strike-slip.

Fold A bend in rock layers caused by crustal movement.

Fossil Any preserved evidence of pre-existing life. It may be the remains of a plant or animal that has turned to stone or has left its impression in rock.

Galaxy A huge gathering of stars, gas and dust, bound by gravity and having a mass ranging from 100,000 to 10 trillion times that of the Sun.

Geological time The division of the history of Earth, from the time of its formation, into intervals of varying length defined by geological events. The longest episodes are called eons, which are divided into eras, periods and epochs.

Glaciation The expansion of glaciers and ice sheets to cover a substantial area of Earth's surface; an ice age.

Glacier A large mass of ice formed by the buildup of snow on a mountain or a continent. It moves slowly downhill or outward.

Gondwana The southern supercontinent fragment comprising New Zealand, Antarctica, Australia, South America, Africa and India. It existed as a separate landmass from 650 million years ago and only began to break up 130 million years ago.

Greenhouse effect The warming caused by certain gases in the atmosphere. These "greenhouse" gases allow sunlight to reach Earth's surface, where it is absorbed and reradiated as heat. The gases then absorb this heat and reradiate it back to Earth.

Habitat An area where the physical and chemical conditions exist to support a particular community of organisms.

Hardness The extent to which the surface particles of a mineral can scratch or be scratched.

Humidity The amount of water vapor in air.

Hypocenter The place within Earth where energy in strained rocks is suddenly released as earthquake waves.

Ice core A long, columnar sample of ice extracted from a glacier.

Ice sheet An ice mass resting on land that covers more than about 20,000 square miles (50,000 km²). A similar ice mass with a smaller area is called an ice cap.

Ice shelf The part of an ice shelf or ice cap that extends over the sea surface.

Igneous rock Rock that forms when magma cools and hardens. Intrusive igneous rock solidifies underground and extrusive igneous rock solidifies above ground.

Invertebrate General term for animals without backbones, such as worms, mollusks and insects.

Laurasia One of the two continents that formed when the supercontinent Pangea separated. It includes Europe, North America and Asia (not India). Similarity of plants and animals of these countries is explained by this former connection.

Lava Molten rock that has erupted onto Earth's surface.

Lithosphere The rigid outer part of Earth, consisting of the crust and the uppermost part of the mantle.

Luster The way light falling on the surface of a mineral is absorbed or reflected (compare sheen).

Magma Hot, liquid rock or a mush of liquid rock and crystals found beneath the surface of Earth. When magma erupts onto Earth's surface, it is called lava.

Magma chamber A pool of magma in the upper part of the lithosphere from which volcanic materials may erupt.

Magnetic field A region surrounding a magnetic object, within which an iron-rich body will experience a magnetic force.

Mantle The layer between Earth's crust and outer core; it is semi-solid rock with the consistency of modeling clay.

Mercalli scale A scale based on direct observation that divides earthquakes into 12 categories according to the damage they cause. It is an inaccurate measure of earthquake energy.

Metal Any of a number of elements that are shiny, moldable and will conduct electricity. Many are mineral compounds.

Metamorphic rock Rock formed by the transformation of a pre-existing rock as a result of heat and/or pressure.

Meteor A streak of light in the night sky caused by a lump of rock entering Earth's atmosphere from space. Before the rock enters the atmosphere it is known as a meteoroid. If it lands on Earth's surface, it is called a meteorite.

Mid-oceanic ridge A long, submerged mountain range that runs through the ocean between continents; the boundary where two plates are pulled apart and new plate material is added. Formed by the upwelling of hot basaltic magma.

Milky Way The galaxy in which our Solar System is located.

Mineral A naturally occurring substance that has a characteristic chemical composition and typically a crystalline structure, imparting such properties as hardness, luster, cleavage, streak and relative density by which it may be identified.

Monsoon A seasonal change in wind direction that brings a major change in the weather. The winter monsoon is dry and the summer monsoon rainy.

Ocean One of the five great bodies of seawater defined by continental margins, the Equator and other arbitrary divisions.

Ocean trench A deep, narrow undersea valley formed when the oceanic crust of one tectonic plate collides with and dives beneath the crust of another plate.

Orbit The path of an object as it moves through space under the control of another's gravity.

Ore A mineral or rock that contains a particular metal in a concentration high enough to make its extraction commercially viable. Hematite (iron) and chalcopyrite (copper) are examples.

Pangea A supercontinent; a single landmass that formed as a result of the collision of all the continents during the Permian period and broke up during the Jurassic into Laurasia and Gondwana. These, in turn, broke into the present continents.

Photosphere The visible surface of the Sun or any other star.

Plate tectonics A theory that explains continental drift, seafloor spreading, earthquakes and volcanic activity by proposing that Earth's crust consists of a number of rigid sections (plates) that move in relation to each other over a less rigid asthenosphere.

Prokaryote An organism, usually single-celled, in which the cell has no nucleus or membrane-bound organelles. Bacteria are prokaryotes.

Pyroclastic flow A dense, heated mixture of volcanic gas, ash and rock fragments that travels at great speed down volcanic slopes. It forms as a result of the collapse of an eruption column or a lava dome.

Richter scale An open-ended scale rating the magnitude of an earthquake based on the amount of energy released. Each number on the scale represents an increase 10 times greater than the one below it.

Rift valley A wide valley that forms as Earth's crust is stretched apart and a central section drops downward as a result of normal faulting.

Rifting The process of splitting continental plates. Upwelling magma pulls the continent apart; as the rift widens, water floods in to form a new ocean.

Rodinia The earliest known supercontinent. It formed about 2200 million years ago and extended from about 60°N almost to the South Pole. It broke apart about 1000 million years ago.

Rotation The spin of a planet, satellite or star on its axis.

Satellite Any small object orbiting a larger one.

Seafloor spreading Movement caused by convection currents in Earth's mantle forcing molten rock to ooze up through cracks in thin oceanic crust. As the lava in the cracks cools, it pushes the seafloor outward.

Sedimentary rock Rock formed near Earth's surface from pieces of other rocks or plant or animal remains, or by the buildup of chemical solids.

Seismic waves Energy waves that travel through Earth after an earthquake, often causing great destruction.

Sheen The reflection of light from structures, such as lamellae, or cracks, within a mineral (compare luster).

Soil A mixture of mineral particles and decomposed organic material.

Solar flare A sudden release of magnetic energy in or near the Sun's corona emitting radiation into space.

Solar wind A ceaseless, but variable, high-speed stream of extreme charged particles flowing out into space from the Sun.

Solstice One of the two days each year (June 21-22 and December 22-23) when the noonday Sun is directly overhead at either the Tropic of Cancer or Tropic of Capricorn, marking midsummer day in the illuminated hemisphere and midwinter day in the other hemisphere.

Streak The mark of powdered mineral left when a mineral is rubbed against unglazed white porcelain; the color of the streak is used in mineral identification.

Subduction The sliding of a dense oceanic plate under the edge of a more buoyant plate, which is usually continental. Eventually, the sinking plate will be remelted into magma.

Sublimation The change of ice directly into water vapor without passing through a liquid phase. The change from water vapor to ice is called deposition.

Sunspot A dark, highly magnetic region on the Sun's surface that is cooler than the surrounding area.

Tectonic plates Rigid pieces of Earth's lithosphere that move over the semi-solid asthenosphere.

Tethys Sea The body of water partially enclosed by the C-shaped Pangean supercontinent. It was closed when Pangea split into Laurasia and Gondwana.

Tornado A spinning column of air that can measure up to 1 mile (1.6 km) in diameter, move at up to 65 miles per hour (105 km/h) and generate winds of up to 300 miles per hour (482 km/h).

Transform fault A fault or plate margin along which rocks move in opposite directions or at different speeds.

Tropical cyclone An area of low atmospheric pressure over a tropical ocean that produces torrential rain, winds in excess of 75 miles per hour (120 km/h) and a storm surge. Tropical cyclones are called hurricanes in the Atlantic and Caribbean, typhoons in the Pacific, southern Indian Ocean and China Sea, and cyclones in the Bay of Bengal.

Tropics Latitudes 23.5°N and 23.5°S, between which there is at least one day a year when the noonday Sun is directly overhead.

Tsunami The Japanese word for "harbor wave." It is a shock wave caused by an earthquake, volcanic eruption or sediment slide on the seafloor that travels across the ocean at great speed and grows as it enters shallow water and slows down.

Vent A pipe inside a volcano through which lava and gas move from the magma chamber and erupt on the surface.

Vertebrate General term for animals that have a backbone, including mammals, birds, fish, reptiles and amphibians.

Volcano A naturally occurring vent at Earth's surface through which magma, gas, ash and rock fragments erupt.

Wave A disturbance in a solid, liquid or gas that has a regularly repeating form and through which energy is transmitted.

Wavelength The distance between two successive crests or troughs in a wave.

Weathering The breaking down of rocks by physical and chemical processes, such as wind, rain, freezing and thawing, and reaction with chemicals in water below ground.

Windchill Cooling effect on bare skin of the combination of air temperature and wind speed.

Index

Credits

PHOTOGRAPHS

t=top; l=left; r=right; tl=top left; tcl=top center left; tc=top center; tcr=top center right; tr=top right; cl=center left; c=center; cr=center right; b=bottom; bl=bottom left; bcl=bottom center left; bc=bottom center; bcr=bottom center right; br=bottom right

AAP=Australian Associated Press; AUS=Auscape International; CBT=Corbis; DS=Digital Stock; GI=Getty Images; iS=istockphoto.com; ISP=Institute for Solar Physics; MP=Minden Pictures; NASA=National Aeronautics and Space Administration; NHM=Natural History Museum; NHPA=Natural History Photographic Agency; NOAA= National Oceanic and Atmospheric Administration; NOAO=National Optical Astronomy Observatory; PD=Photodisc; PL=photolibrary.com; SH=Shutterstock; SOHO=Solar and Heliospheric Observatory; USGS=United States Geographical Survey

Front cover t MP; b PD; **Spine** SH; **Back cover** CBT
2c MP; **5**c GI; **6–7**c USGS; **8–9**c USGS; **10**c PL; cl CBT; cr USGS; **11**c, cr CBT; cl NASA; **12**c AUS; **14–15**c CBT; **16**b, cl PL; c MP; **17**c PL; cl AUS; bl NOAO; **20**bcl, bl NASA **21**c PL; **22**cl NASA; **23**bc PL; br NASA; **24**c PL; cl NASA; **25**b SOHO; t PL; **27**b, bc PD; tc SH; **28**bl CBT; br, cr SOHO; **29**c PL; **30**b NASA; **31**c PL; tcr NASA; tr ISP; **32**br NASA; tr AUS; **34**b NASA; c PL; **35**t PL; **36**bc, cr SOHO; tr PL; **37**b SS t PD; **38**r MP; **39**c PL; **40**bl PL; tr AUS; **41**t PL; **42**b PL; **43**bl PL; t MP; **44**bl CBT; tr AUS; **45**bl PL; r AUS; **46**br SH; tr PL; **47**c PD; **48**c, tr PD; **49**tr PL; **50**bl AAP; br MP; **51**r MP; tl PL; **52**tr AUS; **53**br, t PL; **54**tr MP; **55**bl PL; tc, tl, tr MP; **56**b, l PL; cl GI; cr, r CBT; **57**r SH; **58**cr GSPIM/UICN/SSC **59**tl CBT; **60**c PL; **62**cr CBT; **63**c GI; cl CBT; **64**b NASA; cr PL; **66**b MP; c PL; **67**b PL; **68**tr AUS; **69**bl, br PL; t AUS; **70**br NHM; **71**c, l, r PL; **72**br, cr, tr PL; **73**b t PL; c CBT; **74**b, c, t PL; **75**bl, cl, tl PL; **76**cr, tr PL; **77**br, l PL; **79**bl, br PL; t GI; **80**bl PL; **81**b MP; c, t PD; **82**b SH; bl PL; cr AUS; **83**bcl, tr SH; bcr PL; **84**bl, r PL; **85**l GI; **86**br, tr GI; l PL; **87**bcl PL; tr GI; **88**bl, r PL; **89**c PL; **90**br CBT; tl PL; tr SH; **91**bc CBT; r PL; **92**bl PL; **93**bl, cr, tl, tr PL; **94**bc, br, cr CBT; **95**b, tl, tr CBT; **96**bl PL; tr CBT; **97**l SH; **98**bl PL; **99**bl, tl PL; tr SH; **100**bl CBT; tr AUS; **101**bl PL; br CBT; **102**bl, tr PL; **103**b, c, tr PL; **104**bl SH; br CBT; tr PL; **105**bl, br PL; **106**r GI; **107**br, cl CBT; tr PSU **108**b CBT; tr SH; **109**tc CBT; tl SH; tr GI; **110**c NASA; **112**c CBT; l GI; **113**c CBT; **114**tr PL; **115**bl, br PL; tcl AUS; **116**br CBT; **117**bl, tl SH; **119**bl PL; tl GI; **120**tr CBT; **121**r CBT; **122**tr CBT; **123**br, tr CBT; **124**br GI; **125**c CBT; **126**bl CBT; **127**r, tl PL; **128**bl CBT; br PL; **129**bl GI; **130**bl SH; tr GI; **131**bl, cr SH; tr PL; **132**bcr PD; bl PL; **133**bl CBT; r NASA; **134**c PL; **135**l, r PL; **136**bc PL; bl NASA; **137**b PL; t CBT; **138**b, tr SH; **139**l SH; **140**tr CBT; **141**bcr PD; bl AUS; tr NHPA; **142**bl PL; **143**br, l CBT; **144**c NASA; **146**c PL; l CBT; r PD; **148**bc, bl, tc PL; **150**cr PL; **151**b CBT; cl MP; tr GI; **152**bl PL; **153**b, t MP; **154**cr NOAA; tr GI; **155**c CBT; **157**bl AAP; **158**b PD; tr PL; **159**b PL; tl GI; **160**c CBT; **162**c CBT; l, r PL; **163**c MP; l PD; **164**tr SH; **165**bcr AUS; tl MP; tr SH; **166**bcr AUS; r PL; **167**l SH; r PL; **168**br CBT; cr, tr PD; **169**br PD; cr, tr SH; **170**b PL; **171**bl CBT; r, tl PL; **172**br, tr PL; **173**bl, tr PL; tl PD; **174**bl, cl PL; br CBT; **175**r PL; tl CBT; **176**b PL; **177**bl, r PL; tl MP; **178**bcr SH; tr CBT; **179**bl PL; cr TPL; **180**c PL; **181**br SH; cl TPL; **182**bcr, cl GI; **183**bl TPL; t SH; **184**c TPL; **185**bcl PL; br TPL; tr SH; **186**b NASA; **187**c PL; t PD; **188**bl CBT; **189**b, tl CBT; tr PL; **190**bl TPL; **191**bl CBT; tl SH; **192**tr PL; **193**l, r PL; **194**b, cr CBT; **195**b, t CBT; **196**b MP; **197**l, r CBT; tl DS; **198**r PL; **199**l NASA; r PL; **200**bl SH; **201**l, r PL; **202**br, tr PL; cl CBT; **203**r PL; **204**bl, br CBT; tr PL; **205**bl PL; br CBT; **206**bl SH; tr NASA; **207**bl PD; tc TPL; **208**bl PL; r CBT; **209**bl, t TPL; **210**br, tr CBT; **211**r NASA; **212**bl SH; tr GI; **213**bl, t CBT; br MP; **214**bl GI; **215**bl, cr CBT; t PL; **216**bl CBT; br SH; tr PL; **217**r MP; **218**bl PL; **219**b MP; bc PD; t, tc SH; **220**bl PL; r CBT; **221**r MP; **222**b CBT; tr PL; **223**b PL; t SH; **224**bl SH; br, tr PL; **225**r CBT; **226**r PL; **227**l CBT; r PD; **228**br, tr CBT; l PD; **229**r CBT; **230**bl PL; **231**bl MP; br GI; tl CBT; **232**tr MP; **233**b GI; tl, tr MP; **234**c CBT; **236**bcr, l SH; tr GI; **237**c PL; **238**bc CBT; br SH; tr NASA; **239**bcl iS; **240**tr SH; **241**b, c, t SH; **242**b Pekka Parviainen tc, tr SH; **243**b SH; **244**b Pekka Parviainen tr GI; **245**bl SH; r Pekka Parviainen **246**c CBT; tr PL; **247**bl PL; br, tc SH; **248**tr AUS; **249**br NASA; br iS; tcl AUS; **250**b CBT; cr GI; tc SH; **251**br NASA; t iS; **252**tr PL; **253**b CBT; t PL; **254**br SH; cr PL; tr DS; **256**bl, tr SH; **257**b GI; tl SH; tr iS; **258**bl CBT; br GI; tr PL; **260**r GI; **261**b SH; **262**b CBT; **263**bl CBT; br SH; t GI; **264**c iS; **265**t GI; **266**b, t PL; **267**bc, tr PL; **268**b NASA; tr GI; **269**t SH; **271**bl, t PD; br iS; **272**tr SH; **273**tc PL; tl, tr GI; **274**bl, r SH; **275**b, t GI; **276**bl PL; **277**bl, tl PL; cl CBT; **278**bl, br, tr PL; **279**b, tr SH; **280**c CBT;

ILLUSTRATIONS

Richard Bonson/The Art Agency 39r
Peter Bull Art Studio 97r, 147bl, 150tr, 154b, 239cr, 243t, 248bl, 252bl, 259r, 261tr, 264bl br, 265b, 269b
Andrew Davies/Creative Communication 52b, 58b, 116bcl bl, 122bl, 150b, 156c, 164b, 168bl, 170c, 172bl, 174tcr, 176tc tr, 179br, 182bl, 187br, 191tr, 194tr, 198l, 202bl, 207br, 210bl, 214tcr, 218c, 222tl, 226cl, 230cl, 232bl, 254l
Chris Forsey 76bl
Mark A. Garlick/space-art.co.uk 18b, 22bcr, cr, 24b, 26bl, 28bcr, tr, 32bcl bl, 35b, 62cl, 65cl, 147lc, 149c
Malcolm Godwin/Moonrunner Design 18tr, 19br, 23t, tr
David Hardy/The Art Agency 22b, 36b
Dean Hudson/Juliana Titin 272b
Map Illustrations 270c
Map Illustrations & Andrew Davies/Creative Communication 114b
Mick Posen/The Art Agency 42t, 49br, 62br, 67t, 68b, 75r, 78b, 101t, 105cr, 112bcr, 117r, 118br, l, tr, 120b, 125br, cr, tr, 129bc, bl, br, cl, 134b, 136r, 139bcr, cr, r, 140b, 142r, 152bc, 156b, 188tr, 192b, 200tl, 205tr, 240b, 251bl, 255cc, 260bl, cl
Peter Scott/The Art Agency 178bl
Guy Troughton 54bc, bl, 58bl, 59r

Captions

page 1 Often called the Blue Planet, more than 70 percent of Earth's surface is covered by water.
page 2 The Grand Canyon in Arizona, USA, was formed over millions of years by the steady flow of the Colorado River.
page 4–5 Earth is a living planet and volcanism is one of the major agents of geological change. Here, molten lava erupts from the Kimanura volcano, Democratic Republic of Congo.
page 6–7 A desert wildlife population is sustained by subterranean waters of the Ugab River in Namibia. This river flows for only a few days each year above ground.
page 8–9 Storms are a perennial feature of our atmosphere. Lightning strikes the Earth about 100 times every second
page 12–13 Clearly visible from space, the Great Barrier Reef in Queensland, Australia, is the largest reef on Earth.
page 280–1 From ancient times, humans have strived to understand the mysteries of our planet. Although Earth has now been mapped to the smallest detail, our understanding of our home is not yet complete.